Complete MathSmart

Grade 2

Copyright © 2011 **Popular Book Company (Canada) Limited**

Printed in China

ISBN: 978-1-897164-12-9

ontents

Section I

	Overview	5
1.	2-digit Numbers	6
2.	Addition and Subtraction to 20	10
3.	Shapes	12
4.	Addition to 100	14
5.	Subtraction to 100	18
	Midway Review	22
6.	More about Addition and Subtraction	26
7.	Money	30
8.	Measurement	34
9.	Probability	36
10.	Pictographs	38
	Final Review	42

Section II

	Overview	47
1.	Addition and Subtraction Facts to 20	48
2.	More about Addition Facts	52
3.	Relating Subtraction to Addition	56
4.	Adding and Subtracting Using Counting	60
5.	Adding without Regrouping I	64
6.	Adding without Regrouping II	68
7.	Adding with Regrouping I	72
8.	Adding with Regrouping II	76
	Midway Review	80
9.	Subtracting without Regrouping I	84
10.	Subtracting without Regrouping II	88
11.	Subtracting with Regrouping I	92
12.	Subtracting with Regrouping II	96
13.	Estimating Sums and Differences	100
14.	Checking Subtraction by Using Addition	104
15.	More Addition and Subtraction	108
16.	Addition and Subtraction with Money	112
	Final Review	116

Section III

	Overview	121
	Review	122
1.	Numbers to 50	126

ISBN: 978-1-897164-12-9

2.	Addition	130
3.	Subtraction	134
4.	Patterning	138
5.	Measurement I	142
6.	Geometry I	146
7.	Data Management	150
	Progress Test	154
8.	Numbers to 100	158
9.	More about Addition and Subtraction	162
10.	Money	166
11.	Measurement II	170
12.	Geometry II	174
13.	Fractions	178
14.	Probability	182
	Final Test	186

Section IV

	Overview	193
1.	3-digit Numbers	194
2.	Addition and Subtraction	196
3.	Multiplication	200
4.	Money	204
5.	Pictographs	208
6.	More about Addition and Subtraction	212
	Midway Review	216
7.	4-digit Numbers	220
8.	Division	224
9.	Measurement	228
10.	More about Multiplication and Division	230
11.	Bar Graphs	234
12.	Probability	238
	Final Review	240

Parents' Guide	245
Answers	249

ISBN: 978-1-897164-12-9

ISBN: 978-1-897164-12-9

Overview

Section I provides children with opportunities to develop and practise addition and subtraction skills up to 100 with carrying and regrouping.

In addition, the Geometry units teach children how to classify 2-D and 3-D shapes, and find lines of symmetry.

Data Management topics include charts, pictographs and bar graphs. Children are encouraged to use real objects, pictures or bars to show information. At this stage, the number of items for comparison is limited to no more than 4.

In the Measurement units, children learn to select appropriate non-standard units for measuring the passage of time and the length, weight and height of different objects.

Money applications include sums up to 100¢.

1 2-digit Numbers

Fill in the missing numbers.

① 38 39 ___ ___ 42 ___ ___ 45

② 29 ___ 27 ___ ___ 24 ___ 22

③ ___ 57 ___ ___ 54 53 ___ 51

Put the numbers in order from the biggest to the smallest.

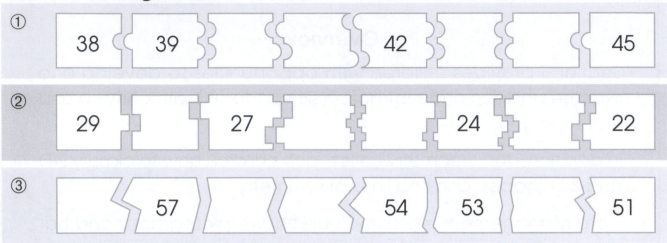

④ 42 23 54 37 : ____ , ____ , ____ , ____

⑤ 25 11 64 50 : ____ , ____ , ____ , ____

⑥ 30 47 81 90 : ____ , ____ , ____ , ____

Help the bird count by 4's to get to the nest. Colour its path.

⑦

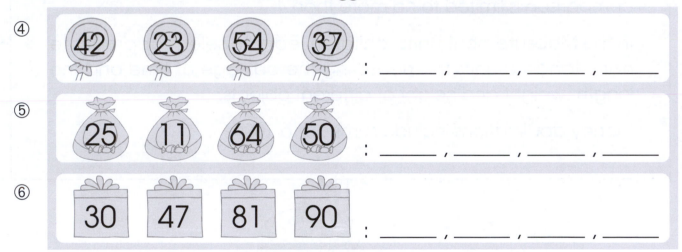

4	8	12	18	24	30	38
6	10	16	20	22	36	40
12	20	22	24	36	40	44
16	14	24	28	32	42	48

ISBN: 978-1-897164-12-9

Fill in the missing numbers in the patterns. Then circle the correct words and write the numbers.

⑧ 12 , 14 , 16 , 18 , _____ , _____ , _____

Pattern : increase / decrease by _____

⑨ 55 , 50 , 45 , 40 , _____ , _____ , _____

Pattern : increase / decrease by _____

⑩ 20 , 30 , 40 , 50 , _____ , _____ , _____

Pattern : increase / decrease by _____

⑪ 85 , 84 , 83 , 82 , _____ , _____ , _____

Pattern : increase / decrease by _____

Colour the flowers. Then answer the questions.

⑫ Colour the 19th ❀ blue and the 21st ❀ yellow.

⑬ How many ❀ are there from the 15th to the 20th? _____ ❀

⑭ How many ❀ are there in all? _____ ❀

⑮ How many more ❀ must Sally plant so that there are 29 ❀ in all? _____ ❀

ISBN: 978-1-897164-12-9

Fill in the missing days. Then answer the questions.

⑯

September						
SUN	MON	TUE	WED	THU	FRI	SAT
	1	2				6
	8		11			
14		17				20
				25	26	
28	30					

⑰ Debbie's birthday is September 18th. What day of the week is it? _____

⑱ Tommy's birthday is September 27th. What day of the week is it? _____

⑲ How many Mondays are there in September? _____

⑳ How many Fridays are there in September? _____

㉑ Lucy's birthday party is on the 3rd Sunday in September. What is the date of her party? _____

㉒ Prima's birthday party is on the day after September 23rd. What is the date of her party? _____

㉓ What day of the week is October 1st? _____

㉔ Matthew's birthday party is on the day before October 3rd. What is the date of his birthday? _____

COMPLETE MATHSMART (GRADE 2)   ISBN: 978-1-897164-12-9

Write the numbers for the children.

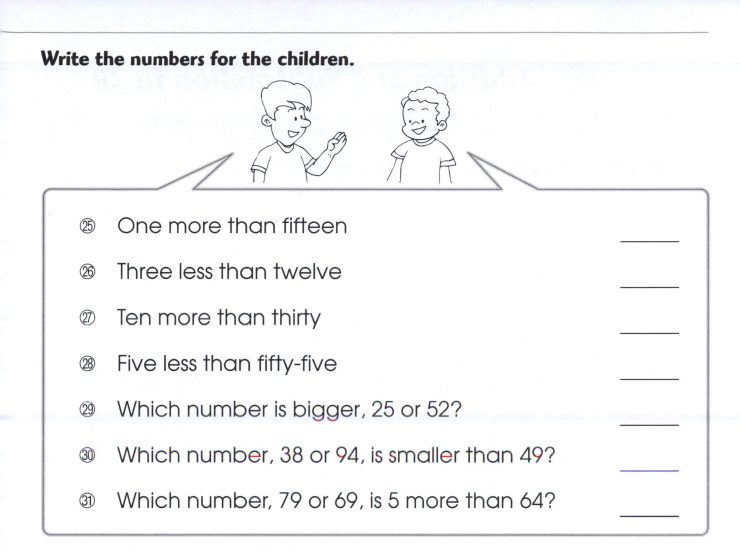

㉕ One more than fifteen   _____

㉖ Three less than twelve   _____

㉗ Ten more than thirty   _____

㉘ Five less than fifty-five   _____

㉙ Which number is bigger, 25 or 52?   _____

㉚ Which number, 38 or 94, is smaller than 49?   _____

㉛ Which number, 79 or 69, is 5 more than 64?   _____

Cross out X the wrong number and write the correct one in the box for each chain.

㉜ 41 ~ 40 ~ 39 ~ ~~36~~ ~ 37 ~ 36 ~ 35 ~ 34   ☐

㉝ 86 ~ 84 ~ 88 ~ 80 ~ 78 ~ 76 ~ 74 ~ 72   ☐

㉞ 50 ~ 45 ~ 40 ~ 38 ~ 30 ~ 25 ~ 20 ~ 15   ☐

㉟ 78 ~ 79 ~ 82 ~ 84 ~ 86 ~ 88 ~ 90 ~ 92   ☐

㊱ 32 ~ 28 ~ 24 ~ 22 ~ 16 ~ 12 ~ 8 ~ 4   ☐

2 Addition and Subtraction to 20

Use the family of facts to fill in the missing numbers.

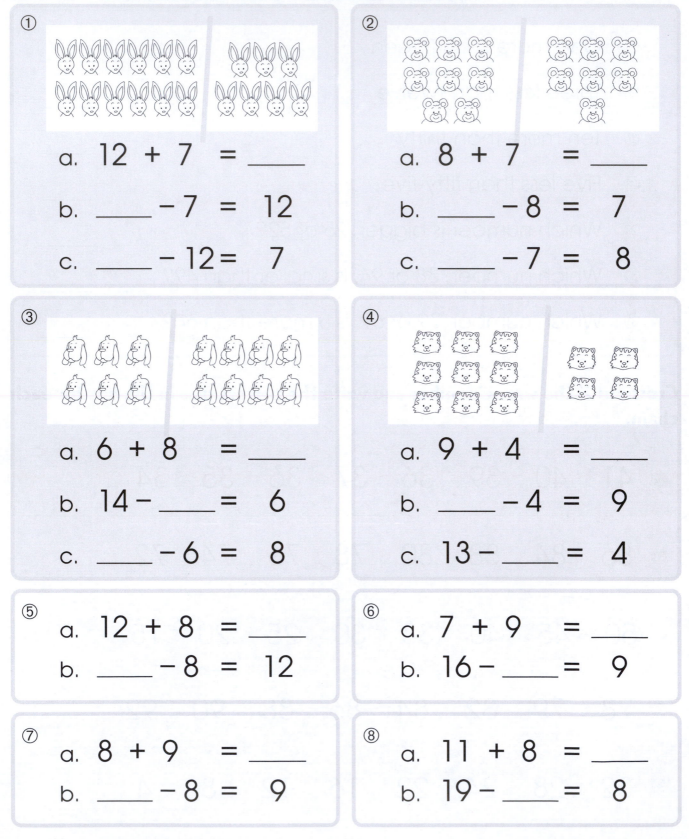

①

a. 12 + 7 = ____

b. ____ − 7 = 12

c. ____ − 12 = 7

②

a. 8 + 7 = ____

b. ____ − 8 = 7

c. ____ − 7 = 8

③

a. 6 + 8 = ____

b. 14 − ____ = 6

c. ____ − 6 = 8

④

a. 9 + 4 = ____

b. ____ − 4 = 9

c. 13 − ____ = 4

⑤

a. 12 + 8 = ____

b. ____ − 8 = 12

⑥

a. 7 + 9 = ____

b. 16 − ____ = 9

⑦

a. 8 + 9 = ____

b. ____ − 8 = 9

⑧

a. 11 + 8 = ____

b. 19 − ____ = 8

ISBN: 978-1-897164-12-9

Look at the pictures. Then answer the questions.

⑨ How many 🕊 are there?   _____ 🕊

⑩ How many 🕊 are there?   _____ 🕊

⑪ How many 🐴 are there?   _____ 🐴

⑫ How many 🐴 are there?   _____ 🐴

⑬ How many birds are there?

_____ + _____ = _____   _____ birds

⑭ How many more 🕊 than 🕊 are there?

_____ − _____ = _____   _____ more

⑮ How many horses are there?

_____ + _____ = _____   _____ horses

⑯ How many more 🐴 than 🐴 are there?

_____ − _____ = _____   _____ more

⑰ How many animals are black?

_____ + _____ = _____   _____ animals

Shapes

Circle the correct name of each shape.

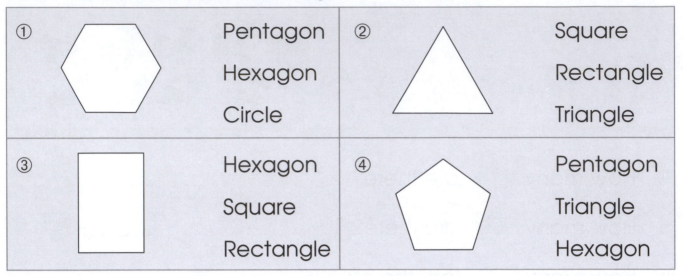

① Pentagon
　 Hexagon
　 Circle

② Square
　 Rectangle
　 Triangle

③ Hexagon
　 Square
　 Rectangle

④ Pentagon
　 Triangle
　 Hexagon

Draw the line of symmetry on each letter.

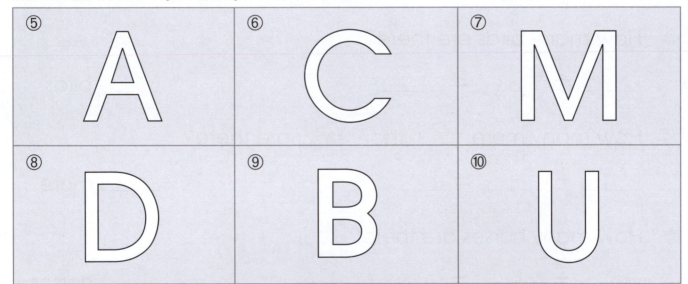

⑤ A
⑥ C
⑦ M
⑧ D
⑨ B
⑩ U

Each letter has two lines of symmetry. Draw them.

⑪ H
⑫ O
⑬ I

ISBN: 978-1-897164-12-9

Look at the pictures. Then write the number in the box to tell how many lines of symmetry each picture has.

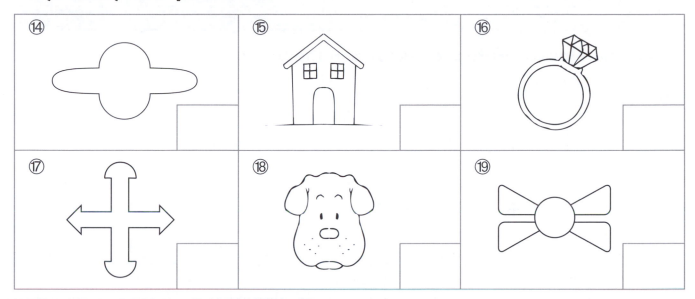

Write the name of each shape.

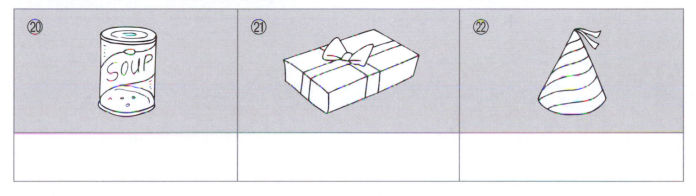

Colour the shapes.

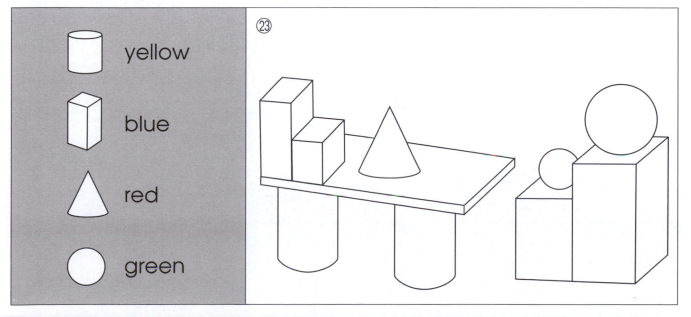

Addition to 100

Count the blocks. Write the numbers in the boxes .

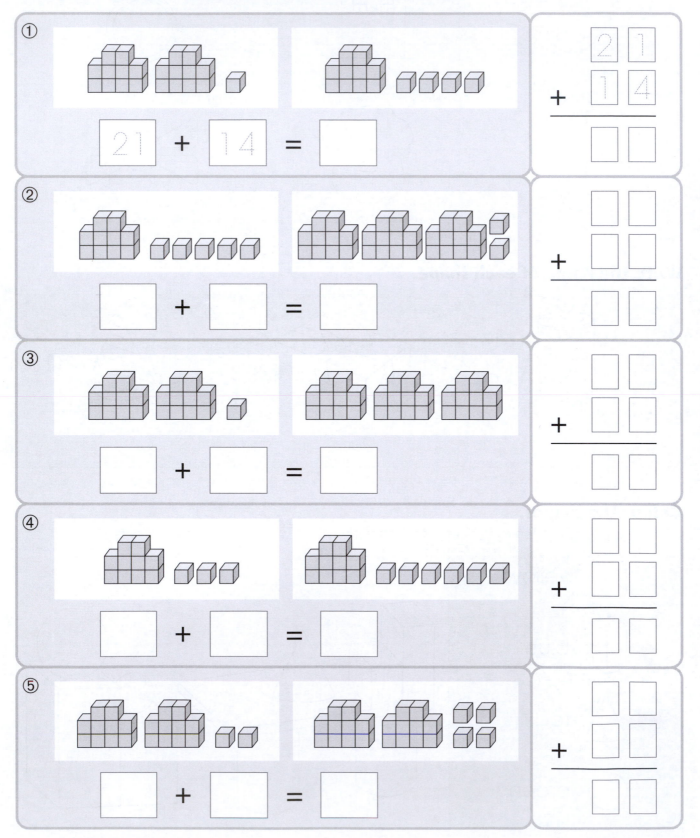

① 21 + 14 =

+ 2 1
  1 4

② + =

+

③ + =

+

④ + =

+

⑤ + =

+

ISBN: 978-1-897164-12-9

In each group, circle ten marbles not in the bottles and add the numbers.

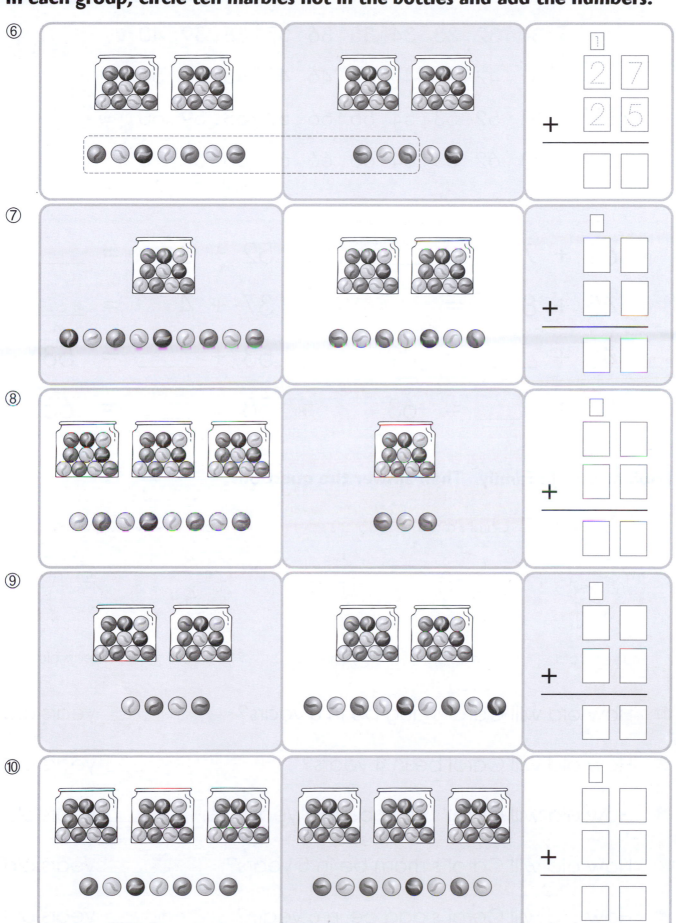

Fill in the missing numbers with the help of the number chart.

31	32	33	34	35	36	37	38	39	40
41	42	43	44	45	46	47	48	49	50
51	52	53	54	55	56	57	58	59	60
61	62	63	64	65	66	67	68	69	70

⑪ 61 + 7 = _____

⑬ 45 + 8 = _____

⑮ 43 + _____ = 49

⑰ 54 + _____ = 63

⑫ 52 + 3 = _____

⑭ 37 + 4 = _____

⑯ 53 + _____ = 58

⑱ 58 + _____ = 66

Look at Carol's family. Then answer the questions.

Carol's dad	Carol's mom	Carol's sister	Carol	Carol's dog
40 years old	38 years old	13 years old	7 years old	2 years old

⑲ How old will Carol's dog be in 5 years? _____ years old

⑳ How old will Carol be in 4 years? _____ years old

㉑ How old will Carol's sister be in 8 years? _____ years old

㉒ How old will Carol's mom be in 5 years? _____ years old

㉓ How old will Carol's dad be in 6 years? _____ years old

ISBN: 978-1-897164-12-9

Complete.

㉔ Sarah collects 12 🐚 . Joe collects 25 🐚 . How many 🐚 do they collect in all?

_____ + _____ = _____

They collect _____ 🐚 in all.

㉕ Bobby has 34 📚 . Stephen has 21 📚 . How many 📚 do they have in all?

_____ + _____ = _____

They have _____ 📚 in all.

㉖ Lucy has 35 🧁 . David has 12 more 🧁 than Lucy. How many 🧁 does David have?

_____ + _____ = _____

David has _____ 🧁 .

㉗ Tom catches 16 🐟 . Pat catches 36 🐟 . How many 🐟 do they catch in all?

_____ + _____ = _____

They catch _____ 🐟 in all.

㉘ Aunt Betty bakes 35 🍪 and 28 🍪 . How many 🍪 🍪 does Aunt Betty bake?

_____ + _____ = _____

Aunt Betty bakes _____ 🍪 🍪 .

Subtraction to 100

Write the numbers with the help of the number chart.

21	22	23	24	25	26	27	28	29	30
31	32	33	34	35	36	37	38	39	40
41	42	43	44	45	46	47	48	49	50
51	52	53	54	55	56	57	58	59	60

① 5 less than 47   _____

② 6 less than 59   _____

③ 4 less than 40   _____

④ 2 less than 55   _____

⑤ 6 less than 31   _____

⑥ 3 less than 42   _____

⑦ 7 less than 53   _____

⑧ 7 less than 35   _____

⑨ 52 is _____ more than 42.

⑩ 45 is _____ more than 43.

⑪ 32 is _____ less than 39.

⑫ 35 is _____ less than 40.

Count how many stickers each child has. Then fill in the blanks.

⑬ Sam gives 10 ☺ to his friends. He has _____ ☺ left.

⑭ Tina gives 4 ☺ to her friends. She has _____ ☺ left.

⑮ Felix gives 6 ☺ to his friends. He has _____ ☺ left.

COMPLETE MATHSMART (GRADE 2) ISBN: 978-1-897164-12-9

Cross out ✗ the correct number of cookies. Find the differences.

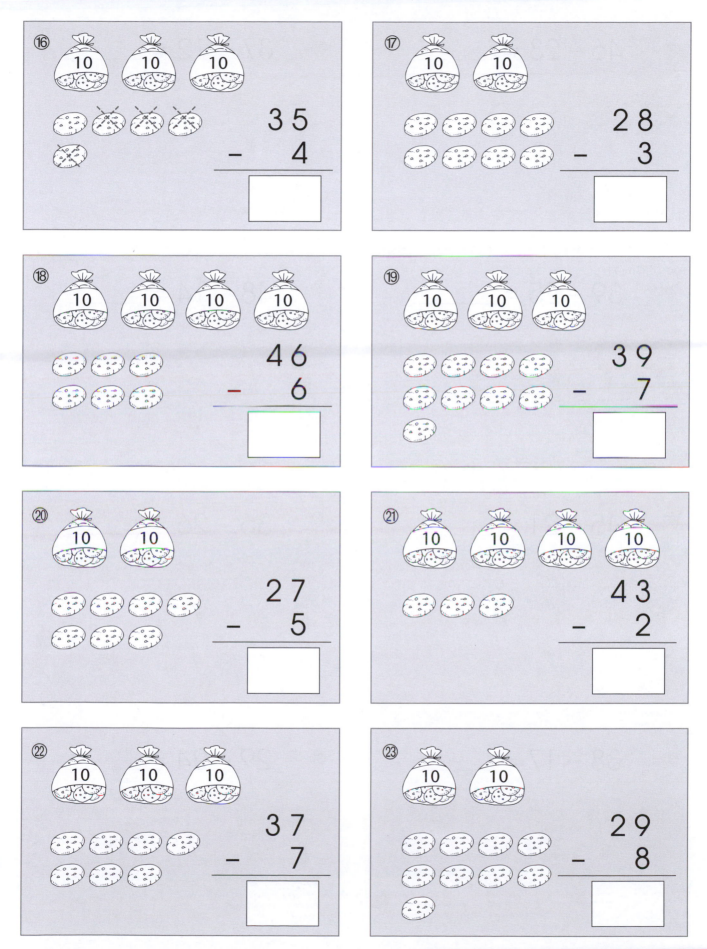

⑯
$$35 - 4$$

⑰
$$28 - 3$$

⑱
$$46 - 6$$

⑲
$$39 - 7$$

⑳
$$27 - 5$$

㉑
$$43 - 2$$

㉒
$$37 - 7$$

㉓
$$29 - 8$$

ISBN: 978-1-897164-12-9

Cross out ✗ the correct number of flowers. Find the differences.

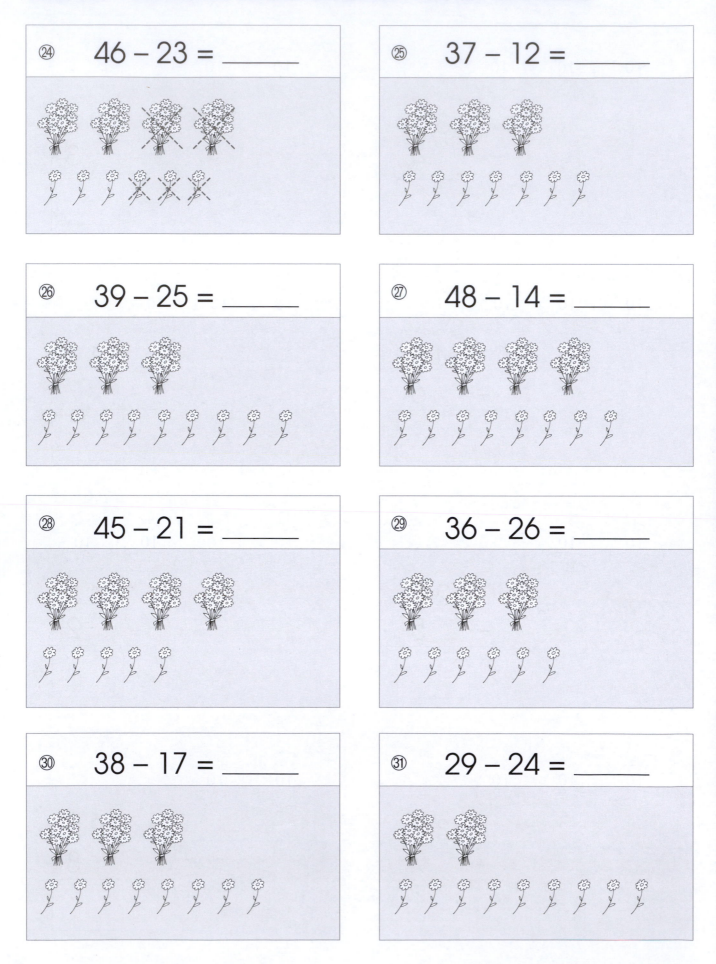

㉔ 46 – 23 = _____

㉕ 37 – 12 = _____

㉖ 39 – 25 = _____

㉗ 48 – 14 = _____

㉘ 45 – 21 = _____

㉙ 36 – 26 = _____

㉚ 38 – 17 = _____

㉛ 29 – 24 = _____

ISBN: 978-1-897164-12-9

Complete.

32 Cathy has 32 🍭 . She gives 2 to Billy. How many 🍭 does Cathy have now?

_____ – _____ = _____

Cathy has _____ 🍭 now.

33 George has 45 🪙 . He has 4 more than Joe. How many 🪙 does Joe have?

_____ – _____ = _____

Joe has _____ 🪙 .

34 There are 56 🧁 in the store. Uncle John buys 5 of them. How many 🧁 are left in the store?

_____ – _____ = _____

_____ 🧁 are left in the store.

35 There are 38 👦 and 6 👧 in the class. How many more 👦 than 👧 are in the class?

_____ – _____ = _____

_____ more 👦 than 👧 are in the class.

36 Aunt Betty has 68 🍪 . She gives 8 to May. How many 🍪 does Aunt Betty have now?

_____ – _____ = _____

Aunt Betty has _____ 🍪 now.

ISBN: 978-1-897164-12-9

Midway Review

Count by 2's to help Little Squirrel find the food he likes. Colour the path.

①

2	4	5	7	9	11	13	26
6	6	10	12	28	30	32	34
12	8	6	14	26	30	33	36
14	10	12	18	24	25	27	29
16	12	16	20	22	26	29	30
20	14	16	18	22	24	26	28

Use the numbers to answer the questions.

44   66   50   96   9
14   39   8   54   70

② Which number is the largest? _____

③ Which number is the smallest? _____

④ How many numbers are smaller than 60? _____

⑤ How many 2-digit numbers are there? _____

⑥ Which number is 10 less than 76? _____

⑦ Which number is 5 more than 65? _____

⑧ Which number plus 20 is 70? _____

⑨ Which two numbers should be put in the following pattern?

_____ , 24, 34, 44, _____   _____ ; _____

ISBN: 978-1-897164-12-9

Count and write the numbers. Find the sums.

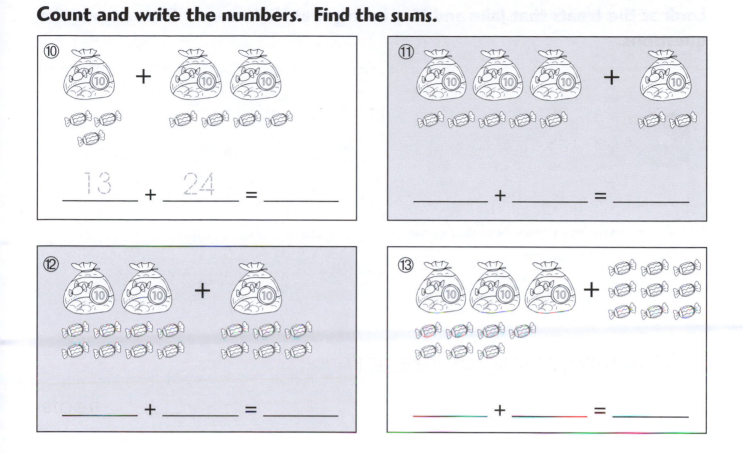

⑩ _13_ + _24_ = _____

⑪ _____ + _____ = _____

⑫ _____ + _____ = _____

⑬ _____ + _____ = _____

Count and write the numbers. Find the differences.

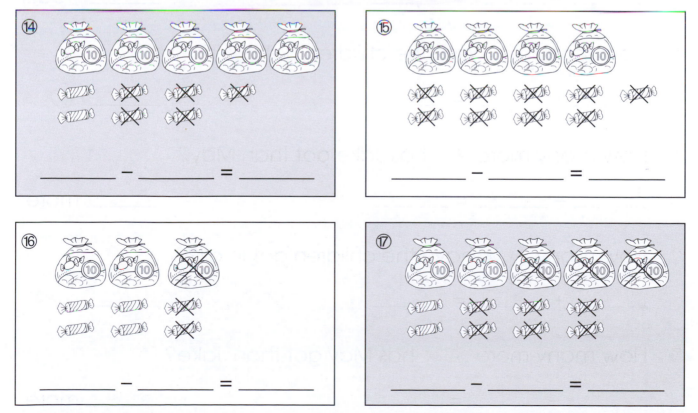

⑭ _____ − _____ = _____

⑮ _____ − _____ = _____

⑯ _____ − _____ = _____

⑰ _____ − _____ = _____

ISBN: 978-1-897164-12-9

Look at the treats that Jake and May have got at Halloween. Then answer the
questions.

⑱ How many treats has Jake got?

_____ + _____ = _____   _____ treats

⑲ How many treats has May got?

_____ + _____ = _____   _____ treats

⑳ How many 🍬 have the children got in all?

_____ + _____ = _____   _____ 🍬

㉑ How many more 🍬 has Jake got than May?

_____ – _____ = _____   _____ more

㉒ How many 🍬 have the children got in all?

_____ + _____ = _____   _____ 🍬

㉓ How many more 🍬 has May got than Jake?

_____ – _____ = _____   _____ more

ISBN: 978-1-897164-12-9

㉔ If May gives 6 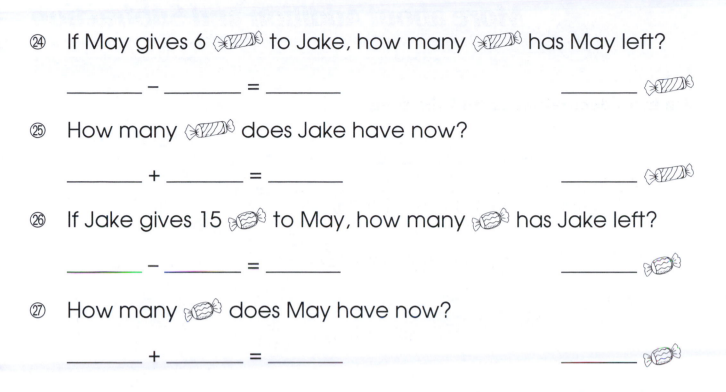 to Jake, how many candies has May left?

_____ – _____ = _____   _____ candy

㉕ How many candies does Jake have now?

_____ + _____ = _____   _____ candy

㉖ If Jake gives 15 candies to May, how many candies has Jake left?

_____ – _____ = _____   _____ candy

㉗ How many candies does May have now?

_____ + _____ = _____   _____ candy

These are Jake's containers for holding his candies. Write the name of each shape.

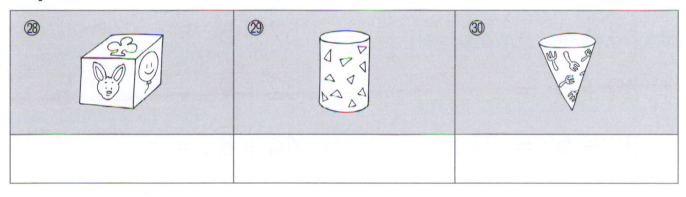

㉘	㉙	㉚

Look at the pictures on the containers. Draw their lines of symmetry.

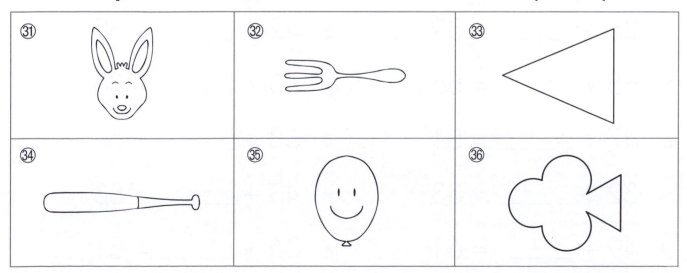

㉛	㉜	㉝
㉞	㉟	㊱

ISBN: 978-1-897164-12-9

Use Eva's decoration to find the sums.

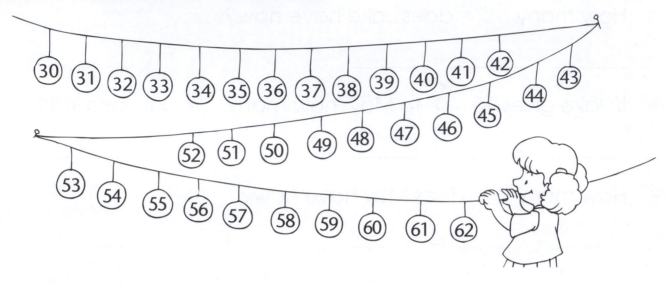

① 35 + 3 = _____

② 46 + 2 = _____

③ 53 + 4 = _____

④ 57 + 5 = _____

⑤ 49 + 8 = _____

⑥ 32 + 9 = _____

⑦ 33 + 5 = _____

⑧ 44 + 8 = _____

⑨ 47 + 11 = _____

⑩ 36 + 13 = _____

⑪ 35 + _____ = 39

⑫ 42 + _____ = 50

⑬ 55 + _____ = 56

⑭ 33 + _____ = 36

⑮ 47 + _____ = 51

⑯ 58 + _____ = 64

⑰ 32 + _____ = 33

⑱ 43 + _____ = 53

⑲ 49 + _____ = 61

⑳ 36 + _____ = 51

ISBN: 978-1-897164-12-9

Use Little Squirrel's maze to find the differences.

58 59 60 61 62 63 64 65
66
67
74 73 72 71 70 69 68
75
76 77 78 79 80 81 82 83 84 85

㉑ $73 - 2 =$ _____

㉒ $63 - 3 =$ _____

㉓ $84 - 3 =$ _____

㉔ $78 - 6 =$ _____

㉕ $70 - 5 =$ _____

㉖ $82 - 4 =$ _____

㉗ $63 - 5 =$ _____

㉘ $81 - 2 =$ _____

㉙ $77 - 9 =$ _____

㉚ $67 - 8 =$ _____

㉛ $65 -$ _____ $= 63$

㉜ $84 -$ _____ $= 81$

㉝ $77 -$ _____ $= 72$

㉞ $79 -$ _____ $= 70$

㉟ $62 -$ _____ $= 59$

㊱ $80 -$ _____ $= 73$

㊲ $71 -$ _____ $= 63$

㊳ $64 -$ _____ $= 58$

㊴ $82 -$ _____ $= 70$

㊵ $79 -$ _____ $= 69$

㊶ $77 -$ _____ $= 65$

㊷ $84 -$ _____ $= 71$

Complete each family of facts.

㊸ $18 - 7 = 11$

7 ___ $+$ ___ $=$ ___
___ $-$ 11 $=$ ___

㊹ $16 + 5 = 21$

___ $-$ ___ $=$ ___
___ $-$ ___ $=$ ___

㊺ $24 + 6 = 30$

___ $-$ ___ $=$ ___
___ $-$ ___ $=$ ___

㊻ $35 - 10 = 25$

___ $+$ ___ $=$ ___
___ $-$ ___ $=$ ___

㊼ $35 + 3 = 38$

___ $-$ ___ $=$ ___
___ $-$ ___ $=$ ___

㊽ $34 - 5 = 29$

___ $+$ ___ $=$ ___
___ $-$ ___ $=$ ___

㊾ $86 - 5 = 81$

___ $+$ ___ $=$ ___
___ $-$ ___ $=$ ___

㊿ $77 + 6 = 83$

___ $-$ ___ $=$ ___
___ $-$ ___ $=$ ___

51 $69 + 8 = 77$

___ $-$ ___ $=$ ___
___ $-$ ___ $=$ ___

52 $40 - 9 = 31$

___ $+$ ___ $=$ ___
___ $-$ ___ $=$ ___

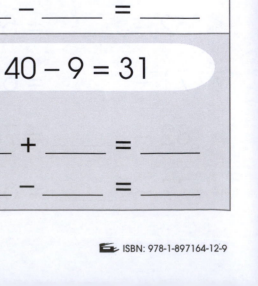 ISBN: 978-1-897164-12-9

Count and write how many stickers each child has. Then answer the questions.

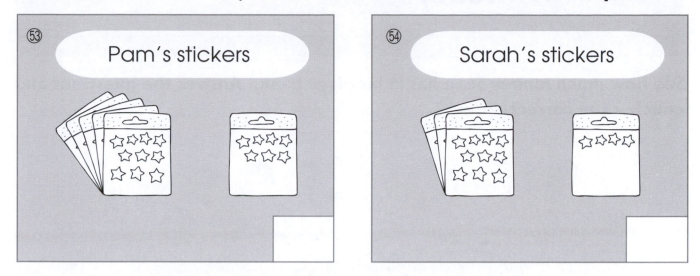

㊽ How many ☆ do the children have in all?

_____ = _____   _____ ☆

㊾ How many more ☆ does Pam have than Sarah?

_____ = _____   _____ ☆

㊿ A sticker album has space for 60 ☆ . If Pam pastes all her ☆ in the album, how many more ☆ can she put in?

_____ = _____   _____ more

㊹ If Sarah also pastes all her ☆ in the album, how many more ☆ can she put in it ?

_____ = _____   _____ more

㊺ If Pam gives 15 ☆ to Sarah, how many ☆ has she left?

_____ = _____   _____ ☆

㊿ How many ☆ does Sarah have now?

_____ = _____   _____ ☆

 **Money**

See how much money Sean has in his piggy bank. Answer the questions and check ✔ the correct answers.

① a. How many  does Sean have? _____

   b. What is the total value of the ? _____ ¢

② a. How many does Sean have? _____

   b. What is the total value of the ? _____ ¢

③ a. How many does Sean have? _____

   b. What is the total value of the ? _____ ¢

④ Which coin has the biggest size? A B C

⑤ Which coin has the greatest value? A B C

⑥ Which coin is worth less than 5¢? A B C

ISBN: 978-1-897164-12-9

Show 2 different ways the children can pay for their food by checking ✔ the coins used.

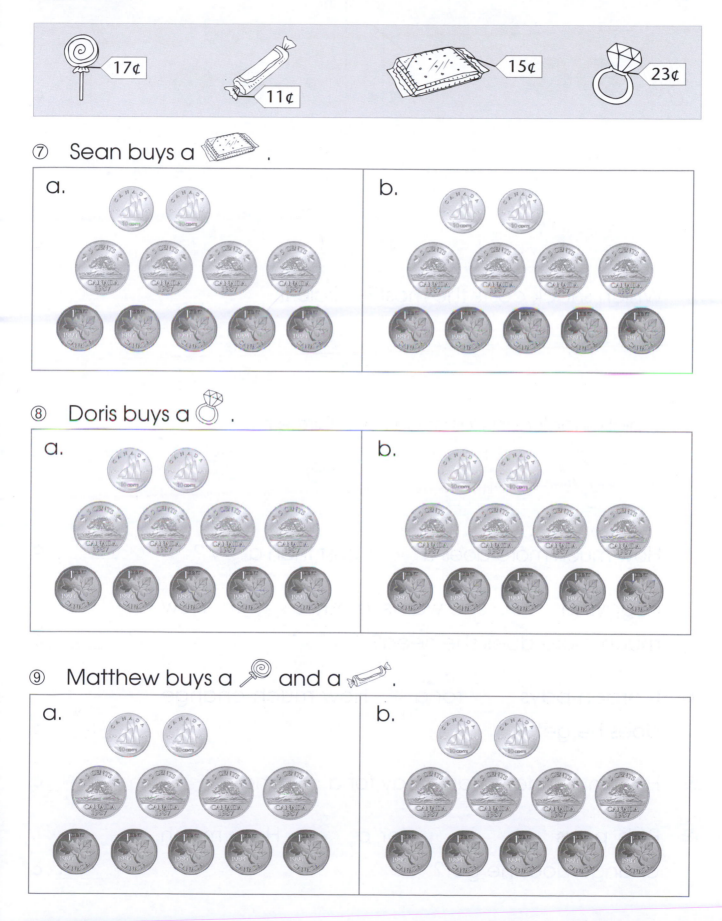

17¢   11¢   15¢   23¢

⑦ Sean buys a ▱ .

a.

b.

⑧ Doris buys a 💍 .

a.

b.

⑨ Matthew buys a 🍭 and a 🍬 .

a.

b.

Write how much each snack costs. Answer the questions.

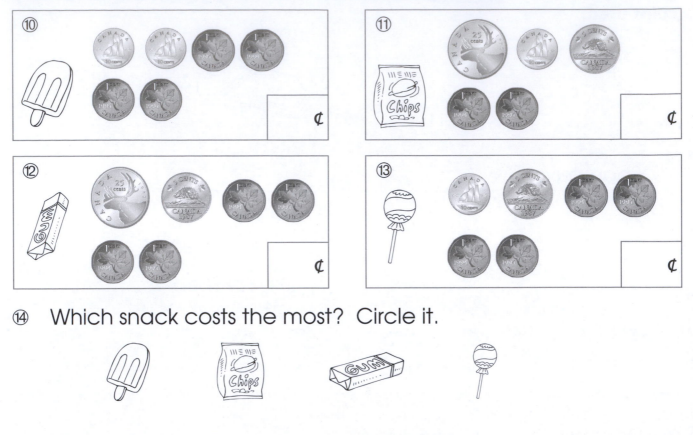

⑭ Which snack costs the most? Circle it.

⑮ Which snack costs less than 20¢? Circle it.

⑯ How much more does a 〈gum〉 cost than a 〈popsicle〉? _____ ¢

⑰ Peggy has 〈coin〉. She wants to buy a 〈gum〉. How
   much more does she need? _____ ¢

⑱ Gordon pays 〈coin〉 for a 〈lollipop〉. How much change
   does he get? _____ ¢

⑲ How much does Paula pay for a 〈popsicle〉 and a 〈chips〉? _____ ¢

⑳ Bob pays 〈coin〉 〈coin〉 〈coin〉 for a 〈chips〉. How much
   change does he get? _____ ¢

     ISBN: 978-1-897164-12-9

See how much Uncle Anthony and Aunt Sandra have. Answer the questions.

㉑ How many coins does Uncle Anthony have? _____ coins

㉒ How much does Uncle Anthony have? _____ ¢

㉓ How many coins does Aunt Sandra have? _____ coins

㉔ How much does Aunt Sandra have? _____ ¢

㉕ How many more coins does Uncle Anthony have than Aunt Sandra? _____ more

㉖ How much more does Aunt Sandra have than Uncle Anthony? _____ ¢

㉗ Uncle Anthony buys a 28¢. How much has he left? _____ ¢

㉘ Aunt Sandra gives 27¢ to Tommy. How much has she left? _____ ¢

㉙ After giving the money to Tommy, does Aunt Sandra have enough money to buy a for 45¢? _____

Measurement

Look at the pictures. Then write the times to complete the sentences.

① Jeffrey goes to bed at _____ .

② Jeffrey watches TV at _____ .

③ Jeffrey eats lunch at _____ .

④ Jeffrey wakes up at _____ .

See how heavy each person is. Then write their names to complete the sentences.

⑤ Rita and _____ weigh the same.

⑥ Sam is heavier than _____ .

⑦ Alan and _____ are both heavier than either _____

or _____ .

⑧ The lightest person is _____ .

ISBN: 978-1-897164-12-9

Gordon uses his lollipops to measure the lengths and widths of the pictures. Help him fill in the numbers and circle the correct words.

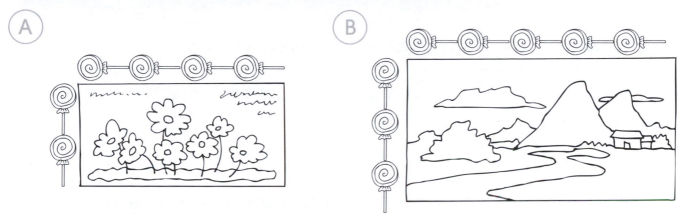

⑨ The length of A has the same length as _____ 🍭 .

⑩ The width of A has the same length as _____ 🍭 .

⑪ The length of B is a little longer than the length of _____
🍭 .

⑫ The width of B is almost equal to the length of _____ 🍭 .

⑬ The length of A is _____   shorter / longer   than the length of B.

⑭ The width of B is _____   shorter / longer   than the width of A.

In each group, check ✔ the one that holds the most water.

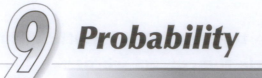

Probability

Look at the spinners. Then check ✔ the correct answers.

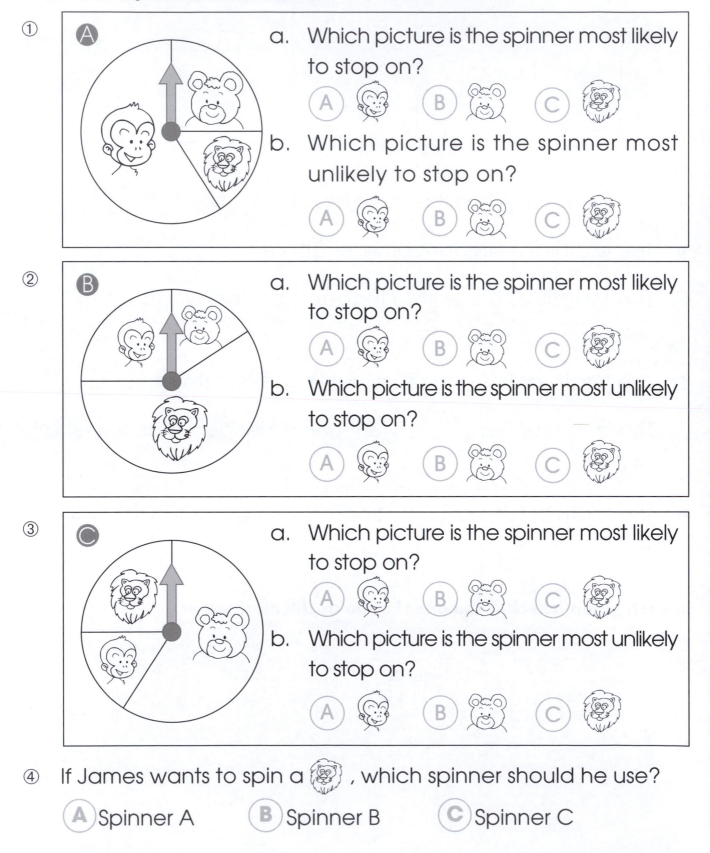

①

A

a. Which picture is the spinner most likely to stop on?

Ⓐ 🐵   Ⓑ 🐻   Ⓒ 🦁

b. Which picture is the spinner most unlikely to stop on?

Ⓐ 🐵   Ⓑ 🐻   Ⓒ 🦁

②

B

a. Which picture is the spinner most likely to stop on?

Ⓐ 🐵   Ⓑ 🐻   Ⓒ 🦁

b. Which picture is the spinner most unlikely to stop on?

Ⓐ 🐵   Ⓑ 🐻   Ⓒ 🦁

③

C

a. Which picture is the spinner most likely to stop on?

Ⓐ 🐵   Ⓑ 🐻   Ⓒ 🦁

b. Which picture is the spinner most unlikely to stop on?

Ⓐ 🐵   Ⓑ 🐻   Ⓒ 🦁

④ If James wants to spin a 🦁 , which spinner should he use?

Ⓐ Spinner A   **Ⓑ** Spinner B   **Ⓒ** Spinner C

   ISBN: 978-1-897164-12-9

Aunt Molly has a lot of juices. Jenny is going to pick a box of juice. Help Jenny check ✔ the correct answers.

⑤ Which kind of juice is Jenny most likely to pick?

Ⓐ [apple]   Ⓑ [orange]   Ⓒ [Fruit Punch]

⑥ Which kind of juice is Jenny most unlikely to pick?

Ⓐ [orange]   Ⓑ [Fruit Punch]   Ⓒ [grape]

⑦ Which is the best word to describe the chance of picking a [Coke] ?

Ⓐ Never   Ⓑ Maybe   Ⓒ Likely

⑧ Is there a better chance that Jenny will pick a [apple] , [grape] or [Fruit Punch] ?

Ⓐ [apple]   Ⓑ [grape]   Ⓒ [Fruit Punch]

Circle the best word for each sentence.

⑨ When you flip a coin, it is   impossible / probable / likely   to have the coin landing on its head.

⑩ When you toss a die, it is   impossible / probable / likely   to get a 7.

ISBN: 978-1-897164-12-9

Pictographs

Mr Vann recorded the weather on his holiday. Use his graph to answer the questions.

Weather on Mr Vann's Holiday

① How many days were ☀ ? _____ days

② How many days were 🌧 ? _____ days

③ How many days were ☁ ? _____ days

④ How many more days were ☀ than 🌧 ? _____ more

⑤ How many more days were ☁ than 🌧 ? _____ more

⑥ How many days were not 🌧 ? _____ days

⑦ Was there more 🌧 than ☁ on

Mr Vann's holidays? _____

⑧ How long was Mr Vann's holiday? _____ days

⑨ Which weather occurred the most? Colour it. ☀ 🌧 ☁

   ISBN: 978-1-897164-12-9

Use the graph to answer the questions.

Number of Pets in Pet Shop

⑩ How many cats are white?   _____ cats

⑪ How many cats are black?   _____ cats

⑫ How many dogs are white?   _____ dogs

⑬ How many dogs are black?   _____ dogs

⑭ How many cats are there in all?   _____ cats

⑮ How many dogs are there in all?   _____ dogs

⑯ How many more dogs than cats are there?   _____ more

⑰ How many pets are white?   _____ pets

⑱ How many pets are black?   _____ pets

⑲ How many more pets in black than in white
    are there?   _____ more

⑳ How many pets are there in the pet shop?   _____ pets

See how many boxes of drinks Aunt Daisy buys. Colour the drinks to complete the graph and fill in the blanks.

㉑

Number of Drinks Aunt Daisy Buys

㉒ How many boxes of 🧃 does Aunt Daisy buy?   ＿＿ boxes

㉓ How many boxes of juices does Aunt Daisy
    buy in all?   ＿＿ boxes

㉔ How many boxes of 🥛 does Aunt Daisy buy?   ＿＿ boxes

㉕ How many boxes of milk does Aunt Daisy
    buy in all?   ＿＿ boxes

ISBN: 978-1-897164-12-9

See how many cards Julia has. Help her colour the graphs and fill in the blanks.

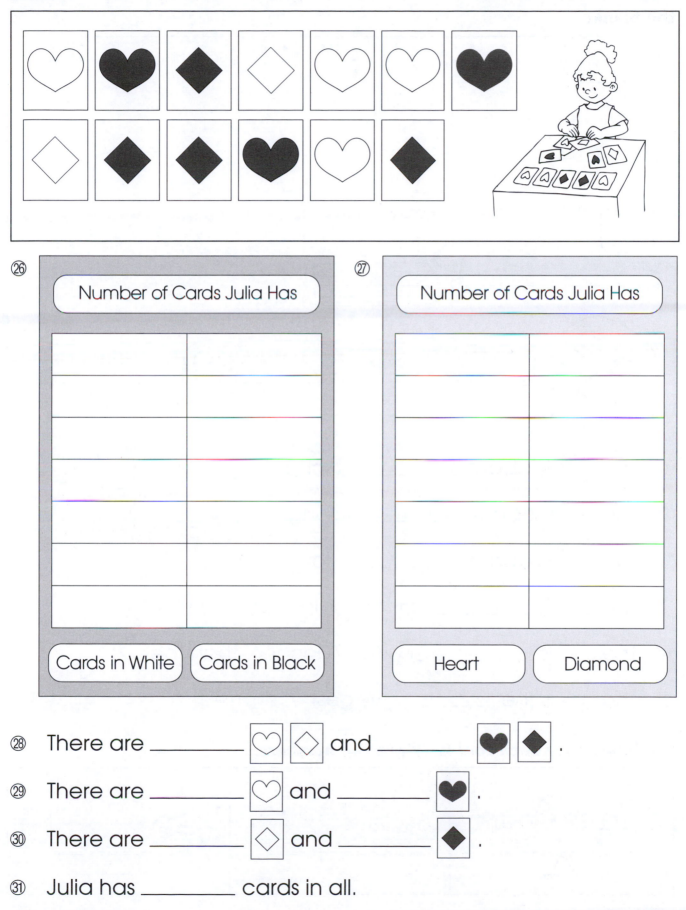

㉖ Number of Cards Julia Has

Cards in White	Cards in Black

㉗ Number of Cards Julia Has

Heart	Diamond

㉘ There are _____ ♡ ◇ and _____ ♥ ◆ .

㉙ There are _____ ♡ and _____ ♥ .

㉚ There are _____ ◇ and _____ ◆ .

㉛ Julia has _____ cards in all.

ISBN: 978-1-897164-12-9

Final Review

Mr Jenkin uses his nails to measure the lengths of the tools. Help him fill in the blanks.

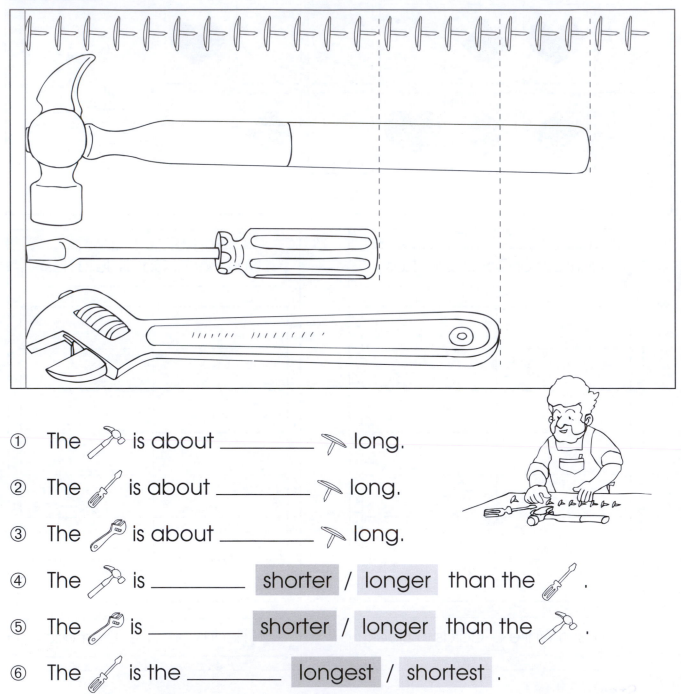

① The 🔨 is about _____ ⚒ long.

② The 🪛 is about _____ ⚒ long.

③ The 🔧 is about _____ ⚒ long.

④ The 🔨 is _____ shorter / longer than the 🪛 .

⑤ The 🔧 is _____ shorter / longer than the 🔨 .

⑥ The 🪛 is the _____ longest / shortest .

See how heavy each tool is. Write the numbers.

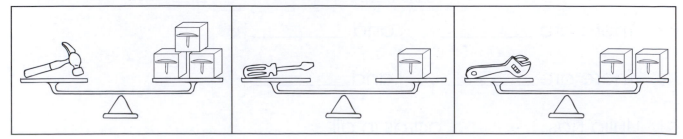

ISBN: 978-1-897164-12-9

⑦ The 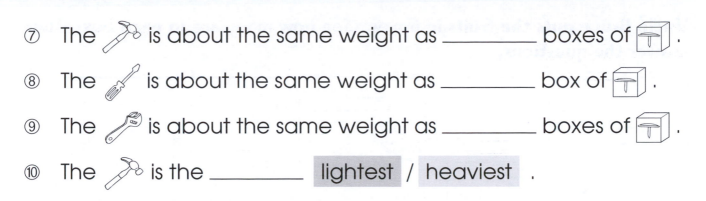 is about the same weight as _____ boxes of 📦 .

⑧ The ✎ is about the same weight as _____ box of 📦 .

⑨ The ⚙ is about the same weight as _____ boxes of 📦 .

⑩ The 🔨 is the _____ lightest / heaviest .

Mr Jenkin sells the tools in a garage sale. Write the price of each tool. Then answer the questions.

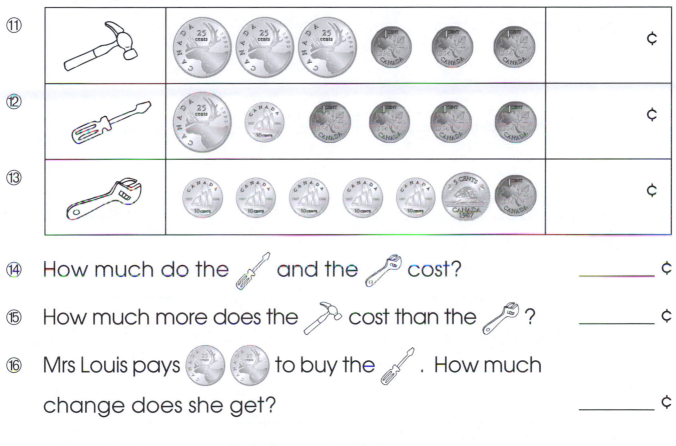

		¢
⑪		¢
⑫		¢
⑬		¢

⑭ How much do the ✎ and the ⚙ cost? _____ ¢

⑮ How much more does the 🔨 cost than the ⚙ ? _____ ¢

⑯ Mrs Louis pays 🪙 🪙 to buy the ✎ . How much
change does she get? _____ ¢

See what time Mr Jenkin started and finished the sale.   Draw the clock hands.

⑰ Start Time   10:30 a.m.   ⑱ Finish Time   4:00 p.m.

Uncle Bruce puts the fruits in boxes. See how many are in each box. Then answer the questions.

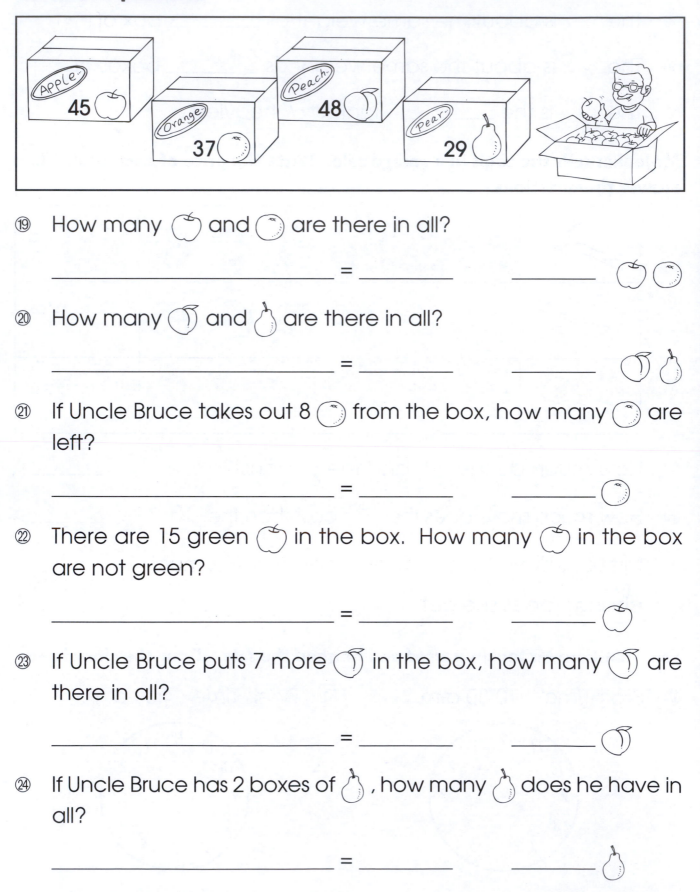

⑲ How many 🍎 and 🍑 are there in all?

_____ = _____   _____ 🍎🍑

⑳ How many 🍑 and 🍐 are there in all?

_____ = _____   _____ 🍑🍐

㉑ If Uncle Bruce takes out 8 🍊 from the box, how many 🍊 are left?

_____ = _____   _____ 🍊

㉒ There are 15 green 🍎 in the box. How many 🍎 in the box are not green?

_____ = _____   _____ 🍎

㉓ If Uncle Bruce puts 7 more 🍑 in the box, how many 🍑 are there in all?

_____ = _____   _____ 🍑

㉔ If Uncle Bruce has 2 boxes of 🍐 , how many 🍐 does he have in all?

_____ = _____   _____ 🍐

   ISBN: 978-1-897164-12-9

Look at the graphs. Then answer the questions.

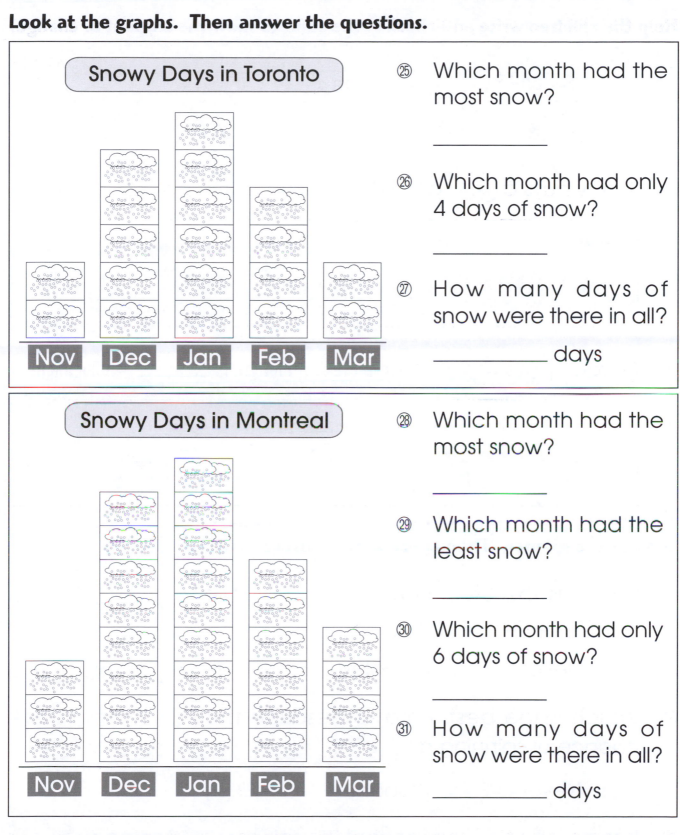

Snowy Days in Toronto

Nov Dec Jan Feb Mar

㉕ Which month had the most snow?

_____

㉖ Which month had only 4 days of snow?

_____

㉗ How many days of snow were there in all?

_____ days

Snowy Days in Montreal

Nov Dec Jan Feb Mar

㉘ Which month had the most snow?

_____

㉙ Which month had the least snow?

_____

㉚ Which month had only 6 days of snow?

_____

㉛ How many days of snow were there in all?

_____ days

㉜ Which city had more snow? _____

㉝ How many more days of snow did Montreal have than Toronto in February? _____ more days

Help the children write and check ✔ the coins to show the amount or change.

㉞ Sandy buys a  and a ⬭ . She has to pay _____ ¢.

㉟ Gordon pays 🪙🪙 for a ◎ . He gets _____ ¢ change.

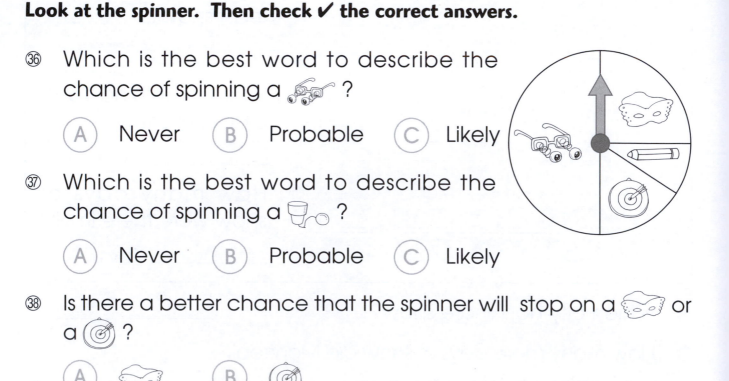

Look at the spinner. Then check ✔ the correct answers.

㊱ Which is the best word to describe the chance of spinning a 👓 ?

Ⓐ Never   Ⓑ Probable   Ⓒ Likely

㊲ Which is the best word to describe the chance of spinning a ⬭ ?

Ⓐ Never   Ⓑ Probable   Ⓒ Likely

㊳ Is there a better chance that the spinner will stop on a 🎭 or a ◎ ?

Ⓐ 🎭   Ⓑ ◎

ISBN: 978-1-897164-12-9

Section II

Overview

In Section I, children developed addition and subtraction skills up to 100, including money applications.

They also had opportunities to work with 2- and 3-dimensional shapes, organize and analyse data using charts, pictographs and bar graphs, and use non-standard units in measuring height, length and weight.

In this section, addition and subtraction skills are emphasized. Many exercises are provided for drill and practice with 2-digit numbers. Mastery of mental arithmetic is the goal of those exercises.

ISBN: 978-1-897164-12-9

1 Addition and Subtraction Facts to 20

Jack has 11 🍭 . Jane has 7 🍭 .

1. How many more 🍭 does Jack have than Jane?

   $11 - 7 = 4$ 4 more 🍭 .

2. How many 🍭 do they have in all?

   $11 + 7 = 18$ 18 🍭 in all.

HINTS:

- Read each problem carefully to see whether to add or subtract.
- Watch the sign.

Add or subtract.

①
$$\begin{array}{r} 12 \\ +\ \ 6 \\ \hline 18 \end{array}$$

②
$$\begin{array}{r} 18 \\ -\ \ 4 \\ \hline \end{array}$$

③
$$\begin{array}{r} 15 \\ -\ \ 7 \\ \hline \end{array}$$

④
$$\begin{array}{r} 14 \\ +\ \ 3 \\ \hline \end{array}$$

⑤
$$\begin{array}{r} 2 \\ +\ 16 \\ \hline \end{array}$$

⑥
$$\begin{array}{r} 17 \\ -\ \ 5 \\ \hline \end{array}$$

⑦ $9 + 5$ = _____

⑧ $11 - 6$ = _____

⑨ $16 - 12$ = _____

⑩ $8 + 6$ = _____

⑪ $3 + 15$ = _____

⑫ $19 - 8$ = _____

⑬ $20 - 7$ = _____

⑭ $7 + 6$ = _____

⑮ $2 + 8 + 5$ = _____

⑯ $4 + 2 + 7$ = _____

ISBN: 978-1-897164-12-9

Write the missing numbers.

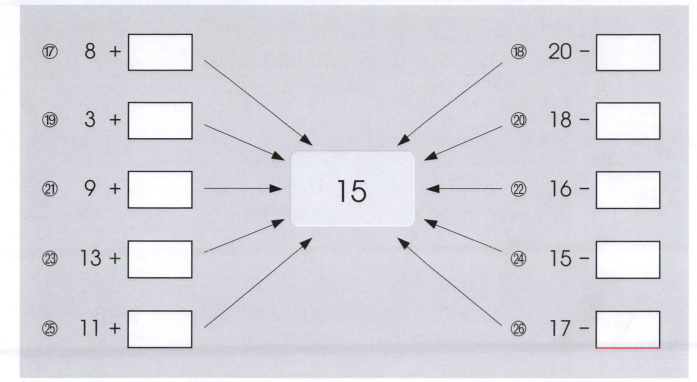

⑰ 8 + ☐

⑲ 3 + ☐

㉑ 9 + ☐

㉓ 13 + ☐

㉕ 11 + ☐

15

⑱ 20 − ☐

⑳ 18 − ☐

㉒ 16 − ☐

㉔ 15 − ☐

㉖ 17 − ☐

Fill in the ◯ with + or −.

㉗
```
  12
◯  7
─────
  19
```

㉘
```
  17
◯   6
─────
  11
```

㉙
```
  12
◯   8
─────
  20
```

㉚
```
  16
◯   4
─────
  12
```

㉛
```
  18
◯ 14
─────
   4
```

㉜
```
   9
◯   7
─────
  16
```

㉝
```
  13
◯   7
─────
   6
```

㉞
```
  19
◯ 17
─────
   2
```

㉟
```
  11
◯   8
─────
   3
```

㊱
```
  12
◯   6
─────
  18
```

㊲
```
  14
◯   6
─────
  20
```

㊳
```
  15
◯   7
─────
   8
```

ISBN: 978-1-897164-12-9

Colour the bones that match each number.

③⑨
8

| 12 − 6 | 18 − 10 | 6 + 2 |

④⓪
13

| 6 + 7 | 16 − 3 | 17 − 5 |

④①
17

| 12 + 5 | 20 − 4 | 9 + 8 |

④②
12

| 6 + 5 | 15 − 3 | 17 − 5 |

④③
10

| 19 − 8 | 3 + 7 | 16 − 6 |

Complete the related number sentences.

④④ $6 + 6 = 12$

a. $6 + 7 = \underline{\hspace{2cm}}$

b. $6 + 8 = \underline{\hspace{2cm}}$

c. $6 + 9 = \underline{\hspace{2cm}}$

d. $6 + 10 = \underline{\hspace{2cm}}$

④⑤ $16 − 8 = 8$

a. $16 − 7 = \underline{\hspace{2cm}}$

b. $16 − 6 = \underline{\hspace{2cm}}$

c. $16 − 5 = \underline{\hspace{2cm}}$

d. $16 − 4 = \underline{\hspace{2cm}}$

ISBN: 978-1-897164-12-9

Complete.

46 Mom buys 12 red ⬤ and 6 green ⬤ .
How many ⬤ does she buy in all?

_____ = _____   _____ ⬤ in all.

47 There are 16 🍬 in the bag. Sue eats 12 🍬 .
How many 🍬 are left in the bag?

_____ = _____   _____ 🍬 left.

48 There are 20 children in the class. 12 of them are boys.
How many girls are there in the class?

_____ = _____   _____ girls.

49 Sue has 10 red 🧱 and 5 green 🧱 .
How many 🧱 does Sue have altogether?

_____ = _____   _____ 🧱 altogether.

Just for Fun

Count by 5's to help Little Bunny get the carrot. Draw the path.

20	25	30	55	60	90
5	20	45	50	65	100
10	15	40	35	70	95
5	20	35	80	75	100
10	25	30	85	90	95

ISBN: 978-1-897164-12-9

2 More about Addition Facts

$$4 + 3 = 7 \qquad 3 + 4 = 7$$
$$4 + 3 = 3 + 4 = 7$$

HINTS:

- Even if the order of an addition changes, the answer is the same.

  e.g. $4 + 3 = 3 + 4 = 7$

- Different addition sentences may give the same SUM.

  e.g. $2 + 3 = 1 + 4 = 5$

Complete the related facts.

①
a. $2 + 3 = \underline{\quad 5 \quad}$

b. $3 + 2 = \underline{\qquad}$

c. $2 + 3 = 3 + 2 = \underline{\qquad}$

②
a. $5 + 3 = \underline{\qquad}$

b. $3 + 5 = \underline{\qquad}$

c. $5 + 3 = 3 + 5 = \underline{\qquad}$

③
a. $4 + 6 = \underline{\qquad}$

b. $6 + 4 = \underline{\qquad}$

c. $4 + 6 = 6 + 4 = \underline{\qquad}$

④
a. $0 + 5 = \underline{\qquad}$

b. $5 + 0 = \underline{\qquad}$

c. $0 + 5 = 5 + 0 = \underline{\qquad}$

⑤
a. $2 + 6 = \underline{\qquad}$

b. $6 + 2 = \underline{\qquad}$

c. $2 + 6 = 6 + 2 = \underline{\qquad}$

ISBN: 978-1-897164-12-9

Write the missing numbers.

⑥ 3 + 8 = 8 + _____

⑦ 5 + 7 = _____ + 5

⑧ 11 + 4 = _____ + 11

⑨ 8 + 9 = 9 + _____

⑩ 10 + _____ = 7 + 10

⑪ 5 + _____ = 6 + 5

⑫ _____ + 12 = 12 + 6

⑬ _____ + 4 = 4 + 13

⑭ 14 + 6 = _____ + 14

⑮ 17 + 2 = 2 + _____

Complete and match.

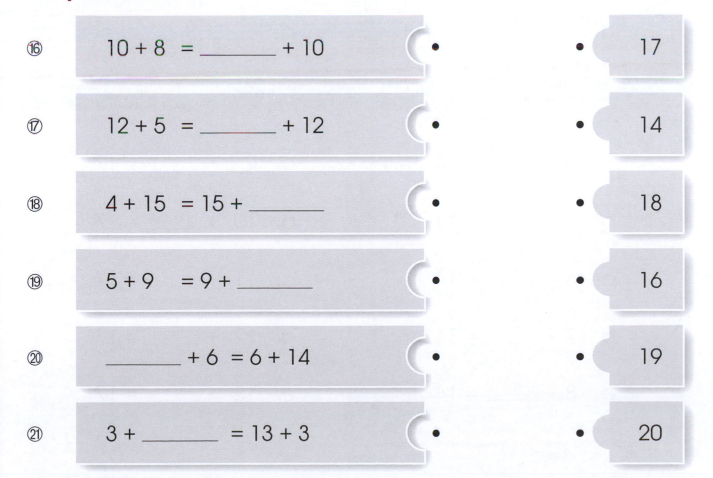

⑯ 10 + 8 = _____ + 10

⑰ 12 + 5 = _____ + 12

⑱ 4 + 15 = 15 + _____

⑲ 5 + 9 = 9 + _____

⑳ _____ + 6 = 6 + 14

㉑ 3 + _____ = 13 + 3

17

14

18

16

19

20

ISBN: 978-1-897164-12-9

Write different addition sentences for each sum.

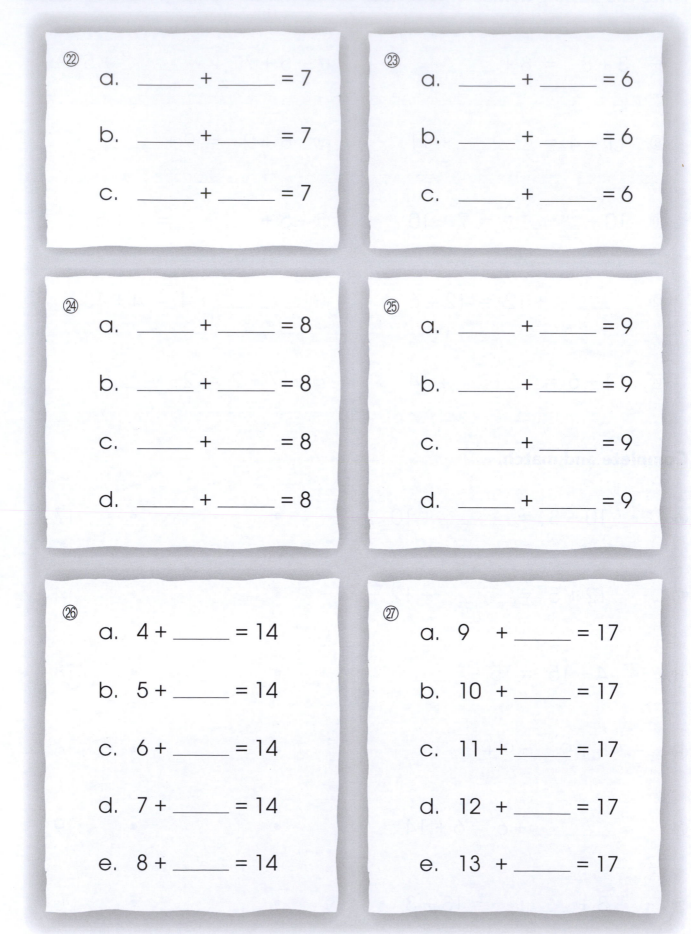

㉒
a. _____ + _____ = 7

b. _____ + _____ = 7

c. _____ + _____ = 7

㉓
a. _____ + _____ = 6

b. _____ + _____ = 6

c. _____ + _____ = 6

㉔
a. _____ + _____ = 8

b. _____ + _____ = 8

c. _____ + _____ = 8

d. _____ + _____ = 8

㉕
a. _____ + _____ = 9

b. _____ + _____ = 9

c. _____ + _____ = 9

d. _____ + _____ = 9

㉖
a. 4 + _____ = 14

b. 5 + _____ = 14

c. 6 + _____ = 14

d. 7 + _____ = 14

e. 8 + _____ = 14

㉗
a. 9 + _____ = 17

b. 10 + _____ = 17

c. 11 + _____ = 17

d. 12 + _____ = 17

e. 13 + _____ = 17

ISBN: 978-1-897164-12-9

The children are playing darts. Look at their scores. Complete each number sentence. Find their scores in the 2nd round.

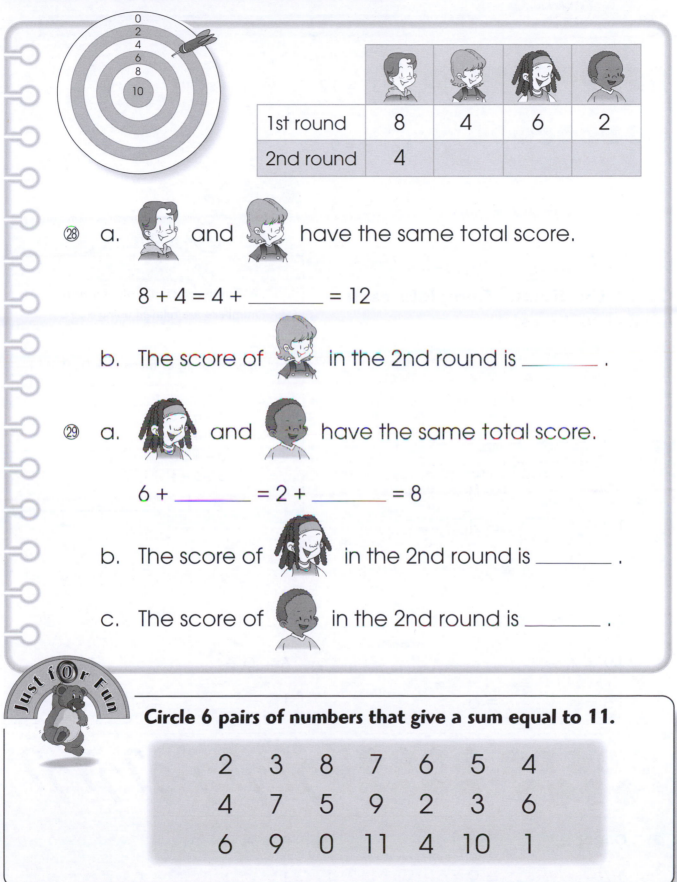

1st round	8	4	6	2
2nd round	4			

㉘ a. ☺ and ☺ have the same total score.

8 + 4 = 4 + _____ = 12

b. The score of ☺ in the 2nd round is _____ .

㉙ a. ☺ and ☺ have the same total score.

6 + _____ = 2 + _____ = 8

b. The score of ☺ in the 2nd round is _____ .

c. The score of ☺ in the 2nd round is _____ .

Just for Fun

Circle 6 pairs of numbers that give a sum equal to 11.

2 3 8 7 6 5 4

4 7 5 9 2 3 6

6 9 0 11 4 10 1

3 Relating Subtraction to Addition

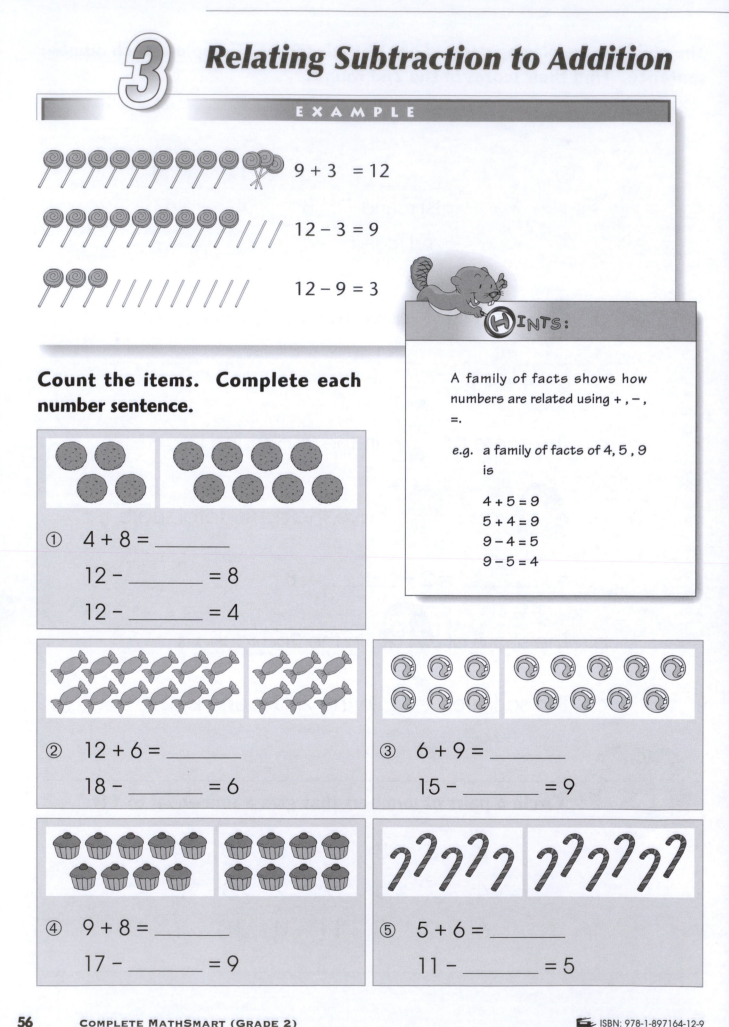

$9 + 3 = 12$

$12 - 3 = 9$

$12 - 9 = 3$

HINTS:

A family of facts shows how numbers are related using + , − , =.

e.g. a family of facts of 4, 5 , 9 is

$4 + 5 = 9$
$5 + 4 = 9$
$9 - 4 = 5$
$9 - 5 = 4$

Count the items. Complete each number sentence.

① $4 + 8 = $ _____

$12 - $ _____ $= 8$

$12 - $ _____ $= 4$

② $12 + 6 = $ _____

$18 - $ _____ $= 6$

③ $6 + 9 = $ _____

$15 - $ _____ $= 9$

④ $9 + 8 = $ _____

$17 - $ _____ $= 9$

⑤ $5 + 6 = $ _____

$11 - $ _____ $= 5$

Complete each family of facts.

⑥ 8 — 6 — 14

___8___ + _____ = _____

___6___ + _____ = _____

14 − ___8___ = _____

14 − _____ = ___8___

⑦ 5 — 6 — 11

_____ + _____ = _____

_____ + _____ = _____

_____ − _____ = _____

_____ − _____ = _____

⑧ 4 — 9 — 13

_____ + _____ = _____

_____ + _____ = _____

_____ − _____ = _____

_____ − _____ = _____

⑨ 12 — 7 — 19

_____ + _____ = _____

_____ + _____ = _____

_____ − _____ = _____

_____ − _____ = _____

⑩ 7 — 9 — 16

_____ + _____ = _____

_____ + _____ = _____

_____ − _____ = _____

_____ − _____ = _____

⑪ 11 — 6 — 17

_____ + _____ = _____

_____ + _____ = _____

_____ − _____ = _____

_____ − _____ = _____

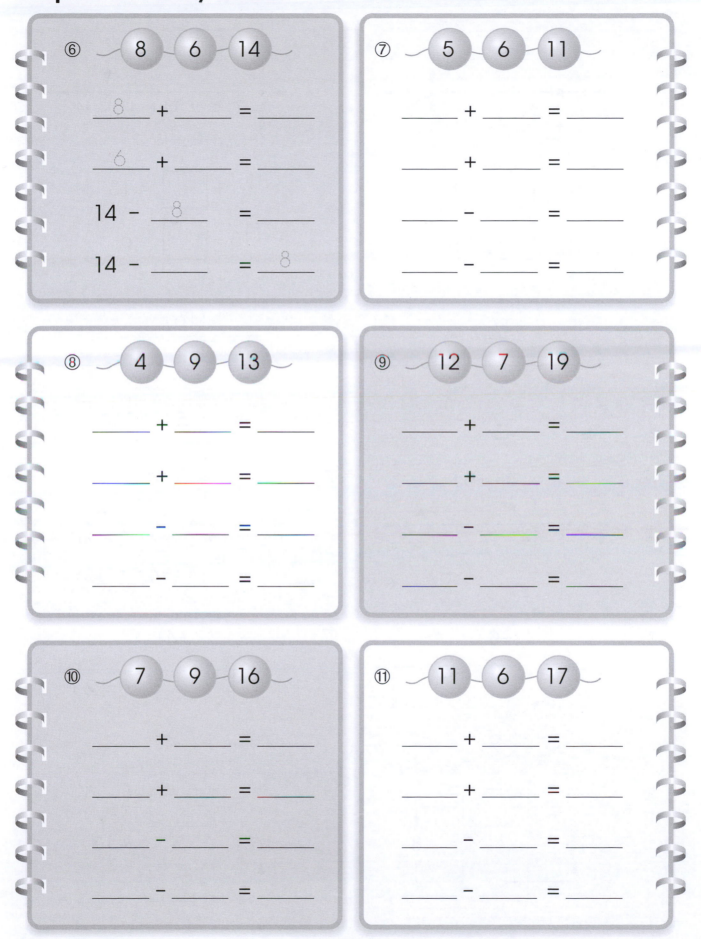

ISBN: 978-1-897164-12-9

Write the missing numbers.

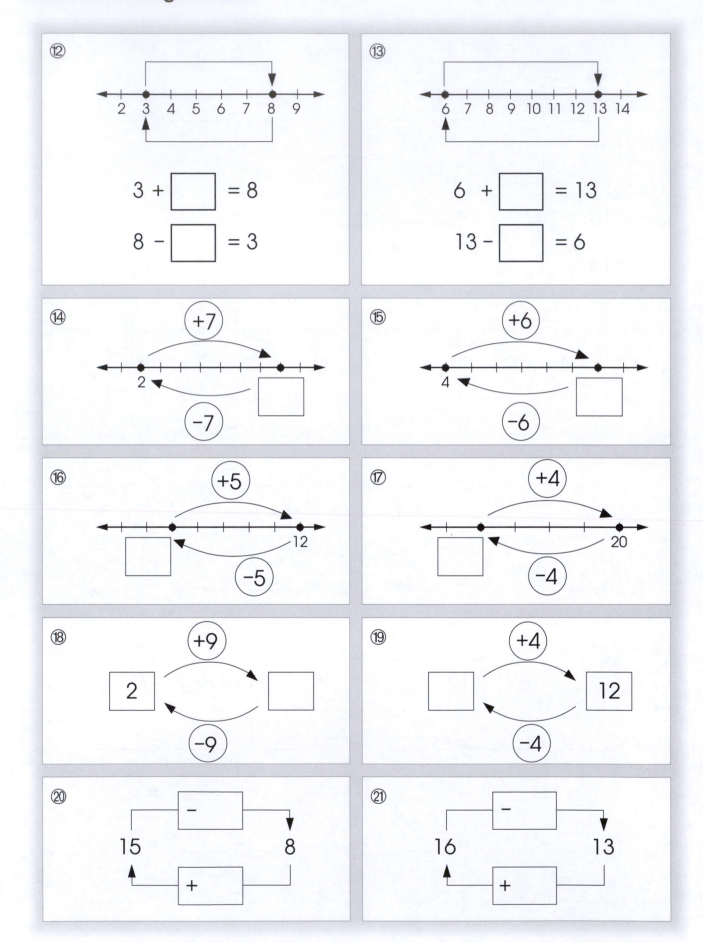

⑫

$3 + \boxed{} = 8$

$8 - \boxed{} = 3$

⑬

$6 + \boxed{} = 13$

$13 - \boxed{} = 6$

⑭ +7 / 2 / −7

⑮ +6 / 4 / −6

⑯ +5 / 12 / −5

⑰ +4 / 20 / −4

⑱ 2 / +9 / −9

⑲ +4 / 12 / −4

⑳ 15 − 8 +

㉑ 16 − 13 +

ISBN: 978-1-897164-12-9

Use the family of facts. Fill in the missing numbers.

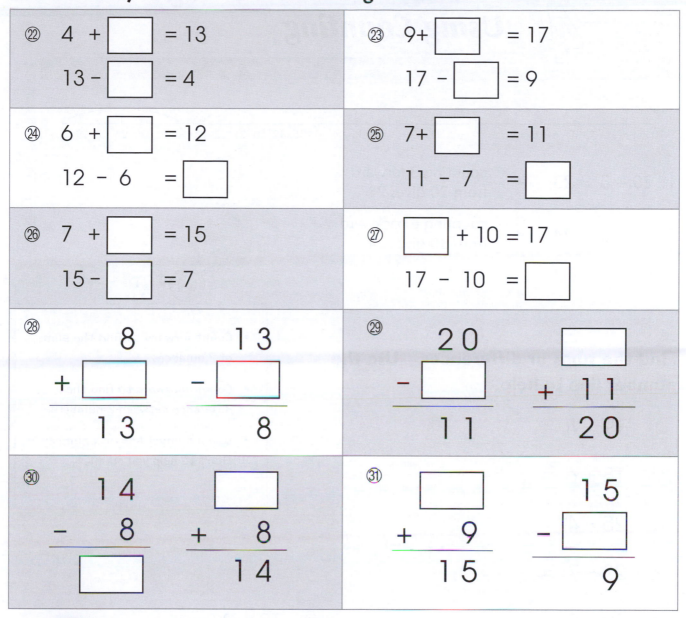

㉒ 4 + ☐ = 13

13 − ☐ = 4

㉓ 9 + ☐ = 17

17 − ☐ = 9

㉔ 6 + ☐ = 12

12 − 6 = ☐

㉕ 7 + ☐ = 11

11 − 7 = ☐

㉖ 7 + ☐ = 15

15 − ☐ = 7

㉗ ☐ + 10 = 17

17 − 10 = ☐

㉘
```
   8          13
 + ☐        − ☐
 ───        ───
  13          8
```

㉙
```
  20          ☐
 − ☐       + 11
 ───        ───
  11         20
```

㉚
```
  14          ☐
 −  8       +  8
 ───        ───
   ☐         14
```

㉛
```
   ☐          15
 +  9       −  ☐
 ───        ───
  15           9
```

Colour the squares red, the rectangles yellow, the triangles blue and the circles green.

ISBN: 978-1-897164-12-9

4 Adding and Subtracting Using Counting

number line from 0 to 30

1. $20 + 3 = 23$ ← counting 3 forward from 20 gives 23

2. $30 - 6 = 24$ ← counting 6 backward from 30 gives 24

HINTS:

- Count forward to find the sum of 2 numbers.

- Count backward to find the difference between 2 numbers.

- Use a number line or a number chart to help you count.

Find the sums or differences. Use the number line to help.

① $19 + 4 =$ _____

② $18 + 6 =$ _____

③ $25 - 4 =$ _____

④ $23 - 7 =$ _____

⑤ $29 - 5 =$ _____

⑥ $18 + 9 =$ _____

⑦ $16 + 6 =$ _____

⑧ $26 - 5 =$ _____

⑨ $27 - 8 =$ _____

⑩ $20 + 8 =$ _____

⑪ $30 - 12 =$ _____

⑫ $16 + 10 =$ _____

⑬ $22 + 7 =$ _____

⑭ $28 - 6 =$ _____

⑮ $17 + 9 =$ _____

⑯ $27 - 9 =$ _____

⑰ $24 + 6 =$ _____

⑱ $22 - 8 =$ _____

Add or subtract. Use the number chart to help.

51	52	53	54	55	56	57	58	59	60
61	62	63	64	65	66	67	68	69	70
71	72	73	74	75	76	77	78	79	80
81	82	83	84	85	86	87	88	89	90

⑲ 65 – 8 = _____

⑳ 78 – 11 = _____

㉑ 52 + 6 = _____

㉒ 68 + 7 = _____

㉓ 84 – 12 = _____

㉔ 81 + 8 = _____

㉕ 77 + 9 = _____

㉖ 90 – 11 = _____

㉗ 58 + 8 = _____

㉘ 62 – 6 = _____

㉙
```
   6 2
 –   1
 _____
```

㉚
```
   7 0
 + 1 4
 _____
```

㉛
```
   8 9
 – 1 0
 _____
```

㉜
```
   6 9
 +   5
 _____
```

㉝
```
   8 1
 +   7
 _____
```

㉞
```
   9 0
 –   8
 _____
```

㉟
```
   7 5
 – 2 0
 _____
```

㊱
```
   6 3
 + 1 7
 _____
```

Count and complete the addition sentences.

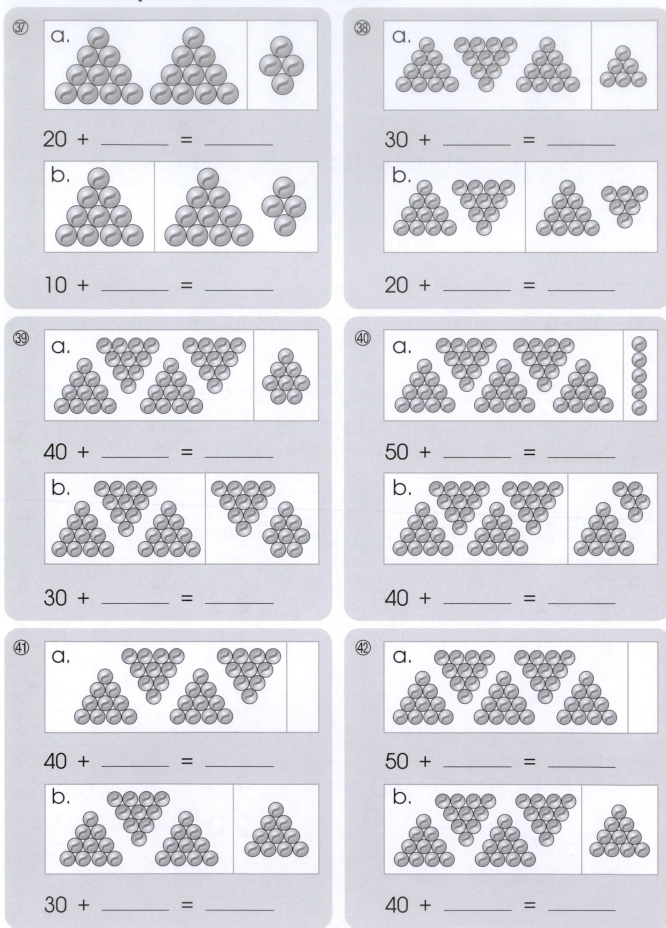

㊲
a.

20 + _____ = _____

b.

10 + _____ = _____

㊳
a.

30 + _____ = _____

b.

20 + _____ = _____

㊴
a.

40 + _____ = _____

b.

30 + _____ = _____

㊵
a.

50 + _____ = _____

b.

40 + _____ = _____

㊶
a.

40 + _____ = _____

b.

30 + _____ = _____

㊷
a.

50 + _____ = _____

b.

40 + _____ = _____

ISBN: 978-1-897164-12-9

Cross out and count. Complete the subtraction sentences.

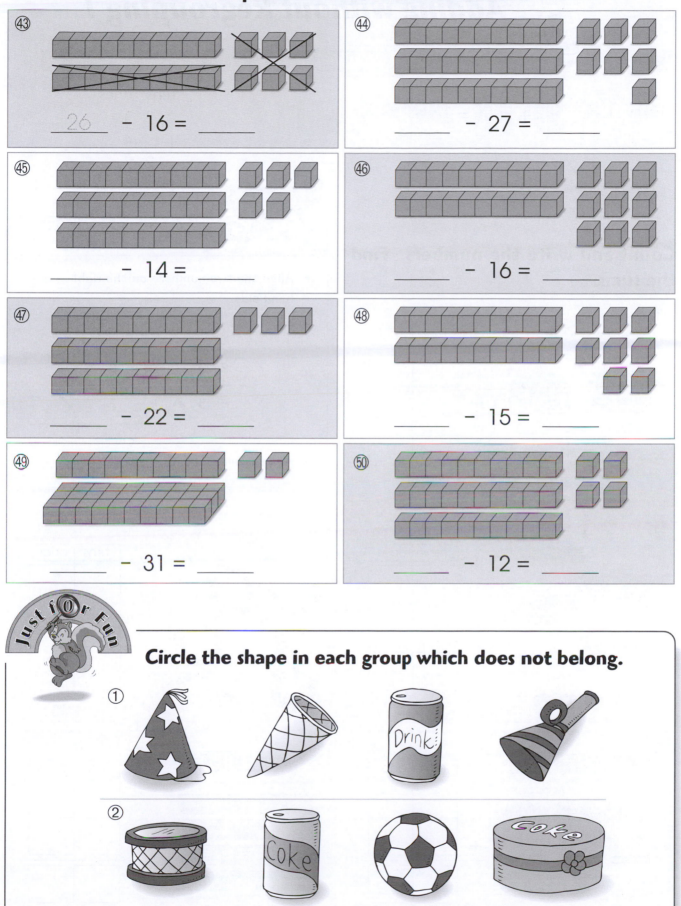

43   _26_ – 16 = _____

44   _____ – 27 = _____

45   _____ – 14 = _____

46   _____ – 16 = _____

47   _____ – 22 = _____

48   _____ – 15 = _____

49   _____ – 31 = _____

50   _____ – 12 = _____

Just for Fun

Circle the shape in each group which does not belong.

① party hat   cone   Drink can   horn

② drum   Coke can   soccer ball   Coke box

ISBN: 978-1-897164-12-9

5 Adding without Regrouping I

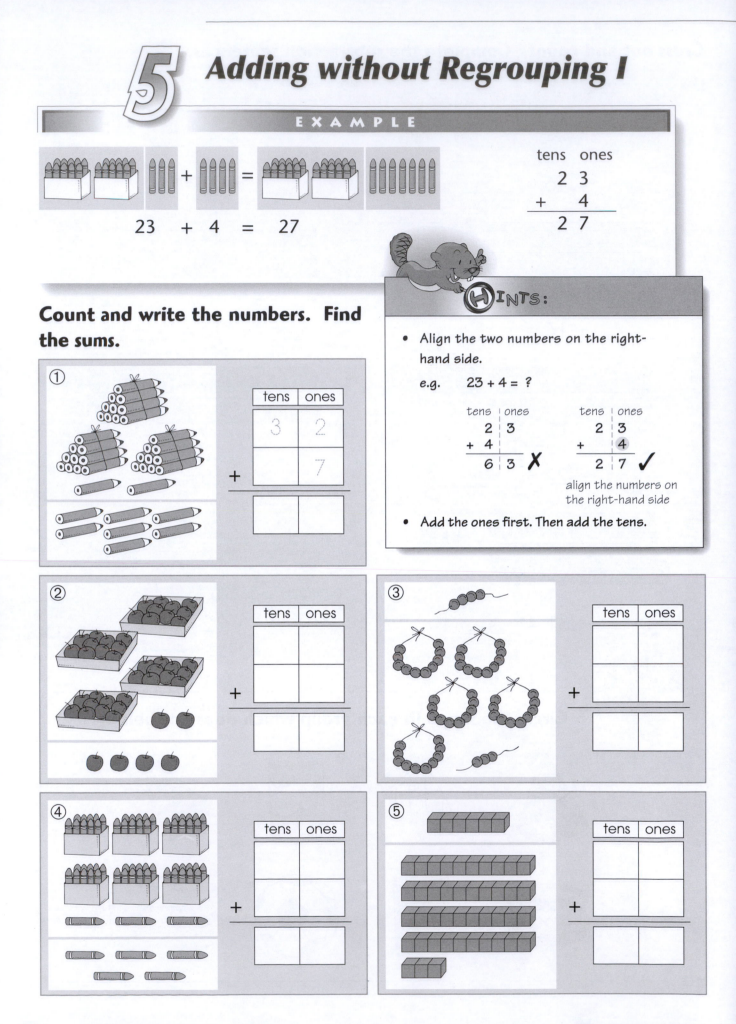

Count and write the numbers. Find the sums.

HINTS:

- Align the two numbers on the right-hand side.

  e.g.   23 + 4 = ?

  align the numbers on the right-hand side

- Add the ones first. Then add the tens.

Add.

⑥
$$26 + 3 = \boxed{}$$

⑦
$$41 + 8 = \boxed{}$$

⑧
$$2 + 36 = \boxed{}$$

⑨
$$62 + 6 = \boxed{}$$

⑩
$$2 + 55 = \boxed{}$$

⑪
$$73 + 4 = \boxed{}$$

⑫
$$84 + 5 = \boxed{}$$

⑬
$$17 + 2 = \boxed{}$$

⑭
$$32 + 6 = \boxed{}$$

⑮
$$8 + 51 = \boxed{}$$

⑯
$$60 + 7 = \boxed{}$$

⑰
$$75 + 3 = \boxed{}$$

⑱
$$44 + 4 = \boxed{}$$

⑲
$$80 + 6 = \boxed{}$$

⑳
$$27 + 2 = \boxed{}$$

㉑
$$5 + 90 = \boxed{}$$

㉒ $4 + 12 = $ _____

㉓ $31 + 7 = $ _____

㉔ $65 + 3 = $ _____

㉕ $42 + 6 = $ _____

㉖ $22 + 5 = $ _____

㉗ $4 + 52 = $ _____

㉘ $3 + 24 = $ _____

㉙ $15 + 3 = $ _____

Find the sums. Write the letters in ㊴ to solve the riddle.

㉚ **i**   34
   +   4

㉛ **p**   22
   +   6

㉝ **e**   53
   +   6

㉜   61
   +   5   **l**

m
㉞   41
  +   7

㉟ **n**   70
   +   5

㊱ **o**   85
   +   2

㊳   92
   +   4   **c**

㊲   23
   +   4   **a**

Riddle : Little Bear is lost. Who should he ask for help?

㊴

28	87	66	38	96	59	48	27	75

The | | | | | | | | | .

ISBN: 978-1-897164-12-9

Complete.

40 Sue has 32 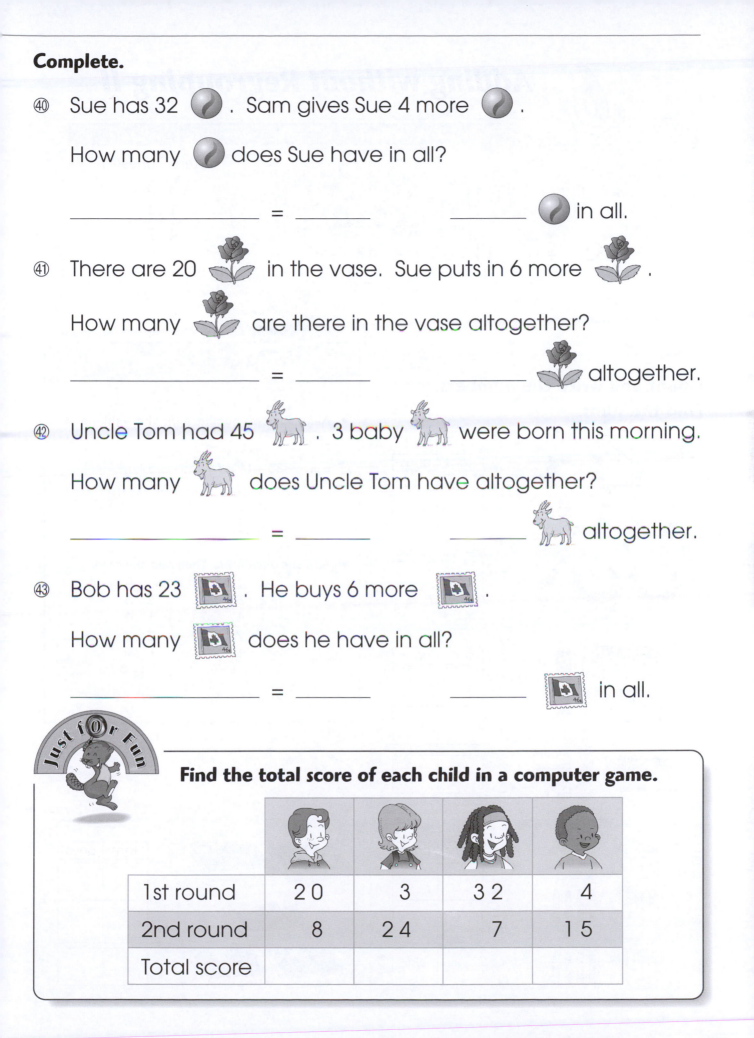 . Sam gives Sue 4 more .

How many does Sue have in all?

_____ = _____ _____ in all.

41 There are 20 in the vase. Sue puts in 6 more .

How many are there in the vase altogether?

_____ = _____ _____ altogether.

42 Uncle Tom had 45 . 3 baby were born this morning.

How many does Uncle Tom have altogether?

_____ = _____ _____ altogether.

43 Bob has 23 . He buys 6 more .

How many does he have in all?

_____ = _____ _____ in all.

Just for Fun

Find the total score of each child in a computer game.

1st round	2 0	3	3 2	4
2nd round	8	2 4	7	1 5
Total score				

ISBN: 978-1-897164-12-9

6 Adding without Regrouping II

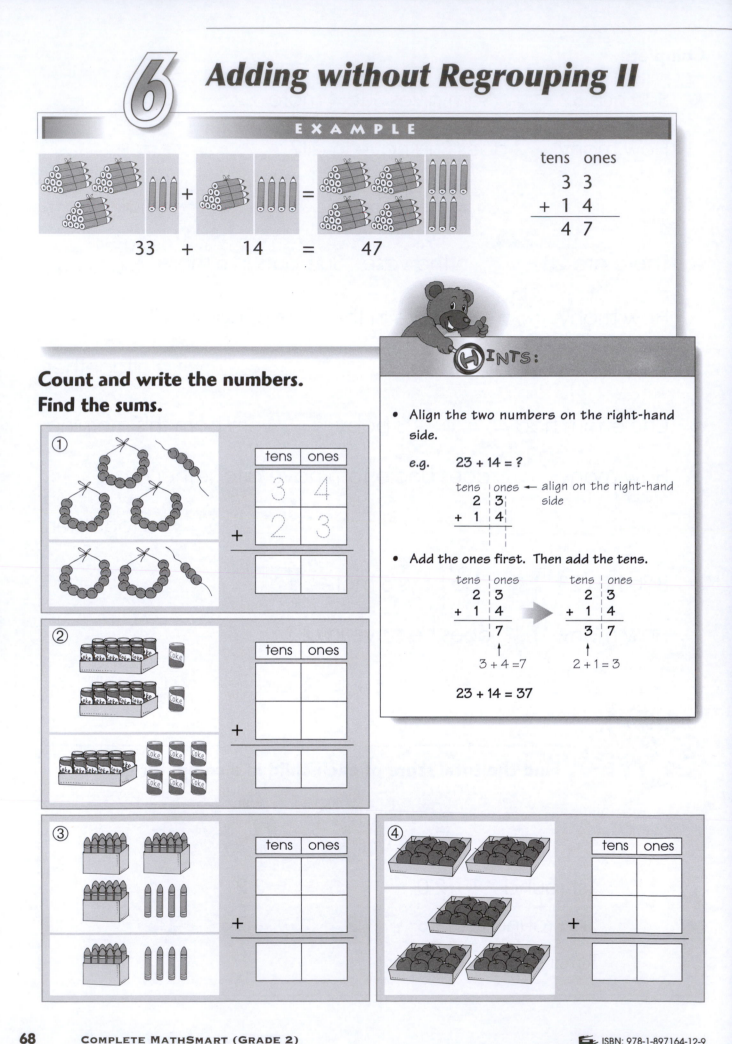

33 + 14 = 47

	tens	ones
	3	3
+	1	4
	4	7

Count and write the numbers.
Find the sums.

HINTS:

- Align the two numbers on the right-hand side.

  e.g.   23 + 14 = ?

tens	ones	← align on the right-hand side
2	3	
+ 1	4	

- Add the ones first. Then add the tens.

tens	ones		tens	ones
2	3	→	2	3
+ 1	4		+ 1	4
	7		3	7

  3 + 4 = 7   2 + 1 = 3

  23 + 14 = 37

①
tens	ones
3	4
2	3

②
tens	ones

③
tens	ones

④
tens	ones

ISBN: 978-1-897164-12-9

Add.

⑤
```
   1 2
 + 2 6
```
☐

⑥
```
   3 4
 + 4 3
```
☐

⑦
```
   5 3
 + 1 4
```
☐

⑧
```
   6 1
 + 1 7
```
☐

⑨
```
   4 5
 + 2 2
```
☐

⑩
```
   1 5
 + 4 3
```
☐

⑪
```
   7 0
 + 2 1
```
☐

⑫
```
   8 2
 + 1 0
```
☐

⑬
```
   3 1
 + 1 6
```
☐

⑭
```
   2 0
 + 5 3
```
☐

⑮
```
   4 2
 + 3 6
```
☐

⑯
```
   5 4
 + 2 2
```
☐

⑰
```
   6 3
 + 3 0
```
☐

⑱
```
   4 4
 + 4 4
```
☐

⑲
```
   1 3
 + 3 3
```
☐

⑳
```
   2 5
 + 1 1
```
☐

㉑ $22 + 22 =$ _____

㉒ $16 + 31 =$ _____

㉓ $34 + 52 =$ _____

㉔ $40 + 28 =$ _____

㉕ $66 + 20 =$ _____

㉖ $73 + 15 =$ _____

㉗ $45 + 14 =$ _____

㉘ $84 + 12 =$ _____

ISBN: 978-1-897164-12-9

Find the sums. Arrange the answers in correct counting order in ㊳, starting with the smallest number.

㉙
$$\begin{array}{r} 34 \\ + 13 \\ \hline \end{array}$$

㉚
$$\begin{array}{r} 12 \\ + 26 \\ \hline \end{array}$$

㉛
$$\begin{array}{r} 28 \\ + 31 \\ \hline \end{array}$$

㉜
$$\begin{array}{r} 26 \\ + 43 \\ \hline \end{array}$$

㉝
$$\begin{array}{r} 42 \\ + 15 \\ \hline \end{array}$$

㉞
$$\begin{array}{r} 51 \\ + 27 \\ \hline \end{array}$$

㉟
$$\begin{array}{r} 53 \\ + 35 \\ \hline \end{array}$$

㊱
$$\begin{array}{r} 38 \\ + 30 \\ \hline \end{array}$$

㊲
$$\begin{array}{r} 60 \\ + 39 \\ \hline \end{array}$$

㊳

ISBN: 978-1-897164-12-9

Complete the addition sentences.

㊴ Ben has 44 red 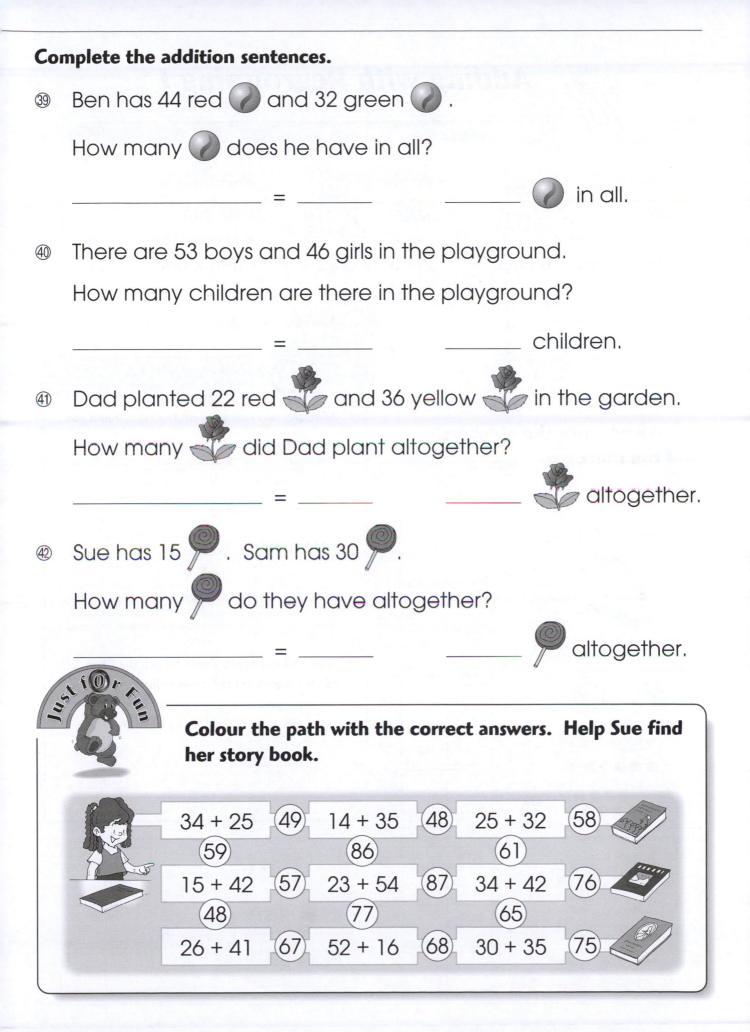 and 32 green .

How many does he have in all?

_____ = _____   _____ in all.

㊵ There are 53 boys and 46 girls in the playground.

How many children are there in the playground?

_____ = _____   _____ children.

㊶ Dad planted 22 red and 36 yellow in the garden.

How many did Dad plant altogether?

_____ = _____   _____ altogether.

㊷ Sue has 15 . Sam has 30 .

How many do they have altogether?

_____ = _____   _____ altogether.

Just f☉r Fun

Colour the path with the correct answers. Help Sue find her story book.

34 + 25	49	14 + 35	48	25 + 32	58
59		86		61	
15 + 42	57	23 + 54	87	34 + 42	76
48		77		65	
26 + 41	67	52 + 16	68	30 + 35	75

ISBN: 978-1-897164-12-9

7 Adding with Regrouping I

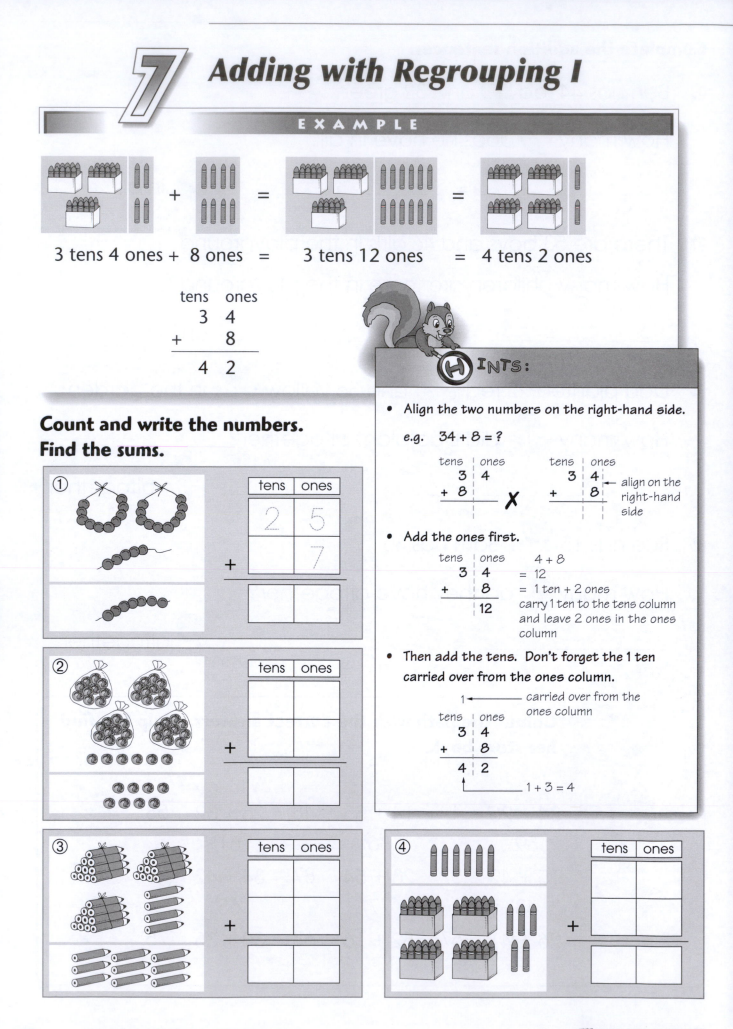

3 tens 4 ones + 8 ones = 3 tens 12 ones = 4 tens 2 ones

	tens	ones
	3	4
+		8
	4	2

Count and write the numbers. Find the sums.

①
tens	ones
2	5
	7

②
tens	ones

③
tens	ones

④
tens	ones

HINTS:

- Align the two numbers on the right-hand side.

  e.g.   34 + 8 = ?

tens	ones
3	4
+	8

  ✗

tens	ones
3	4	← align on the right-hand side
+	8

- Add the ones first.

tens	ones
3	4
+	8
	12

  4 + 8
  = 12
  = 1 ten + 2 ones
  carry 1 ten to the tens column and leave 2 ones in the ones column

- Then add the tens. Don't forget the 1 ten carried over from the ones column.

  1 ← carried over from the ones column

tens	ones
3	4
+	8
4	2

  1 + 3 = 4

ISBN: 978-1-897164-12-9

Add. Remember to regroup.

⑤
```
   16
+   8
```
☐

⑥
```
   23
+   9
```
☐

⑦
```
   32
+   8
```
☐

⑧
```
   46
+   7
```
☐

⑨
```
    7
+ 58
```
☐

⑩
```
   66
+   6
```
☐

⑪
```
   19
+   9
```
☐

⑫
```
   67
+   4
```
☐

⑬
```
   75
+   8
```
☐

⑭
```
   47
+   5
```
☐

⑮
```
    8
+ 28
```
☐

⑯
```
   54
+   6
```
☐

⑰
```
   36
+   8
```
☐

⑱
```
   59
+   2
```
☐

⑲
```
   47
+   9
```
☐

⑳
```
    4
+ 29
```
☐

㉑ 56 + 5 = _____

㉒ 37 + 7 = _____

㉓ 7 + 44 = _____

㉔ 26 + 9 = _____

㉕ 61 + 9 = _____

㉖ 73 + 8 = _____

㉗ 89 + 5 = _____

㉘ 3 + 37 = _____

ISBN: 978-1-897164-12-9

Follow the path. Help Little Squirrel find its food.

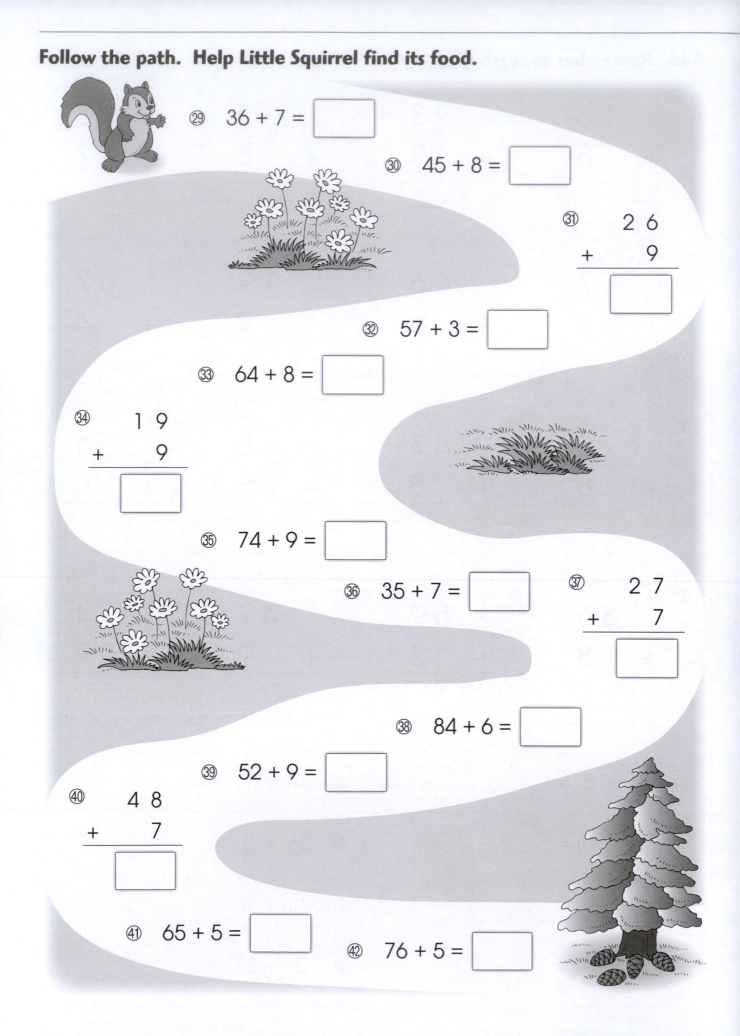

㉙ 36 + 7 = ☐

㉚ 45 + 8 = ☐

㉛ $\begin{array}{r} 2\ 6 \\ +\quad 9 \\ \hline \ \end{array}$

㉜ 57 + 3 = ☐

㉝ 64 + 8 = ☐

㉞ $\begin{array}{r} 1\ 9 \\ +\quad 9 \\ \hline \ \end{array}$

㉟ 74 + 9 = ☐

㊱ 35 + 7 = ☐

㊲ $\begin{array}{r} 2\ 7 \\ +\quad 7 \\ \hline \ \end{array}$

㊳ 84 + 6 = ☐

㊴ 52 + 9 = ☐

㊵ $\begin{array}{r} 4\ 8 \\ +\quad 7 \\ \hline \ \end{array}$

㊶ 65 + 5 = ☐

㊷ 76 + 5 = ☐

ISBN: 978-1-897164-12-9

Complete.

43 Bob has 18 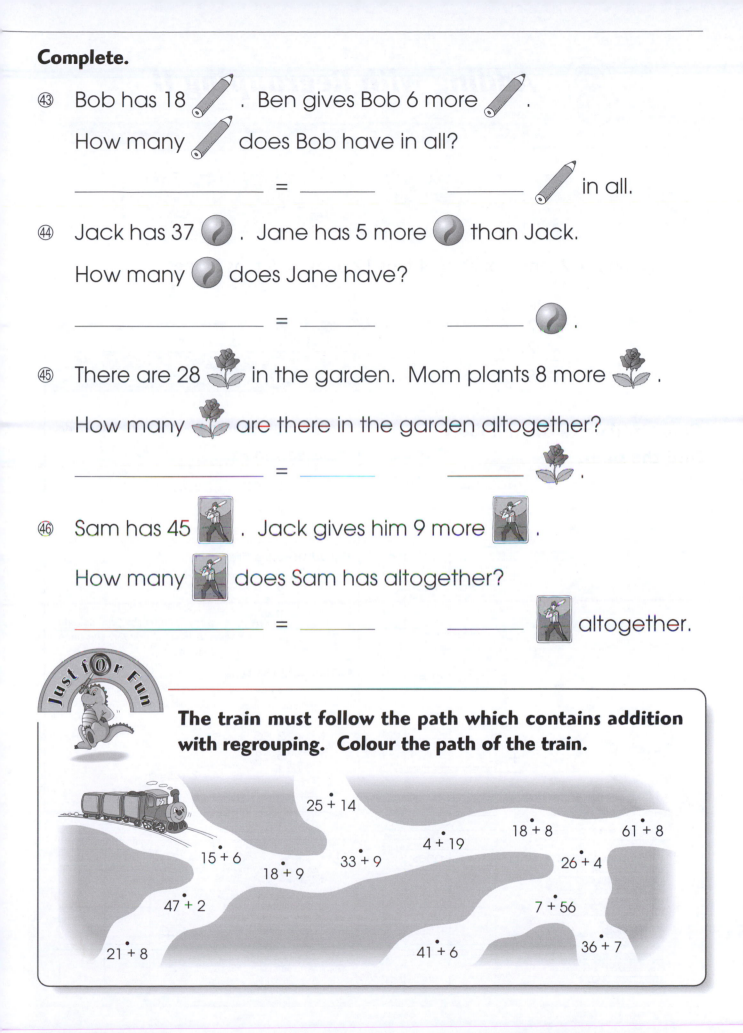. Ben gives Bob 6 more .

How many does Bob have in all?

_____ = _____   _____ in all.

44 Jack has 37 . Jane has 5 more than Jack.

How many does Jane have?

_____ = _____   _____ .

45 There are 28 in the garden. Mom plants 8 more .

How many are there in the garden altogether?

_____ = _____   _____ .

46 Sam has 45 . Jack gives him 9 more .

How many does Sam has altogether?

_____ = _____   _____ altogether.

The train must follow the path which contains addition with regrouping. Colour the path of the train.

25 + 14

15 + 6   33 + 9   4 + 19   18 + 8   61 + 8

18 + 9   26 + 4

47 + 2   7 + 56

21 + 8   41 + 6   36 + 7

E X A M P L E

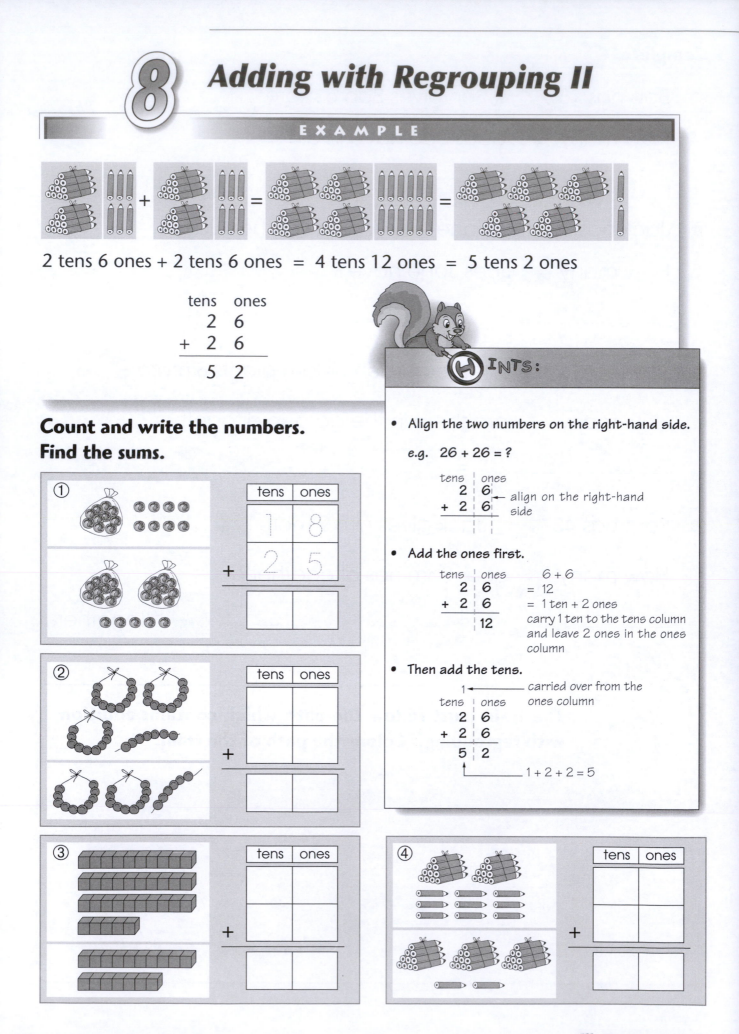

2 tens 6 ones + 2 tens 6 ones = 4 tens 12 ones = 5 tens 2 ones

	tens	ones
	2	6
+	2	6
	5	2

Count and write the numbers.
Find the sums.

①

tens	ones
1	8
2	5

+

②

tens	ones

+

③

tens	ones

+

④

tens	ones

+

HINTS:

- Align the two numbers on the right-hand side.

  e.g.   26 + 26 = ?

tens	ones
2	6	← align on the right-hand side
+ 2	6	

- Add the ones first.

tens	ones	6 + 6
2	6	= 12
+ 2	6	= 1 ten + 2 ones
	12	carry 1 ten to the tens column and leave 2 ones in the ones column

- Then add the tens.

  1 ← carried over from the ones column

tens	ones
2	6
+ 2	6
5	2

  1 + 2 + 2 = 5

ISBN: 978-1-897164-12-9

Add. Remember to regroup.

⑤
```
   3 7
+  1 9
```
[ ]

⑥
```
   2 6
+  3 8
```
[ ]

⑦
```
   4 3
+  2 7
```
[ ]

⑧
```
   4 4
+  3 8
```
[ ]

⑨
```
   6 4
+  1 6
```
[ ]

⑩
```
   5 7
+  2 6
```
[ ]

⑪
```
   3 2
+  5 9
```
[ ]

⑫
```
   1 9
+  4 4
```
[ ]

⑬
```
   2 7
+  5 8
```
[ ]

⑭
```
   3 8
+  4 6
```
[ ]

⑮
```
   5 6
+  1 5
```
[ ]

⑯
```
   4 8
+  4 8
```
[ ]

⑰
```
   6 3
+  2 9
```
[ ]

⑱
```
   5 6
+  3 9
```
[ ]

⑲
```
   1 5
+  4 5
```
[ ]

⑳
```
   2 2
+  4 8
```
[ ]

㉑ 18 + 65 = _____

㉒ 49 + 36 = _____

㉓ 43 + 38 = _____

㉔ 56 + 28 = _____

㉕ 24 + 69 = _____

㉖ 47 + 17 = _____

㉗ 55 + 27 = _____

㉘ 37 + 54 = _____

ISBN: 978-1-897164-12-9

Colour the bookmarks that match each number.

㉙ 44   18 + 26   27 + 15   27 + 17

㉚ 65   32 + 33   36 + 29   22 + 33

㉛ 52   26 + 16   15 + 37   17 + 35

㉜ 63   25 + 38   34 + 27   27 + 36

㉝ 81   54 + 27   63 + 28   45 + 36

㉞ 74   36 + 38   29 + 45   27 + 37

㉟ 91   46 + 45   33 + 59   62 + 29

㊱ 46   23 + 13   19 + 27   36 + 10

ISBN: 978-1-897164-12-9

Complete.

㊲ There are 15 girls and 9 boys in the class.

How many children are there in the class altogether?

_____ = _____   _____ children altogether.

㊳ Bob has 36 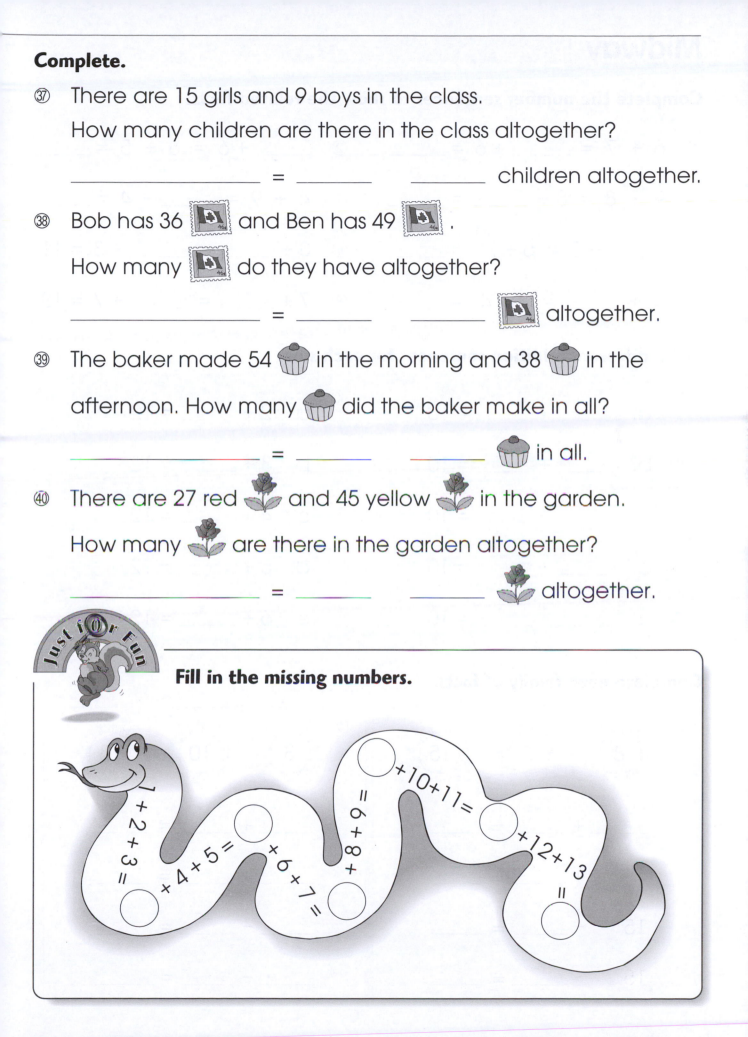 and Ben has 49 .

How many do they have altogether?

_____ = _____   _____ altogether.

㊴ The baker made 54 in the morning and 38 in the

afternoon. How many did the baker make in all?

_____ = _____   _____ in all.

㊵ There are 27 red and 45 yellow in the garden.

How many are there in the garden altogether?

_____ = _____   _____ altogether.

Just for Fun

Fill in the missing numbers.

$1 + 2 + 3 =$

$+ 4 + 5 =$

$+ 6 + 7 =$

$+ 8 + 9 =$

$+ 10 + 11 =$

$+ 12 + 13 =$

Complete the number sentences to show the related facts.

① 6 + 7 = _____ + 6 = _____   ② _____ + 6 = 6 + 5 = _____

③ 9 + 8 = 8 + _____ = _____   ④ 4 + 9 = _____ + 4 = _____

⑤ _____ + 5 = 5 + 7 = _____   ⑥ 3 + _____ = _____ + 3 = 11

⑦ 4 + _____ = 8 + 4 = _____   ⑧ 7 + _____ = _____ + 7 = 18

Write different addition sentences for each sum.

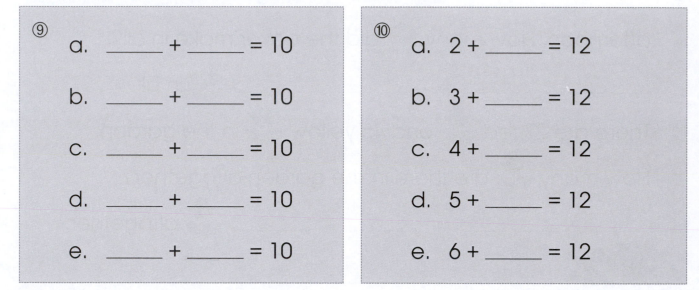

⑨
a. _____ + _____ = 10

b. _____ + _____ = 10

c. _____ + _____ = 10

d. _____ + _____ = 10

e. _____ + _____ = 10

⑩
a. 2 + _____ = 12

b. 3 + _____ = 12

c. 4 + _____ = 12

d. 5 + _____ = 12

e. 6 + _____ = 12

Complete each family of facts.

⑪ 8 7 15

_8_ + _____ = _____

_7_ + _____ = _____

15 − _8_ = _____

15 − _____ = _8_

⑫ 3 10 13

_____ + _____ = _____

_____ + _____ = _____

_____ − _____ = _____

_____ − _____ = _____

ISBN: 978-1-897164-12-9

Write the missing numbers. Use the family of facts.

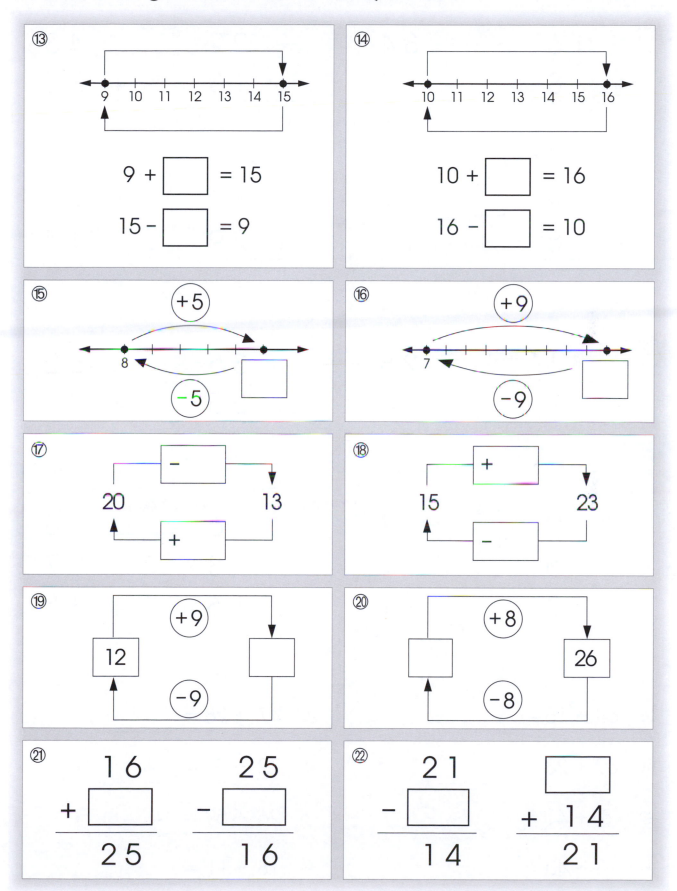

⑬

9 + ☐ = 15

15 – ☐ = 9

⑭

10 + ☐ = 16

16 – ☐ = 10

⑮ +5 −5   8

⑯ +9 −9   7

⑰ –   +   20 ... 13

⑱ +   –   15 ... 23

⑲ +9 −9   12

⑳ +8 −8   26

㉑

16
+ ☐
‾‾‾
2 5

25
– ☐
‾‾‾
1 6

㉒

2 1
– ☐
‾‾‾
1 4

☐
+ 1 4
‾‾‾
2 1

ISBN: 978-1-897164-12-9

Add or subtract.

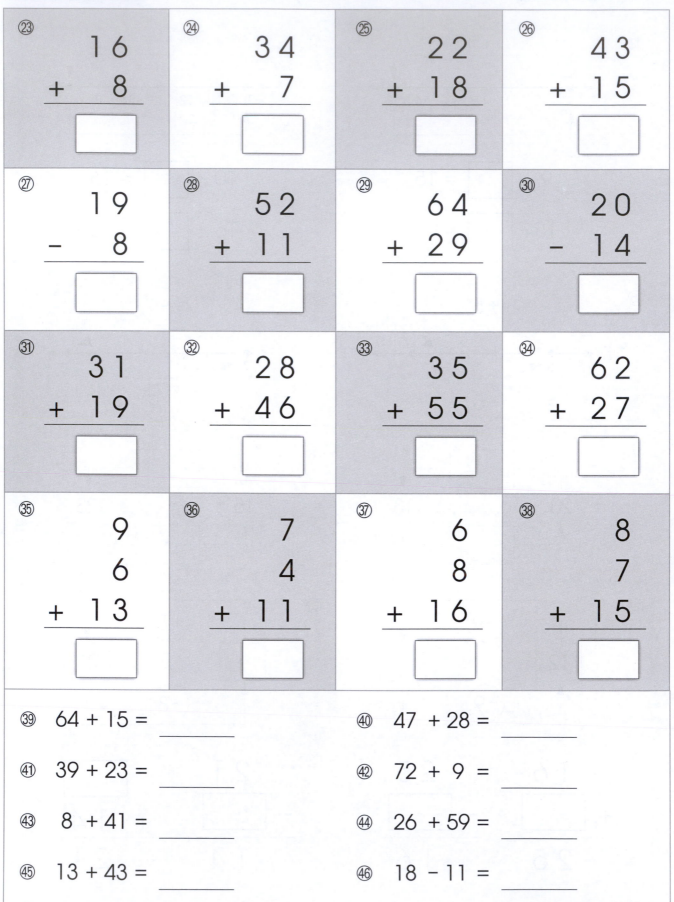

㉓
```
  1 6
+   8
```
☐

㉔
```
  3 4
+   7
```
☐

㉕
```
  2 2
+ 1 8
```
☐

㉖
```
  4 3
+ 1 5
```
☐

㉗
```
  1 9
-   8
```
☐

㉘
```
  5 2
+ 1 1
```
☐

㉙
```
  6 4
+ 2 9
```
☐

㉚
```
  2 0
- 1 4
```
☐

㉛
```
  3 1
+ 1 9
```
☐

㉜
```
  2 8
+ 4 6
```
☐

㉝
```
  3 5
+ 5 5
```
☐

㉞
```
  6 2
+ 2 7
```
☐

㉟
```
    9
    6
+ 1 3
```
☐

㊱
```
    7
    4
+ 1 1
```
☐

㊲
```
    6
    8
+ 1 6
```
☐

㊳
```
    8
    7
+ 1 5
```
☐

㊴ 64 + 15 = _____

㊵ 47 + 28 = _____

㊶ 39 + 23 = _____

㊷ 72 + 9 = _____

㊸ 8 + 41 = _____

㊹ 26 + 59 = _____

㊺ 13 + 43 = _____

㊻ 18 - 11 = _____

ISBN: 978-1-897164-12-9

Count Sue and Sam's cards, and answer the questions.

	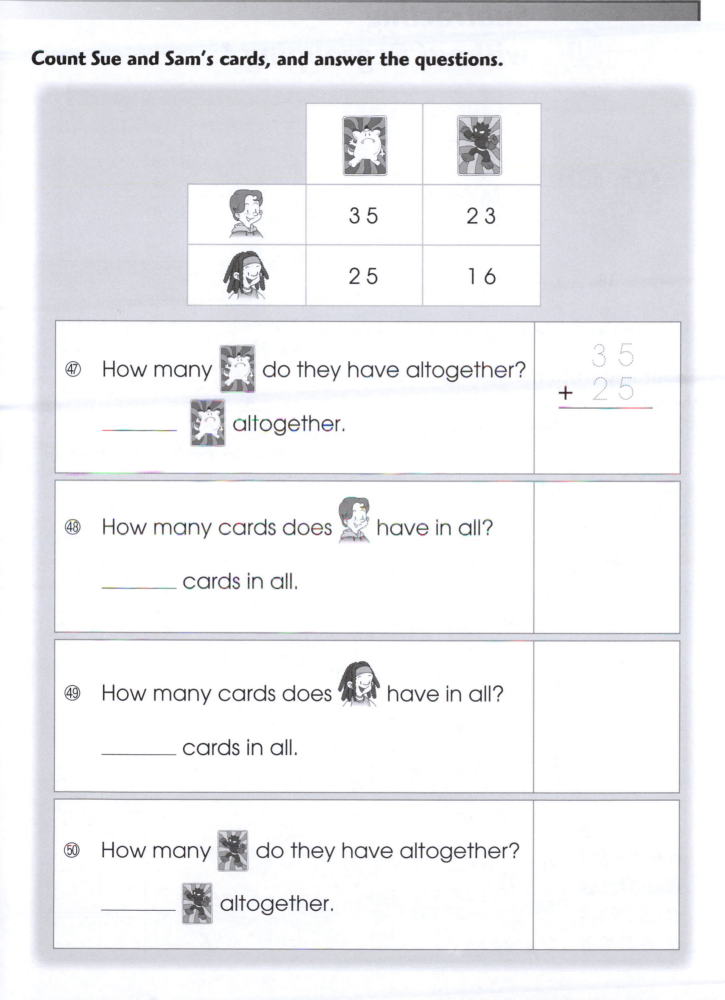	
	3 5	2 3
	2 5	1 6

㊼ How many do they have altogether?

_____ altogether.

$$\begin{array}{r} 3\ 5 \\ +\ 2\ 5 \\ \hline \end{array}$$

㊽ How many cards does have in all?

_____ cards in all.

㊾ How many cards does have in all?

_____ cards in all.

㊿ How many do they have altogether?

_____ altogether.

ISBN: 978-1-897164-12-9

9

Subtracting without Regrouping I

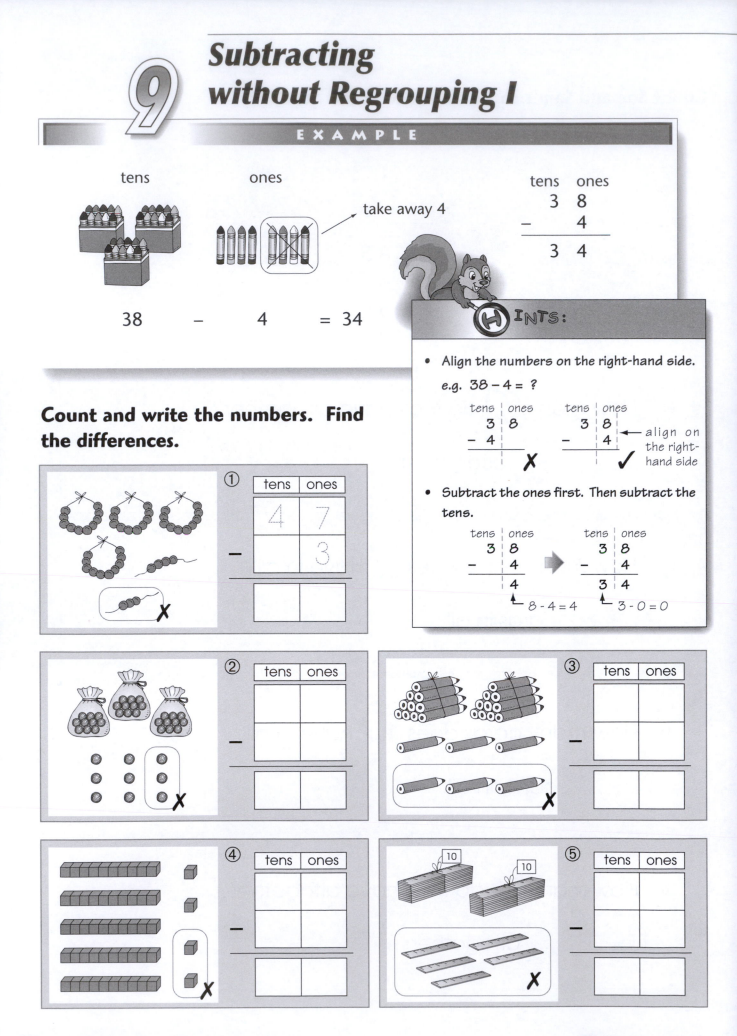

tens   ones

take away 4

tens	ones
3	8
−	4
3	4

38 − 4 = 34

HINTS:

- Align the numbers on the right-hand side.

  e.g. 38 − 4 = ?

tens	ones
3	8
− 4	

  ✗

tens	ones
3	8
−	4

  ← align on the right-hand side ✓

- Subtract the ones first. Then subtract the tens.

tens	ones
3	8
−	4
	4

  ➡

tens	ones
3	8
−	4
3	4

  8 − 4 = 4   3 − 0 = 0

Count and write the numbers. Find the differences.

①
tens	ones
4	7
−	3

②
tens	ones
−	

③
tens	ones
−	

④
tens	ones
−	

⑤
tens	ones
−	

ISBN: 978-1-897164-12-9

Subtract.

⑥
$$\begin{array}{r} 3\,6 \\ -5 \\ \hline \end{array}$$

⑦
$$\begin{array}{r} 2\,7 \\ -6 \\ \hline \end{array}$$

⑧
$$\begin{array}{r} 4\,8 \\ -5 \\ \hline \end{array}$$

⑨
$$\begin{array}{r} 9\,6 \\ -4 \\ \hline \end{array}$$

⑩
$$\begin{array}{r} 5\,5 \\ -3 \\ \hline \end{array}$$

⑪
$$\begin{array}{r} 7\,2 \\ -2 \\ \hline \end{array}$$

⑫
$$\begin{array}{r} 8\,9 \\ -7 \\ \hline \end{array}$$

⑬
$$\begin{array}{r} 4\,6 \\ -3 \\ \hline \end{array}$$

⑭
$$\begin{array}{r} 6\,9 \\ -3 \\ \hline \end{array}$$

⑮
$$\begin{array}{r} 2\,4 \\ -3 \\ \hline \end{array}$$

⑯
$$\begin{array}{r} 5\,7 \\ -2 \\ \hline \end{array}$$

⑰
$$\begin{array}{r} 3\,8 \\ -7 \\ \hline \end{array}$$

⑱
$$\begin{array}{r} 7\,7 \\ -5 \\ \hline \end{array}$$

⑲
$$\begin{array}{r} 1\,8 \\ -6 \\ \hline \end{array}$$

⑳
$$\begin{array}{r} 9\,8 \\ -5 \\ \hline \end{array}$$

㉑
$$\begin{array}{r} 4\,3 \\ -3 \\ \hline \end{array}$$

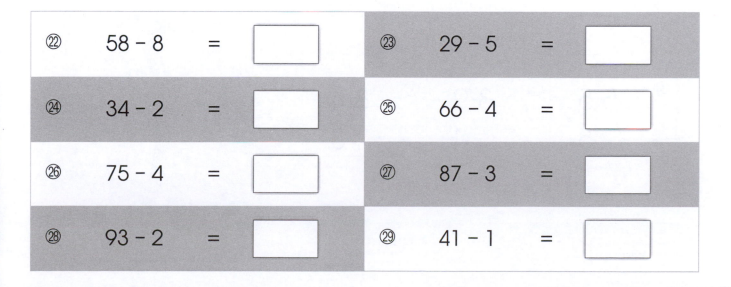

㉒　58 − 8　=　☐　　㉓　29 − 5　=　☐

㉔　34 − 2　=　☐　　㉕　66 − 4　=　☐

㉖　75 − 4　=　☐　　㉗　87 − 3　=　☐

㉘　93 − 2　=　☐　　㉙　41 − 1　=　☐

ISBN: 978-1-897164-12-9

Follow the path. Help Little Monkey get the coconuts.

③⓪
$$\begin{array}{r} 49 \\ -\ \ 5 \\ \hline \end{array}$$

③①
$$\begin{array}{r} 36 \\ -\ \ 2 \\ \hline \end{array}$$

③②
$$\begin{array}{r} 57 \\ -\ \ 4 \\ \hline \end{array}$$

③③
$$\begin{array}{r} 65 \\ -\ \ 3 \\ \hline \end{array}$$

③④
$$\begin{array}{r} 55 \\ -\ \ 5 \\ \hline \end{array}$$

③⑤
$$\begin{array}{r} 39 \\ -\ \ 4 \\ \hline \end{array}$$

③⑥
$$\begin{array}{r} 84 \\ -\ \ 3 \\ \hline \end{array}$$

③⑦
$$\begin{array}{r} 93 \\ -\ \ 3 \\ \hline \end{array}$$

③⑧
$$\begin{array}{r} 22 \\ -\ \ 1 \\ \hline \end{array}$$

③⑨
$$\begin{array}{r} 49 \\ -\ \ 8 \\ \hline \end{array}$$

④⓪
$$\begin{array}{r} 84 \\ -\ \ 3 \\ \hline \end{array}$$

④①
$$\begin{array}{r} 37 \\ -\ \ 6 \\ \hline \end{array}$$

④②
$$\begin{array}{r} 65 \\ -\ \ 2 \\ \hline \end{array}$$

④③
$$\begin{array}{r} 66 \\ -\ \ 3 \\ \hline \end{array}$$

④④
$$\begin{array}{r} 58 \\ -\ \ 6 \\ \hline \end{array}$$

ISBN: 978-1-897164-12-9

Complete.

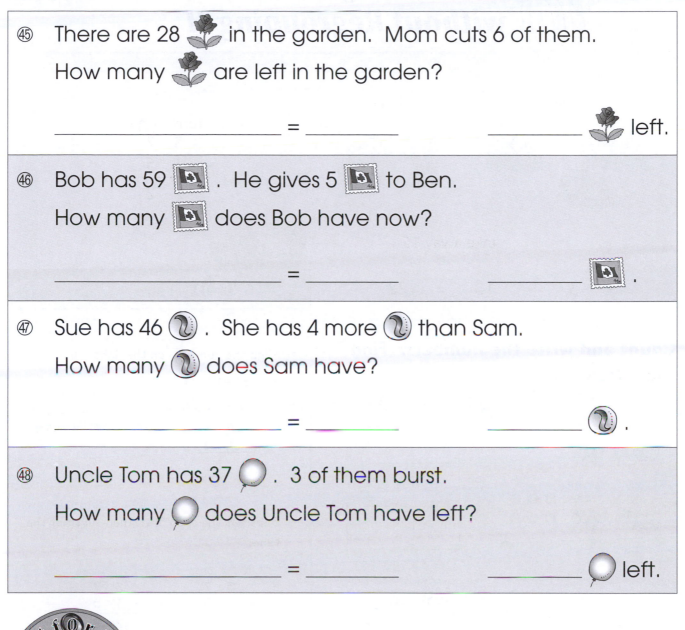

㊺ There are 28 🌹 in the garden. Mom cuts 6 of them.

How many 🌹 are left in the garden?

_____ = _____   _____ 🌹 left.

㊻ Bob has 59 🏳 . He gives 5 🏳 to Ben.

How many 🏳 does Bob have now?

_____ = _____   _____ 🏳 .

㊼ Sue has 46 ⚾ . She has 4 more ⚾ than Sam.

How many ⚾ does Sam have?

_____ = _____   _____ ⚾ .

㊽ Uncle Tom has 37 🎈 . 3 of them burst.

How many 🎈 does Uncle Tom have left?

_____ = _____   _____ 🎈 left.

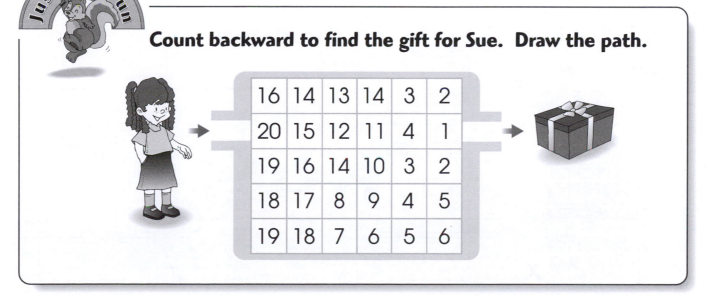

Just for Fun

Count backward to find the gift for Sue. Draw the path.

16	14	13	14	3	2
20	15	12	11	4	1
19	16	14	10	3	2
18	17	8	9	4	5
19	18	7	6	5	6

10 Subtracting without Regrouping II

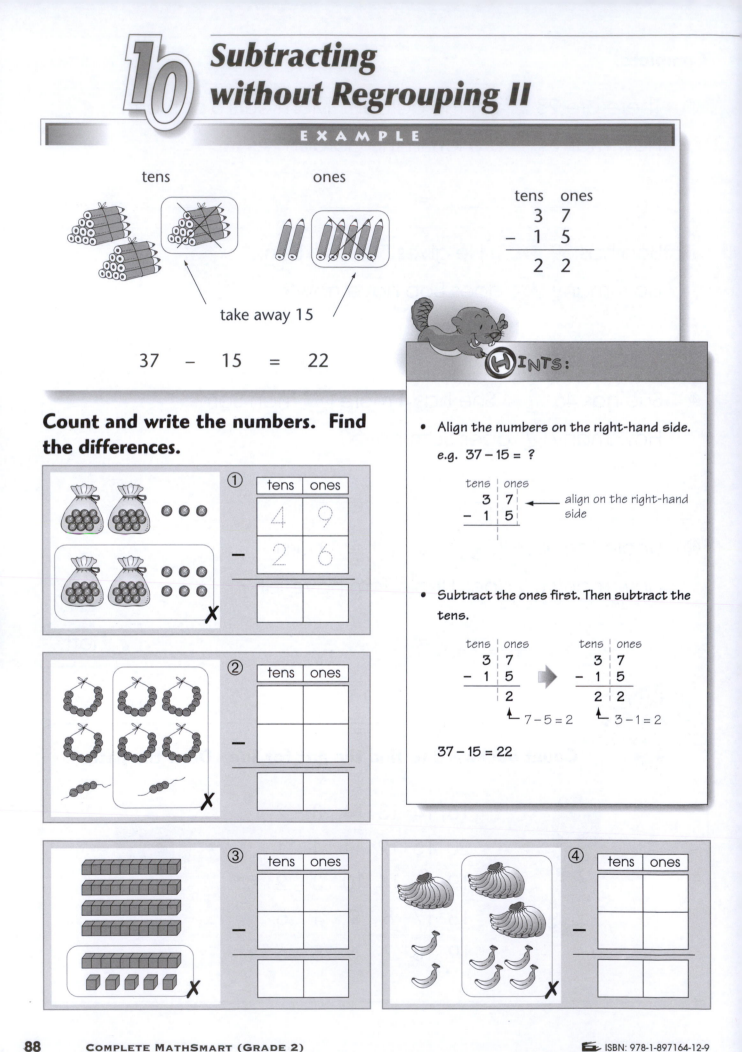

tens   ones

take away 15

37   −   15   =   22

tens	ones
3	7
− 1	5
2	2

Count and write the numbers. Find the differences.

①

tens	ones
4	9
− 2	6

②

tens	ones
−	

③

tens	ones
−	

④

tens	ones
−	

HINTS:

- Align the numbers on the right-hand side.

  e.g. 37 − 15 = ?

tens	ones
3	7
− 1	5

  ← align on the right-hand side

- Subtract the ones first. Then subtract the tens.

tens	ones
3	7
− 1	5
	2

  7 − 5 = 2

tens	ones
3	7
− 1	5
2	2

  3 − 1 = 2

  37 − 15 = 22

Subtract.

⑤
```
   3 6
 - 1 2
```
☐

⑥
```
   4 8
 - 2 5
```
☐

⑦
```
   5 7
 - 3 3
```
☐

⑧
```
   6 5
 - 2 4
```
☐

⑨
```
   8 6
 - 5 4
```
☐

⑩
```
   7 4
 - 4 4
```
☐

⑪
```
   9 6
 - 6 5
```
☐

⑫
```
   2 9
 - 2 5
```
☐

⑬
```
   5 8
 - 3 7
```
☐

⑭
```
   6 6
 - 4 4
```
☐

⑮
```
   4 3
 - 3 1
```
☐

⑯
```
   8 4
 - 3 0
```
☐

⑰
```
   2 7
 - 1 2
```
☐

⑱
```
   3 3
 - 2 3
```
☐

⑲
```
   1 9
 - 1 5
```
☐

⑳
```
   7 8
 - 4 6
```
☐

㉑ 45 – 22 = ☐   ㉒ 99 – 77 = ☐

㉓ 76 – 30 = ☐   ㉔ 54 – 14 = ☐

㉕ 69 – 58 = ☐   ㉖ 25 – 11 = ☐

㉗ 37 – 21 = ☐   ㉘ 83 – 70 = ☐

ISBN: 978-1-897164-12-9

Find the differences. In each group, colour the balloons with the same answers.

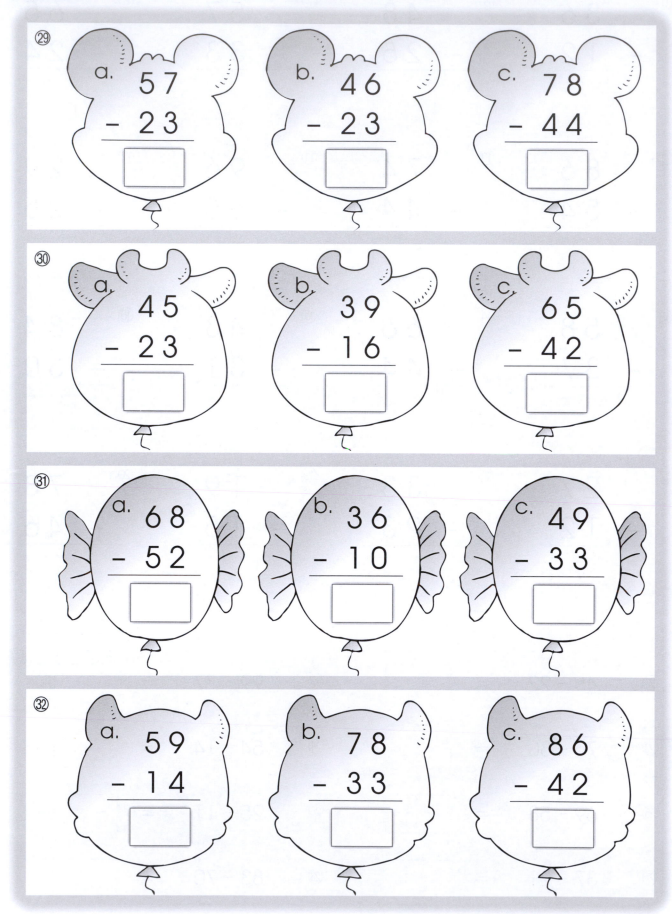

㉙ a. 57
   − 23
   _____

b. 46
   − 23
   _____

c. 78
   − 44
   _____

㉚ a. 45
   − 23
   _____

b. 39
   − 16
   _____

c. 65
   − 42
   _____

㉛ a. 68
   − 52
   _____

b. 36
   − 10
   _____

c. 49
   − 33
   _____

㉜ a. 59
   − 14
   _____

b. 78
   − 33
   _____

c. 86
   − 42
   _____

ISBN: 978-1-897164-12-9

Complete.

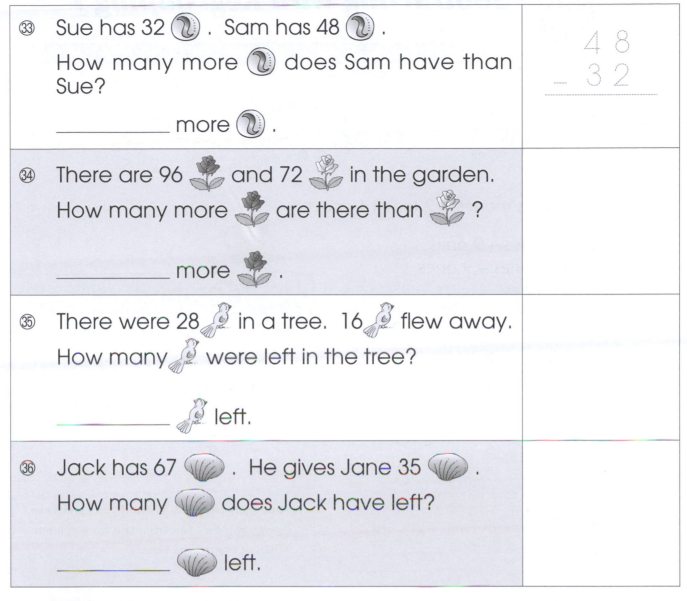

㉝ Sue has 32 🪙 . Sam has 48 🪙 .
How many more 🪙 does Sam have than Sue?

4 8
– 3 2
_____

_____ more 🪙 .

㉞ There are 96 🌹 and 72 🌹 in the garden.
How many more 🌹 are there than 🌹 ?

_____ more 🌹 .

㉟ There were 28 🐦 in a tree. 16 🐦 flew away.
How many 🐦 were left in the tree?

_____ 🐦 left.

㊱ Jack has 67 🐚 . He gives Jane 35 🐚 .
How many 🐚 does Jack have left?

_____ 🐚 left.

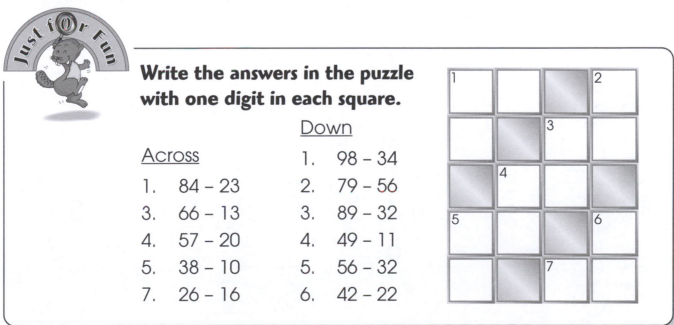

Write the answers in the puzzle with one digit in each square.

Across
1. 84 – 23
3. 66 – 13
4. 57 – 20
5. 38 – 10
7. 26 – 16

Down
1. 98 – 34
2. 79 – 56
3. 89 – 32
4. 49 – 11
5. 56 – 32
6. 42 – 22

ISBN: 978-1-897164-12-9

11 Subtracting with Regrouping I

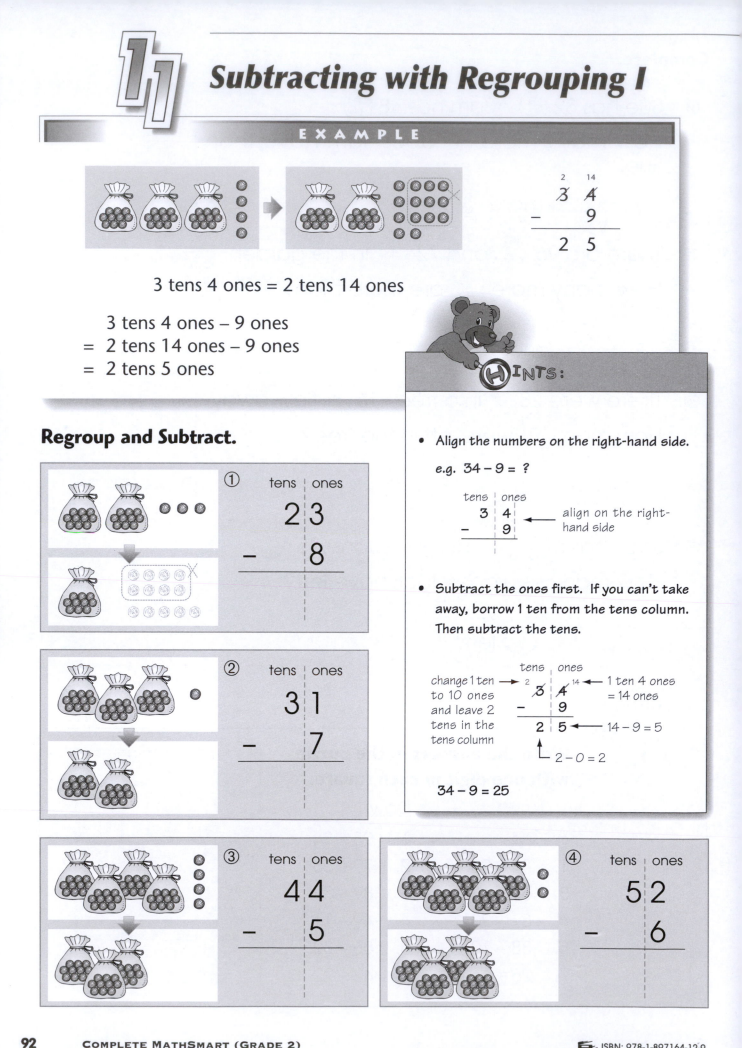

3 tens 4 ones = 2 tens 14 ones

3 tens 4 ones – 9 ones
= 2 tens 14 ones – 9 ones
= 2 tens 5 ones

$$\begin{array}{r} \overset{2}{\cancel{3}}\ \overset{14}{\cancel{4}} \\ -\quad 9 \\ \hline 2\ 5 \end{array}$$

Regroup and Subtract.

①
tens	ones
2	3
–	8

②
tens	ones
3	1
–	7

③
tens	ones
4	4
–	5

④
tens	ones
5	2
–	6

HINTS:

- Align the numbers on the right-hand side.

  e.g. 34 – 9 = ?

tens	ones
3	4	← align on the right-hand side
–	9

- Subtract the ones first. If you can't take away, borrow 1 ten from the tens column. Then subtract the tens.

  change 1 ten to 10 ones and leave 2 tens in the tens column →

tens	ones
$\overset{2}{\cancel{3}}$	$\overset{14}{\cancel{4}}$	← 1 ten 4 ones = 14 ones
–	9
2	5	← 14 – 9 = 5

  └ 2 – 0 = 2

  34 – 9 = 25

ISBN: 978-1-897164-12-9

Subtract. Remember to regroup.

⑤
```
    6 3
  -   6
  _____
```

⑥
```
    4 5
  -   8
  _____
```

⑦
```
    3 4
  -   7
  _____
```

⑧
```
    7 1
  -   9
  _____
```

⑨
```
    2 7
  -   8
  _____
```

⑩
```
    8 4
  -   9
  _____
```

⑪
```
    5 6
  -   8
  _____
```

⑫
```
    4 7
  -   9
  _____
```

⑬
```
    9 0
  -   6
  _____
```

⑭
```
    3 5
  -   9
  _____
```

⑮
```
    7 2
  -   4
  _____
```

⑯
```
    6 6
  -   8
  _____
```

⑰
```
    4 3
  -   7
  _____
```

⑱
```
    2 8
  -   9
  _____
```

⑲
```
    8 1
  -   4
  _____
```

⑳
```
    5 4
  -   6
  _____
```

㉑ $33 - 8 =$

㉒ $74 - 9 =$

㉓ $60 - 5 =$

㉔ $55 - 7 =$

㉕ $81 - 6 =$

㉖ $42 - 9 =$

㉗ $22 - 7 =$

㉘ $93 - 5 =$

ISBN: 978-1-897164-12-9

Subtract. Colour the lily pads if the answers are odd numbers. Help Little Frog find its Mom.

29)
$$\begin{array}{r} 32 \\ -9 \\ \hline \end{array}$$

30)
$$\begin{array}{r} 53 \\ -8 \\ \hline \end{array}$$

33)
$$\begin{array}{r} 25 \\ -7 \\ \hline \end{array}$$

32)
$$\begin{array}{r} 23 \\ -6 \\ \hline \end{array}$$

31)
$$\begin{array}{r} 46 \\ -9 \\ \hline \end{array}$$

34)
$$\begin{array}{r} 64 \\ -9 \\ \hline \end{array}$$

35)
$$\begin{array}{r} 71 \\ -8 \\ \hline \end{array}$$

36)
$$\begin{array}{r} 61 \\ -7 \\ \hline \end{array}$$

38)
$$\begin{array}{r} 37 \\ -9 \\ \hline \end{array}$$

37)
$$\begin{array}{r} 35 \\ -6 \\ \hline \end{array}$$

39)
$$\begin{array}{r} 40 \\ -7 \\ \hline \end{array}$$

COMPLETE MATHSMART (GRADE 2)   ISBN: 978-1-897164-12-9

Complete.

⑭ Jack had 25 🍫 . He ate 8 🍫 . How many 🍫 were left?

_____ = _____   _____ 🍫 left.

㊶ The baker made 52 🥐 . 9 🥐 were sold. How many 🥐 were left?

_____ = _____   _____ 🥐 left.

㊷ Mom plants 40 🌹 in the garden. There are 7 less 🌷 than 🌹 . How many 🌷 are there in the garden?

_____ = _____   _____ 🌷 .

㊸ Uncle Tom has 33 red 🎈 . There are 6 more red 🎈 than yellow 🎈 . How many yellow 🎈 does Uncle Tom have?

_____ = _____   _____ yellow 🎈 .

Just for Fun

Subtract. Fill in the missing numbers.

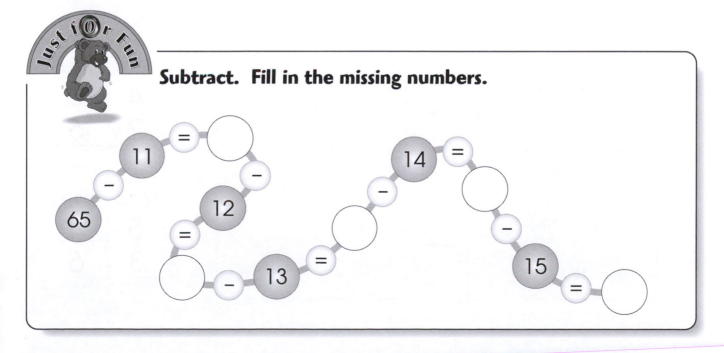

Subtracting with Regrouping II

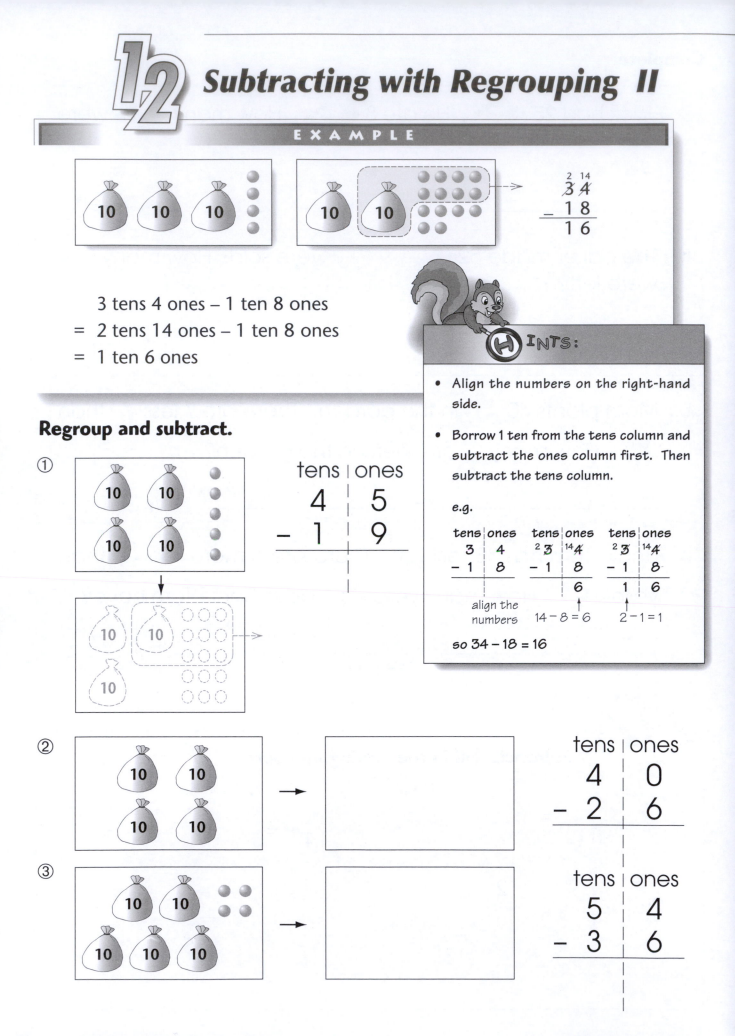

3 tens 4 ones – 1 ten 8 ones

= 2 tens 14 ones – 1 ten 8 ones

= 1 ten 6 ones

Regroup and subtract.

HINTS:

- Align the numbers on the right-hand side.

- Borrow 1 ten from the tens column and subtract the ones column first. Then subtract the tens column.

e.g.

so 34 – 18 = 16

Subtract. Remember to regroup.

④
```
   4 3
 - 2 7
```

⑤
```
   5 6
 - 1 8
```

⑥
```
   3 5
 - 1 9
```

⑦
```
   7 0
 - 2 5
```

⑧
```
   6 1
 - 4 3
```

⑨
```
   8 4
 - 5 6
```

⑩
```
   2 7
 - 1 9
```

⑪
```
   4 6
 - 1 7
```

⑫
```
   7 2
 - 5 5
```

⑬
```
   3 3
 - 1 4
```

⑭
```
   8 5
 - 4 8
```

⑮
```
   9 6
 - 6 9
```

⑯
```
   5 4
 - 3 8
```

⑰
```
   4 0
 - 2 7
```

⑱
```
   2 5
 - 1 6
```

⑲
```
   6 5
 - 3 7
```

⑳ $31 - 14 =$ _____

㉑ $53 - 25 =$ _____

㉒ $64 - 39 =$ _____

㉓ $81 - 44 =$ _____

㉔ $93 - 46 =$ _____

㉕ $41 - 18 =$ _____

㉖ $71 - 59 =$ _____

㉗ $62 - 36 =$ _____

ISBN: 978-1-897164-12-9

Subtract. Colour the eggs that match each number.

㉘ 36

a.
$$\begin{array}{r} 63 \\ -\ 27 \\ \hline \end{array}$$

b.
$$\begin{array}{r} 52 \\ -\ 29 \\ \hline \end{array}$$

c.
$$\begin{array}{r} 52 \\ -\ 16 \\ \hline \end{array}$$

㉙ 37

a.
$$\begin{array}{r} 63 \\ -\ 36 \\ \hline \end{array}$$

b.
$$\begin{array}{r} 74 \\ -\ 37 \\ \hline \end{array}$$

c.
$$\begin{array}{r} 96 \\ -\ 59 \\ \hline \end{array}$$

㉚ 14

a.
$$\begin{array}{r} 41 \\ -\ 27 \\ \hline \end{array}$$

b.
$$\begin{array}{r} 60 \\ -\ 46 \\ \hline \end{array}$$

c.
$$\begin{array}{r} 53 \\ -\ 38 \\ \hline \end{array}$$

㉛ 25

a.
$$\begin{array}{r} 83 \\ -\ 57 \\ \hline \end{array}$$

b.
$$\begin{array}{r} 43 \\ -\ 18 \\ \hline \end{array}$$

c.
$$\begin{array}{r} 62 \\ -\ 37 \\ \hline \end{array}$$

㉜ 44

a.
$$\begin{array}{r} 72 \\ -\ 28 \\ \hline \end{array}$$

b.
$$\begin{array}{r} 63 \\ -\ 29 \\ \hline \end{array}$$

c.
$$\begin{array}{r} 80 \\ -\ 36 \\ \hline \end{array}$$

ISBN: 978-1-897164-12-9

Complete.

③③ There are 92 children in the gym. 37 of them are boys. How many girls are there in the gym?

_____ = _____ _____ girls.

③④ At Sea World, Sue saw 43 🦭 on the rocks and 27 🦭 in the water. How many more 🦭 were there on the rocks than in the water?

_____ = _____ _____ more 🦭.

③⑤ The baker made 55 🧁 in the morning and 39 🧁 in the afternoon. How many more 🧁 did he make in the morning than in the afternoon?

_____ = _____ _____ more 🧁.

③⑥ There were 61 🌭 in the snack bar. 46 🌭 were sold. How many 🌭 were left?

_____ = _____ _____ 🌭 left.

Just for Fun

Add or subtract. Write the letters to find what Sue wants to be.

19 + 27 = [I]   73 − 48   = [E]

52 − 36 = [R]   25 + 46   = [S]

44 − 27 = [G]   4 + 9 + 26 = [N]

A | 71 | 46 | 39 | 17 | 25 | 16 | .

13 Estimating Sums and Differences

23 ——round to the nearest 10——→ 20   3 is smaller than 5, 23 is round down to 20.

36 ——round to the nearest 10——→ 40   6 is greater than 5, 36 is round up to 40.

```
    2 3                            2 0
  + 3 6        estimate         + 4 0
    5 9                            6 0
```
↑   ↑
exact answer   the sum is about 60

HINTS:

- Estimate by rounding all the numbers to the nearest 10. Rounding makes a number smaller or larger.
  e.g. 53 is round down to 50, 58 is round up to 60.

- To round to the nearest 10, look at the ones. If the digit is 5 or more, round up to the nearest 10; otherwise, round down.

The numbers are rounded to the nearest 10. Circle the correct answers.

① 27 ——→ 20   30

② 35 ——→ 30   40

③ 52 ——→ 50   60   ④ 44 ——→ 40   50

⑤ 63 ——→ 60   70   ⑥ 76 ——→ 70   80

⑦ 81 ——→ 80   90   ⑧ 93 ——→ 90   100

⑨ 38 ——→ 38   40   ⑩ 19 ——→ 10   20

Round each number to the nearest 10.

⑪ 31 _____	⑫ 22 _____	⑬ 49 _____
⑭ 58 _____	⑮ 13 _____	⑯ 84 _____
⑰ 7 _____	⑱ 46 _____	⑲ 11 _____
⑳ 69 _____	㉑ 95 _____	㉒ 4 _____

ISBN: 978-1-897164-12-9

Estimate the sums. Compare the estimates with the exact answers.

㉓
a.
```
    3 9
  + 2 7
  _____
```
b. **estimate**
```
    4 0
  + 3 0
  _____
```

㉔
a.
```
    1 6
  + 2 8
  _____
```
b. **estimate**

㉕
a.
```
      8
  + 4 5
  _____
```
b. **estimate**

㉖
a.
```
    5 1
  + 1 4
  _____
```
b. **estimate**

㉗
a.
```
    2 6
  +   7
  _____
```
b. **estimate**

㉘
a.
```
    3 4
  + 5 5
  _____
```
b. **estimate**

㉙ a. 73 + 19 = _____

estimate

b. _____ + _____ = _____

㉚ a. 22 + 66 = _____

estimate

b. _____ + _____ = _____

㉛ a. 33 + 46 = _____

estimate

b. _____ + _____ = _____

㉜ a. 51 + 44 = _____

estimate

b. _____ + _____ = _____

㉝ a. 64 + 27 = _____

estimate

b. _____ + _____ = _____

㉞ a. 13 + 45 = _____

estimate

b. _____ + _____ = _____

Estimate the differences. Compare the estimates with the exact answers.

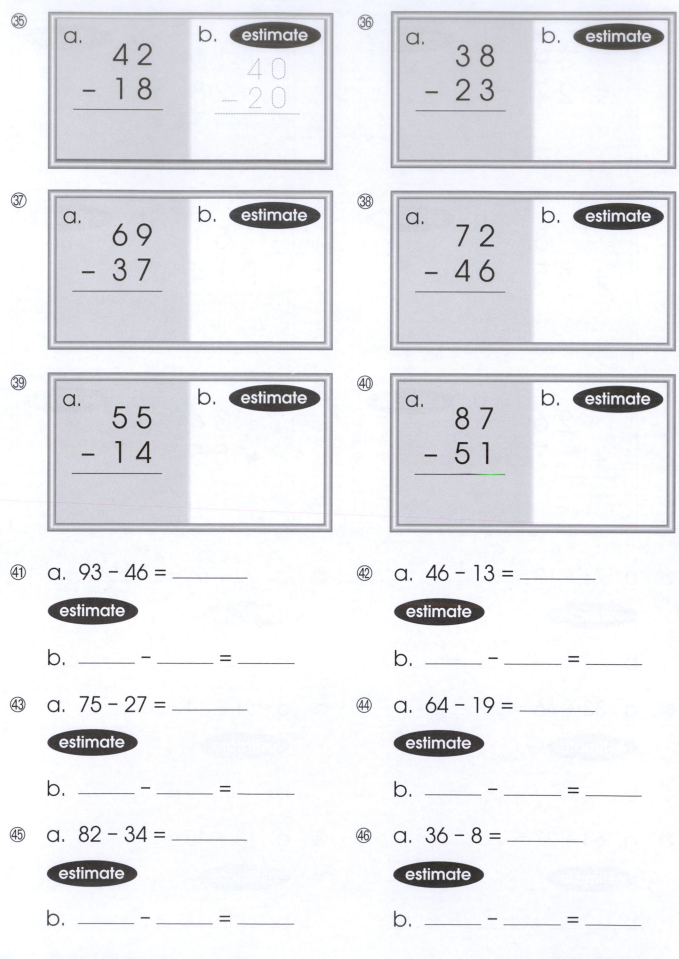

㉟
a.
42
− 18

b. estimate
40
− 20

㊱
a.
38
− 23

b. estimate

㊲
a.
69
− 37

b. estimate

㊳
a.
72
− 46

b. estimate

㊴
a.
55
− 14

b. estimate

㊵
a.
87
− 51

b. estimate

㊶ a. 93 − 46 = _____

estimate

b. _____ − _____ = _____

㊷ a. 46 − 13 = _____

estimate

b. _____ − _____ = _____

㊸ a. 75 − 27 = _____

estimate

b. _____ − _____ = _____

㊹ a. 64 − 19 = _____

estimate

b. _____ − _____ = _____

㊺ a. 82 − 34 = _____

estimate

b. _____ − _____ = _____

㊻ a. 36 − 8 = _____

estimate

b. _____ − _____ = _____

ISBN: 978-1-897164-12-9

Estimate the sums or differences. Circle the correct descriptions.

47 43 – 9

more than 20	less than 20

48 25 + 47

more than 90	less than 90

49 33 + 58

more than 80	less than 80

50 62 – 44

more than 30	less than 30

51 95 – 57

more than 50	less than 50

52 19 + 54

more than 60	less than 60

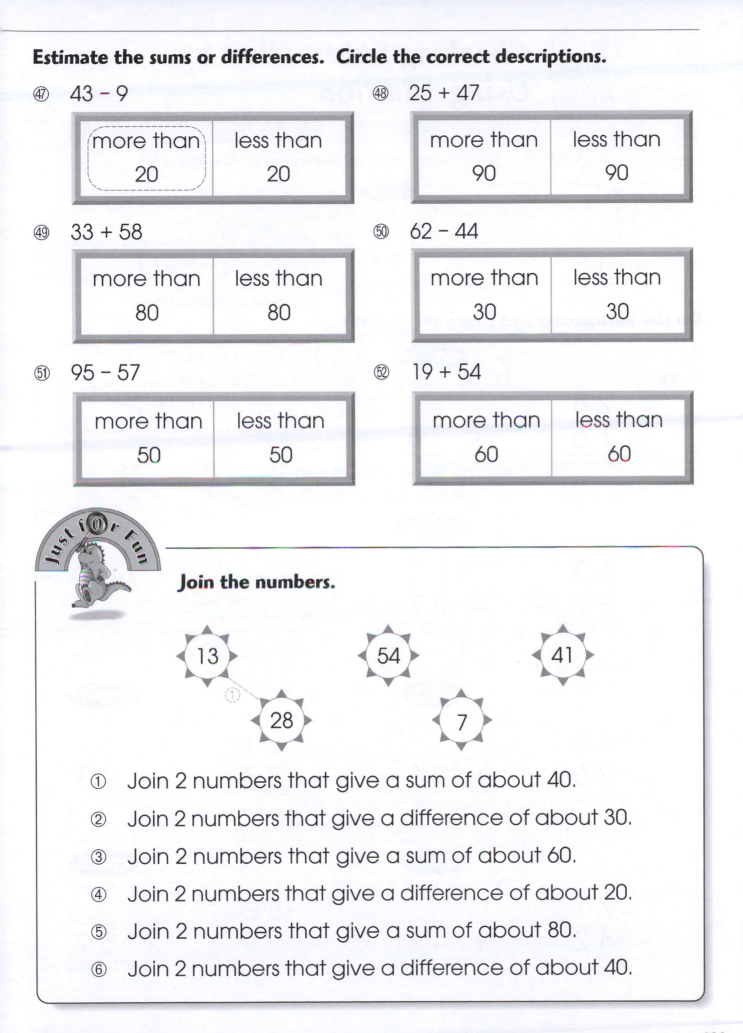

Just for Fun

Join the numbers.

13   54   41

28   7

① Join 2 numbers that give a sum of about 40.

② Join 2 numbers that give a difference of about 30.

③ Join 2 numbers that give a sum of about 60.

④ Join 2 numbers that give a difference of about 20.

⑤ Join 2 numbers that give a sum of about 80.

⑥ Join 2 numbers that give a difference of about 40.

ISBN: 978-1-897164-12-9

14 Checking Subtraction by Using Addition

E X A M P L E

Farmer Joe had 89 🍎 . 52 🍎 were sold. How many 🍎 were left?

```
   8 9
 - 5 2
   3 7
```

check
```
   3 7
 + 5 2
   8 9
```

37 🍎 were left.

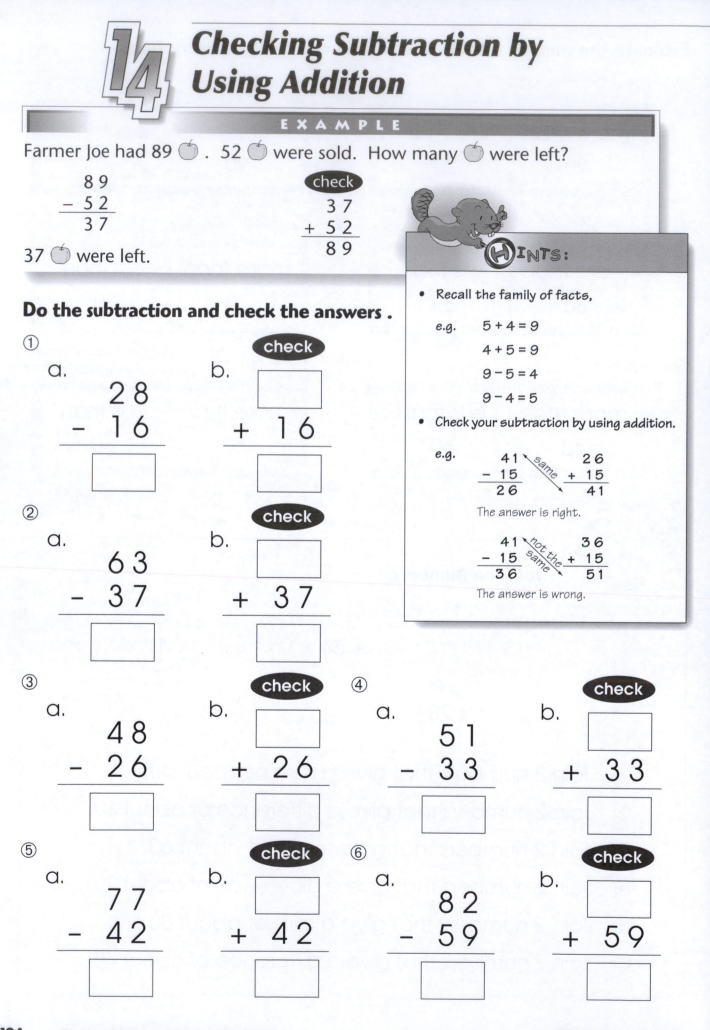

HINTS:

- Recall the family of facts,

  e.g.   5 + 4 = 9
           4 + 5 = 9
           9 − 5 = 4
           9 − 4 = 5

- Check your subtraction by using addition.

  e.g.
  ```
     4 1          2 6
   - 1 5   same + 1 5
     2 6          4 1
  ```
  The answer is right.

  ```
     4 1              3 6
   - 1 5   not the  + 1 5
     3 6    same      5 1
  ```
  The answer is wrong.

Do the subtraction and check the answers .

①
a.
```
   2 8
 - 1 6
```

b. check
```
 + 1 6
```

②
a.
```
   6 3
 - 3 7
```

b. check
```
 + 3 7
```

③
a.
```
   4 8
 - 2 6
```

b. check
```
 + 2 6
```

④
a.
```
   5 1
 - 3 3
```

b. check
```
 + 3 3
```

⑤
a.
```
   7 7
 - 4 2
```

b. check
```
 + 4 2
```

⑥
a.
```
   8 2
 - 5 9
```

b. check
```
 + 5 9
```

ISBN: 978-1-897164-12-9

Subtract and check your answers.

⑦ a. 52 − 8 = _____

check

b. _____ + _____ = _____

⑧ a. 39 − 17 = _____

check

b. _____ + _____ = _____

⑨ a. 45 − 23 = _____

check

b. _____ + _____ = _____

⑩ a. 66 − 39 = _____

check

b. _____ + _____ = _____

⑪ a. 87 − 45 = _____

check

b. _____ + _____ = _____

⑫ a. 23 − 16 = _____

check

b. _____ + _____ = _____

⑬ a. 71 − 33 = _____

check

b. _____ + _____ = _____

⑭ a. 98 − 63 = _____

check

b. _____ + _____ = _____

⑮ a. 32 − 14 = _____

check

b. _____ + _____ = _____

⑯ a. 27 − 6 = _____

check

b. _____ + _____ = _____

⑰ a. 56 − 31 = _____

check

b. _____ + _____ = _____

⑱ a. 45 − 29 = _____

check

b. _____ + _____ = _____

ISBN: 978-1-897164-12-9

Subtract. Complete 1 addition sentence and 1 subtraction sentence to check each answer.

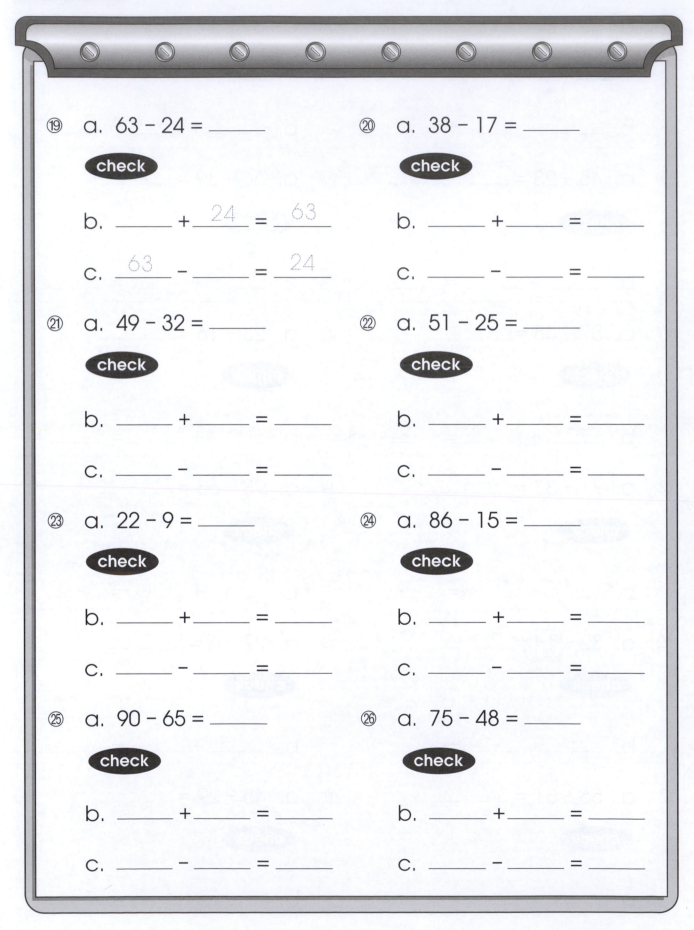

⑲ a. 63 – 24 = _____

check

b. _____ + 24 = 63

c. 63 – _____ = 24

⑳ a. 38 – 17 = _____

check

b. _____ + _____ = _____

c. _____ – _____ = _____

㉑ a. 49 – 32 = _____

check

b. _____ + _____ = _____

c. _____ – _____ = _____

㉒ a. 51 – 25 = _____

check

b. _____ + _____ = _____

c. _____ – _____ = _____

㉓ a. 22 – 9 = _____

check

b. _____ + _____ = _____

c. _____ – _____ = _____

㉔ a. 86 – 15 = _____

check

b. _____ + _____ = _____

c. _____ – _____ = _____

㉕ a. 90 – 65 = _____

check

b. _____ + _____ = _____

c. _____ – _____ = _____

㉖ a. 75 – 48 = _____

check

b. _____ + _____ = _____

c. _____ – _____ = _____

ISBN: 978-1-897164-12-9

Complete and check.

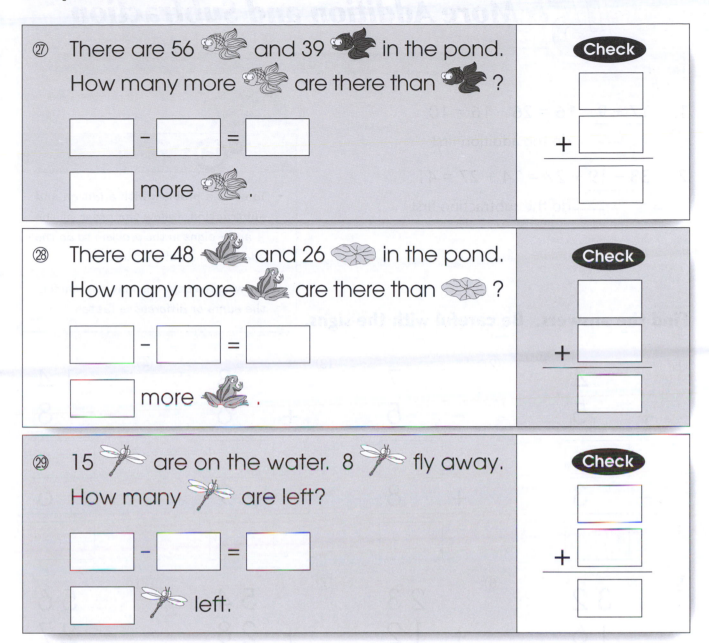

㉗ There are 56 🐟 and 39 🐟 in the pond. How many more 🐟 are there than 🐟 ?

☐ – ☐ = ☐

☐ more 🐟 .

Check

☐
+ ☐
☐

㉘ There are 48 🐸 and 26 🍃 in the pond. How many more 🐸 are there than 🍃 ?

☐ – ☐ = ☐

☐ more 🐸 .

Check

☐
+ ☐
☐

㉙ 15 🦟 are on the water. 8 🦟 fly away. How many 🦟 are left?

☐ – ☐ = ☐

☐ 🦟 left.

Check

☐
+ ☐
☐

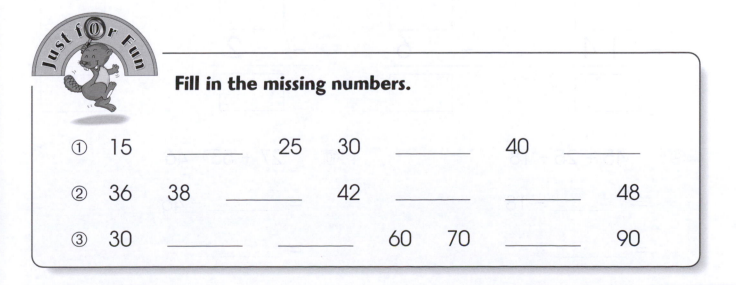

Just for Fun

Fill in the missing numbers.

① 15 _____ 25 30 _____ 40 _____

② 36 38 _____ 42 _____ _____ 48

③ 30 _____ _____ 60 70 _____ 90

15 More Addition and Subtraction

1. 17 + 9 − 16 = 26 − 16 = 10
    └─── do the addition first

2. 33 − 19 + 27 = 14 + 27 = 41
    └─── do the subtraction first

HINTS:

- To solve a problem with addition and subtraction, follow the order of the + and − signs in the problem to do the addition and subtraction.

- Knowing the patterns may help you find the sums or differences faster.

Find the answers. Be careful with the signs.

①
```
    4
+   5
_____
[    ]
−   3
_____
[    ]
```

②
```
    7
−   5
_____
[    ]
+   8
_____
[    ]
```

③
```
    8
+   6
_____
[    ]
−   9
_____
[    ]
```

④
```
   14
−   8
_____
[    ]
+   6
_____
[    ]
```

⑤
```
   32
−  16
_____
[    ]
−  14
_____
[    ]
```

⑥
```
   23
+  12
_____
[    ]
−   6
_____
[    ]
```

⑦
```
   54
+  28
_____
[    ]
−   2
_____
[    ]
```

⑧
```
   56
−  27
_____
[    ]
+   7
_____
[    ]
```

⑨   45 + 25 − 18

= _____ − 18

= _____

⑩   27 + 53 − 46

= _____ − 46

= _____

ISBN: 978-1-897164-12-9

Add.

⑪ 10 + 30 = _40_   ⑫ 40 + 20 = _____

⑬ 16 + 20 = _____   ⑭ 20 + 26 = _____

⑮ 16 + 10 + 10 = _____   ⑯ 10 + 10 + 26 = _____

⑰ 9 + 4 = 10 + _3_

= _____

⑱ 19 + 25 = 20 + _____ = _____

⑲ 29 + 33 = 30 + _____ = _____

⑳ 18 + 35 = 20 + _____ = _____

㉑ 38 + 16 = 40 + _____ = _____

㉒ 4 + 8 = _____ + 10

= _____

㉓ 22 + 18 = _____ + 20 = _____

㉔ 21 + 19 = _____ + 20 = _____

㉕ 16 + 28 = _____ + 30 = _____

㉖ 13 + 29 = _____ + 30 = _____

ISBN: 978-1-897164-12-9

Subtract.

㉗ 50 − 20 = _____

㉘ 36 − 26 = _____

㉙ 64 − 20 = _____

㉚ 53 − 13 = _____

㉛ 73 − 30 = _____

㉜ 48 − 28 = _____

㉝ 60 − 30 = _____

㉞ 76 − 50 = _____

㉟ 87 − 57 = _____

㊱ 38 − 20 = _____

㊲ 49 − 29 = _____

㊳ 96 − 66 = _____

㊴ a. 8 − 5   = _____

㊵ a. 14 − 8 = _____

  b. 18 − 5 = _____

  b. 24 − 8 = _____

  c. 28 − 5 = _____

  c. 34 − 8 = _____

  d. 38 − 5 = _____

  d. 44 − 8 = _____

  e. 48 − 5 = _____

  e. 54 − 8 = _____

㊶ a. 72 − 8   = _____

㊷ a. 67 − 9   = _____

  b. 72 − 18 = _____

  b. 67 − 19 = _____

  c. 72 − 28 = _____

  c. 67 − 29 = _____

  d. 72 − 38 = _____

  d. 67 − 39 = _____

  e. 72 − 48 = _____

  e. 67 − 49 = _____

ISBN: 978-1-897164-12-9

The children are playing with the spinner. Look at the children's scores in 3 rounds of the game. Find their final scores.

	1st round	2nd round	3rd round
	Add 8	Add 4	Subtract 5
	Add 9	Subtract 3	Add 5
	Add 7	Add 6	Subtract 4

means add 5

means subtract 5

43 The final score of is :

_____ = _____

44 The final score of is :

_____ = _____

45 The final score of is :

_____ = _____

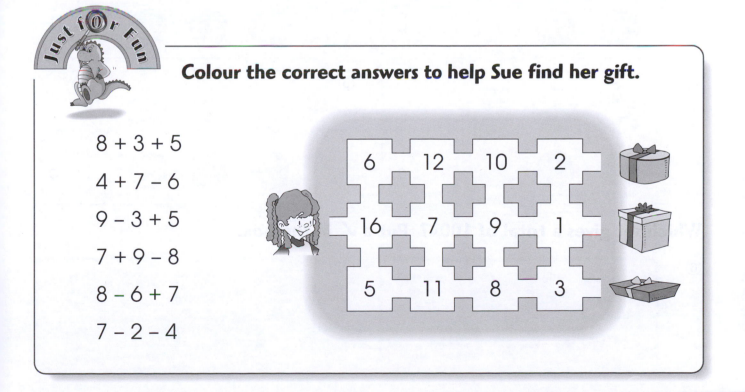

Just for Fun

Colour the correct answers to help Sue find her gift.

8 + 3 + 5

4 + 7 − 6

9 − 3 + 5

7 + 9 − 8

8 − 6 + 7

7 − 2 − 4

6	12	10	2
16	7	9	1
5	11	8	3

ISBN: 978-1-897164-12-9

16 Addition and Subtraction with Money

EXAMPLE

How many cents does Sam have?

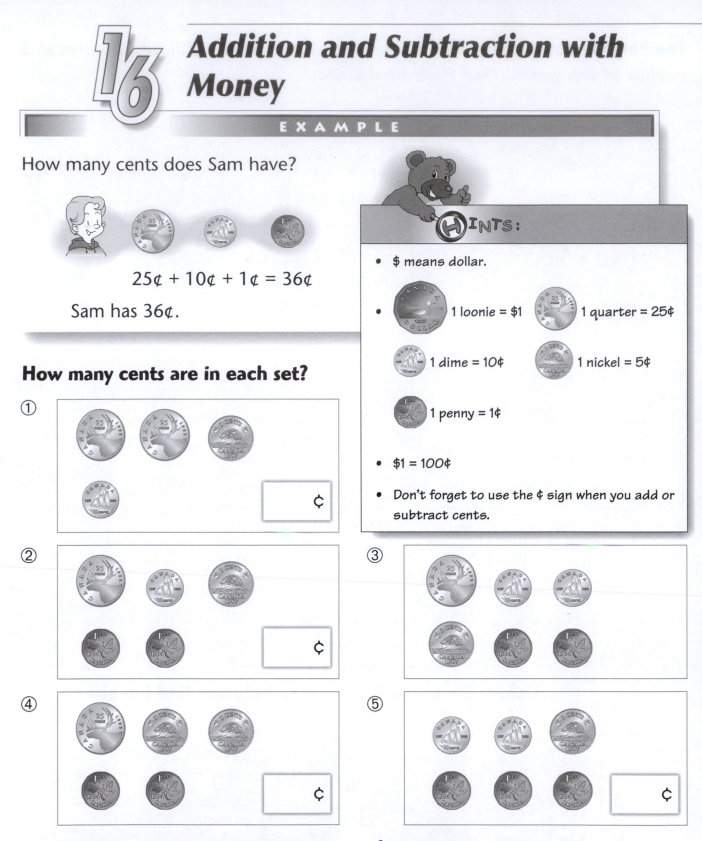

$25¢ + 10¢ + 1¢ = 36¢$

Sam has 36¢.

HINTS:

- $ means dollar.

- 1 loonie = $1   1 quarter = 25¢

- 1 dime = 10¢   1 nickel = 5¢

- 1 penny = 1¢

- $1 = 100¢

- Don't forget to use the ¢ sign when you add or subtract cents.

How many cents are in each set?

① ____ ¢

② ____ ¢   ③

④ ____ ¢   ⑤ ____ ¢

Which set gives a total of 100¢? Put a ✓ in the box.

⑥   ⑦

ISBN: 978-1-897164-12-9

How much change does Sue get?

	Sue has	Sue buys	Change Sue gets
⑧		49¢	_____ ¢ – _____ ¢ = _____ ¢
⑨		85¢	_____ ¢ – _____ ¢ = _____ ¢
⑩		36¢	_____ ¢ – _____ ¢ = _____ ¢
⑪		56¢	_____ ¢ – _____ ¢ = _____ ¢

How much more does Sam need?

	Sam has	Sam wants to buy	Extra amount Sam needs
⑫		67¢	_____ ¢ – _____ ¢ = _____ ¢
⑬		76¢	_____ ¢ – _____ ¢ = _____ ¢
⑭		72¢	_____ ¢ – _____ ¢ = _____ ¢
⑮		28¢	_____ ¢ – _____ ¢ = _____ ¢

Pay with the least number of coins. Write the number of each coin needed.

	25¢	10¢	5¢	1¢
⑯ 54¢				
⑰ 22¢				
⑱ 80¢				
⑲ 47¢				
⑳ 36¢				

Write each price. Then solve the problems.

㉑ ____ ¢	㉒ ____ ¢	㉓ ____ ¢	㉔ ____ ¢

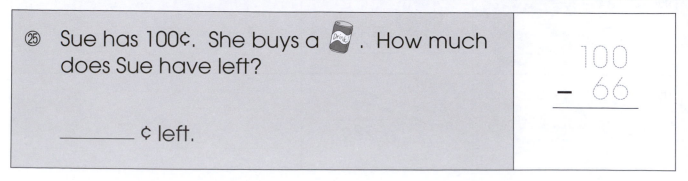

㉕ Sue has 100¢. She buys a Drink. How much does Sue have left?

$$\begin{array}{r} 100 \\ -\ 66 \\ \hline \end{array}$$

_____ ¢ left.

ISBN: 978-1-897164-12-9

㉖ Sam buys a 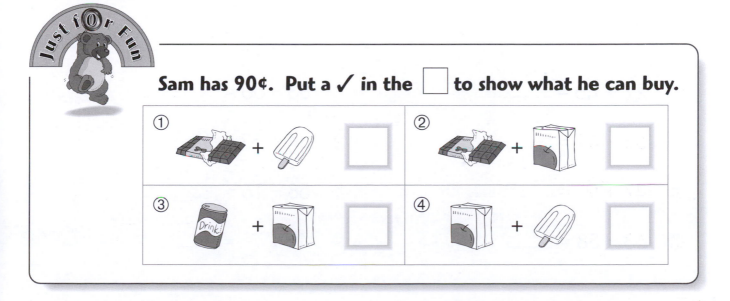 and a . How much does Sam pay in all?

_____ ¢ in all.

㉗ Jack buys a and a . How much does Jack pay in all?

_____ ¢ in all.

㉘ Ben buys a . Bob buys a . How much more does Ben pay than Bob?

_____ ¢ more.

㉙ Sue buys a . Jane buys a . How much less does Jane pay than Sue?

_____ ¢ less.

Just for Fun

Sam has 90¢. Put a ✓ in the ☐ to show what he can buy.

① + ☐ ② + ☐

③ + ☐ ④ + ☐

ISBN: 978-1-897164-12-9

Add or subtract.

①
```
  3 2
+   9
-----
```

②
```
  2 8
+ 1 7
-----
```

③
```
  3 6
-   4
-----
```

④
```
  5 2
-   9
-----
```

⑤
```
  7 9
- 5 1
-----
```

⑥
```
  8 4
- 6 6
-----
```

⑦
```
  4 9
+   8
-----
```

⑧
```
  2 1
+ 4 5
-----
```

⑨
```
  4 6
+ 2 5
-----
```

⑩
```
  9 2
- 3 7
-----
```

⑪
```
  1 8
+ 6 2
-----
```

⑫
```
  6 0
- 4 1
-----
```

⑬
```
  5 8
- 2 2
-----
```

⑭
```
  1 4
+ 5 5
-----
```

⑮
```
  7 3
- 3 0
-----
```

⑯
```
  2 3
+ 4 7
-----
```

⑰ 27 + 46 = _____

⑱ 83 – 56 = _____

⑲ 65 – 49 = _____

⑳ 34 + 57 = _____

㉑ 47 + 9 = _____

㉒ 58 – 16 = _____

㉓ 63 – 38 = _____

㉔ 42 + 7 = _____

ISBN: 978-1-897164-12-9

Estimate the sums or differences by rounding the numbers to the nearest 10. Compare the estimates with the exact answers.

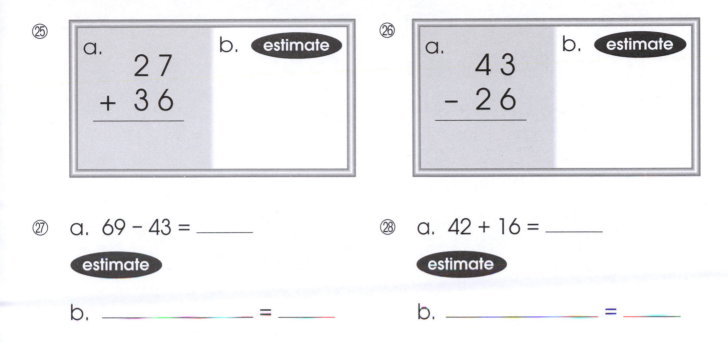

㉕
a.
```
   2 7
 + 3 6
 _____
```
b. estimate

㉖
a.
```
   4 3
 - 2 6
 _____
```
b. estimate

㉗ a. 69 – 43 = _____

estimate

b. _____ = _____

㉘ a. 42 + 16 = _____

estimate

b. _____ = _____

Subtract. Check the answers using addition.

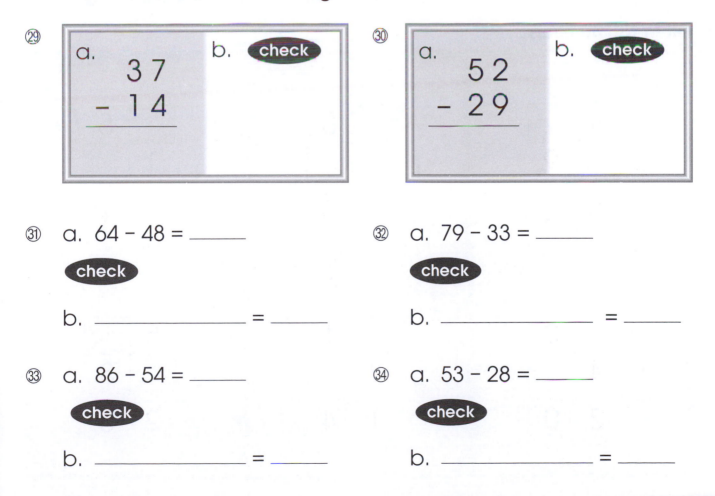

㉙
a.
```
   3 7
 - 1 4
 _____
```
b. check

㉚
a.
```
   5 2
 - 2 9
 _____
```
b. check

㉛ a. 64 – 48 = _____

check

b. _____ = _____

㉜ a. 79 – 33 = _____

check

b. _____ = _____

㉝ a. 86 – 54 = _____

check

b. _____ = _____

㉞ a. 53 – 28 = _____

check

b. _____ = _____

ISBN: 978-1-897164-12-9

Complete.

㉟ $8 + 3 \quad = 10 + \underline{\hspace{2cm}} = \underline{\hspace{2cm}}$

㊱ $19 + 26 = 20 + \underline{\hspace{2cm}} = \underline{\hspace{2cm}}$

㊲ $13 + 29 = \underline{\hspace{2cm}} + 30 = \underline{\hspace{2cm}}$

㊳ $25 + 38 = \underline{\hspace{2cm}} + 40 = \underline{\hspace{2cm}}$

㊴
a. $9 - 6 \quad = \underline{\hspace{2cm}}$

b. $19 - 6 = \underline{\hspace{2cm}}$

c. $29 - 6 = \underline{\hspace{2cm}}$

d. $39 - 6 = \underline{\hspace{2cm}}$

㊵
a. $62 - 9 \quad = \underline{\hspace{2cm}}$

b. $62 - 19 = \underline{\hspace{2cm}}$

c. $62 - 29 = \underline{\hspace{2cm}}$

d. $62 - 39 = \underline{\hspace{2cm}}$

Fill in the numbers.

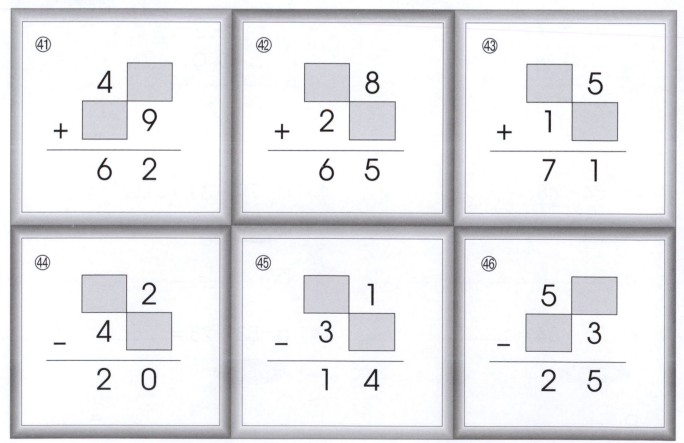

ISBN: 978-1-897164-12-9

Find the answers.

㊼ 9 + 7 − 6 = ______

㊽ 5 + 7 + 8 = ______

㊾ 8 − 3 + 6 = ______

㊿ 7 + 2 − 4 = ______

(51) 69 − 23 + 17

= ______ + 17

= ______

(52) 14 + 35 − 26

= ______ − 26

= ______

(53) 22 + 36 − 49

= ______ − 49

= ______

(54) 72 − 58 + 13

= ______ + 13

= ______

The children are shopping. Put a ✓ in the ☐ to show what they buy.

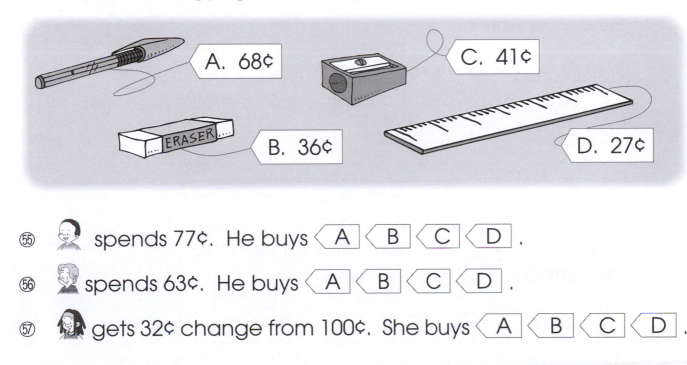

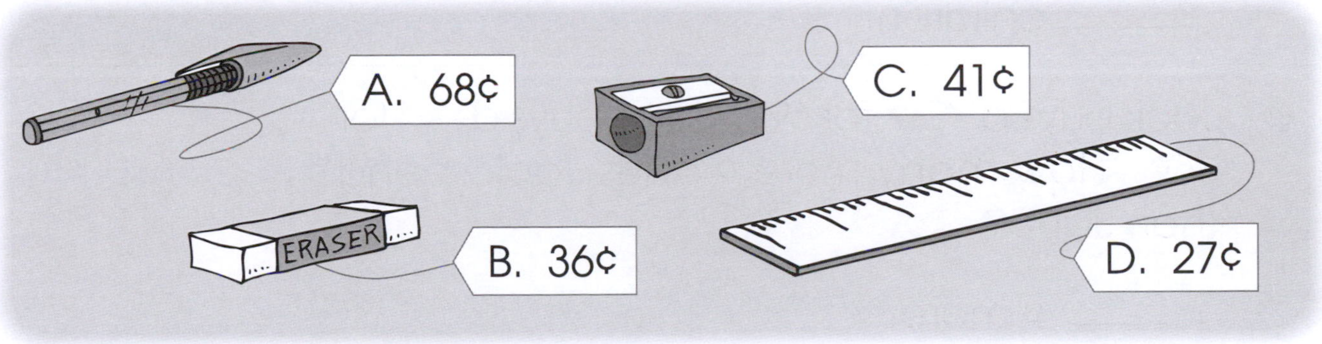
A. 68¢
C. 41¢
ERASER
B. 36¢
D. 27¢

(55)  spends 77¢. He buys ☐ A ☐ B ☐ C ☐ D .

(56)  spends 63¢. He buys ☐ A ☐ B ☐ C ☐ D .

(57)  gets 32¢ change from 100¢. She buys ☐ A ☐ B ☐ C ☐ D .

Complete.

58. Mom buys 8 red 🌹 and 25 yellow 🌹. How many 🌹 does she buy in all?

    $$\begin{array}{r} 8 \\ + 25 \\ \hline \end{array}$$

    _____ 🌹 in all.

59. There are 23 girls and 19 boys on the school bus. How many children are there on the school bus altogether?

    _____ children altogether.

60. Sue has 92¢. She spends 57¢ for a 🥫. How many ¢ does she have left?

    _____ ¢ left.

61. There are 26 children in a class. 17 children are reading. How many children are not reading?

    _____ children.

62. Jack buys a 🍫 for 69¢. Jane buys a 🍭 for 35¢. How many more ¢ does Jack spend than Jane?

    _____ ¢ more.

63. There are 38 🧁 and 45 🍪 in a cake shop. How many 🧁 🍪 are there altogether in the cake shop?

    _____ 🧁 🍪 altogether.

ISBN: 978-1-897164-12-9

Overview

In Section II, addition and subtraction skills were practised. In this section, children are expected to be able to apply the skills in other areas, such as patterning and graphs.

In addition, real-life situations are provided for them to develop other skills, including probability, geometry, fractions, graphing and measuring.

Through practice in naming and stating the value of different coins, children are able to solve problems involving money.

ISBN: 978-1-897164-12-9   COMPLETE MATHSMART (GRADE 2)   **121**

Talia makes some invitation cards and cuts them into different shapes. Name the shapes and count how many squares each card covers.

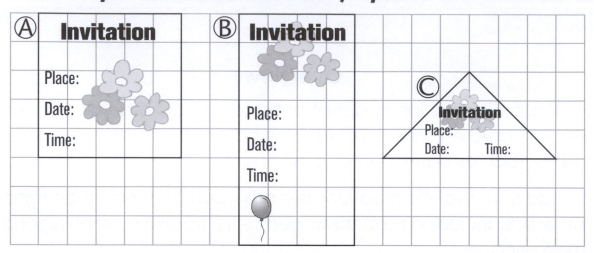

①

	Card A	Card B	Card C
Shape			
Number of squares covered	squares	squares	squares

Find out which cards Talia is going to send to her friends. Do the addition or subtraction on the name cards. Then colour the cards if the answers match the invitation cards.

②

Invitation
Place:
Date:
Time: **11**

| Mary $8 + 3$ | Joe $6 + 6$ | Ray $9 + 4$ | George $7 + 4$ |
| James $5 + 9$ | Vincent $3 + 9$ | Freda $2 + 9$ | Stephen $10 + 1$ |

③

Invitation
Place:
Date:
Time: **7**

| Sean $15 - 7$ | Tina $12 - 5$ | Rose $16 - 9$ | Nathan $18 - 9$ |
| Wayne $10 - 3$ | Roger $16 - 8$ | Sophia $13 - 6$ | John $14 - 8$ |

④

Invitation
Place: **13** Time:
Date:

| Ivy $11 + 2$ | Alfred $8 + 5$ | Lisa $15 - 6$ | Yvonne $16 - 3$ |
| Victoria $9 + 6$ | Jill $7 + 6$ | Tom $12 - 4$ | Bill $17 - 5$ |

ISBN: 978-1-897164-12-9

Look at the things the children are going to buy for Talia. Check ✔ the coins to show the values of the things. Then answer the questions.

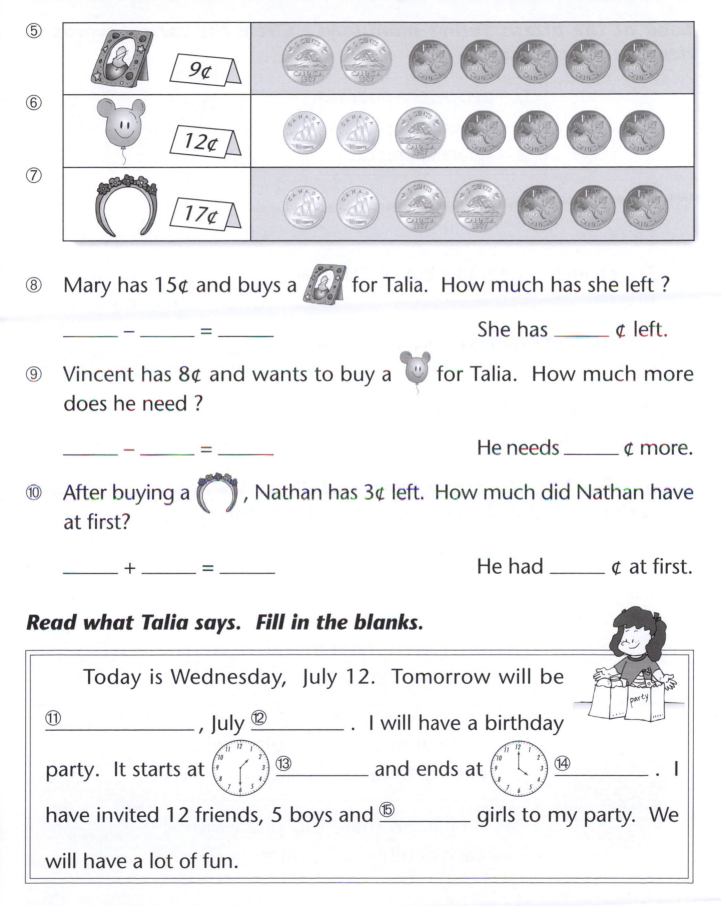

⑧ Mary has 15¢ and buys a 🖼 for Talia. How much has she left ?

_____ − _____ = _____   She has _____ ¢ left.

⑨ Vincent has 8¢ and wants to buy a 🎈 for Talia. How much more does he need ?

_____ − _____ = _____   He needs _____ ¢ more.

⑩ After buying a 👑, Nathan has 3¢ left. How much did Nathan have at first?

_____ + _____ = _____   He had _____ ¢ at first.

Read what Talia says. Fill in the blanks.

Today is Wednesday, July 12. Tomorrow will be

⑪ _____ , July ⑫ _____ . I will have a birthday

party. It starts at ⑬ _____ and ends at ⑭ _____ . I

have invited 12 friends, 5 boys and ⑮ _____ girls to my party. We

will have a lot of fun.

ISBN: 978-1-897164-12-9   COMPLETE MATHSMART (GRADE 2)   **123**

Look at the pizzas Talia's mom buys. Circle the correct words to describe the chances.

```
6 – pepperoni pizzas
1 – vegetarian pizza
2 – Hawaiian pizzas
```

⑯ The chance of getting a box of pepperoni pizza

Often   Sometimes   Never

⑰ The chance of getting a box of Canadian pizza

Often   Sometimes   Never

⑱ The chance of getting a box of vegetarian pizza

Often   Sometimes   Never

⑲ What kind of pizza is Talia more likely to pick, pepperoni or Hawaiian?

Pepperoni   Hawaiian

Talia's mom cuts the pizzas into equal slices. See how many children are going to share the pizzas. Write the numbers.

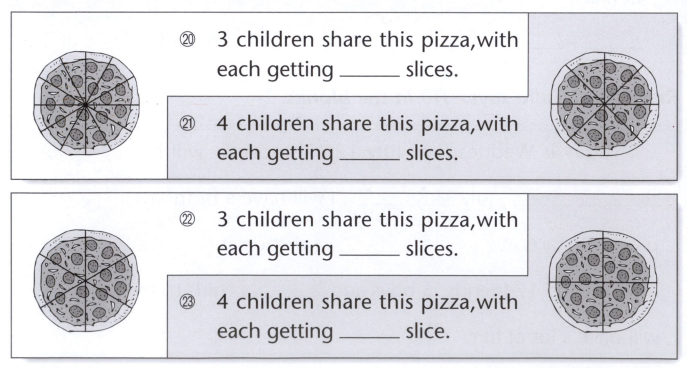

⑳ 3 children share this pizza, with each getting _____ slices.

㉑ 4 children share this pizza, with each getting _____ slices.

㉒ 3 children share this pizza, with each getting _____ slices.

㉓ 4 children share this pizza, with each getting _____ slice.

ISBN: 978-1-897164-12-9

Look at Talia's gifts. Colour the graph and answer the questions.

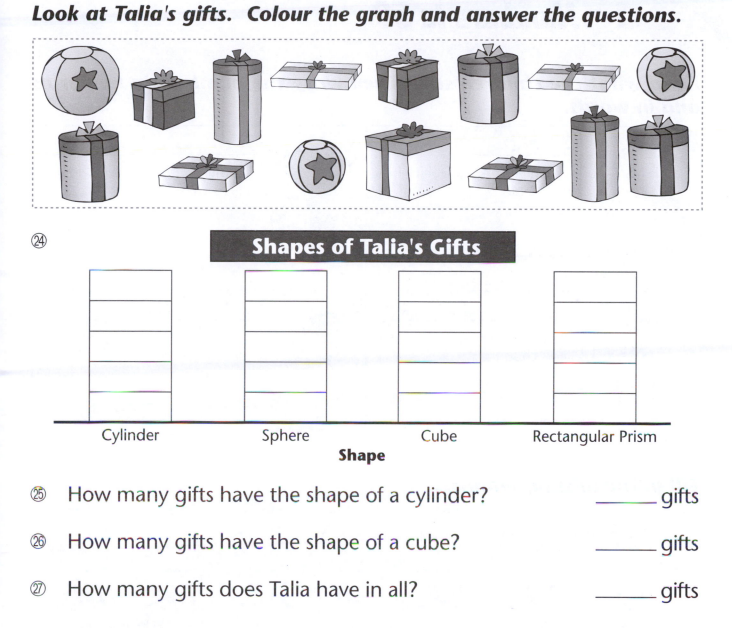

㉔

Shapes of Talia's Gifts

| Cylinder | Sphere | Cube | Rectangular Prism |

Shape

㉕ How many gifts have the shape of a cylinder?   _____ gifts

㉖ How many gifts have the shape of a cube?   _____ gifts

㉗ How many gifts does Talia have in all?   _____ gifts

See how Talia arranges her gifts. What comes next ? Colour the correct pictures.

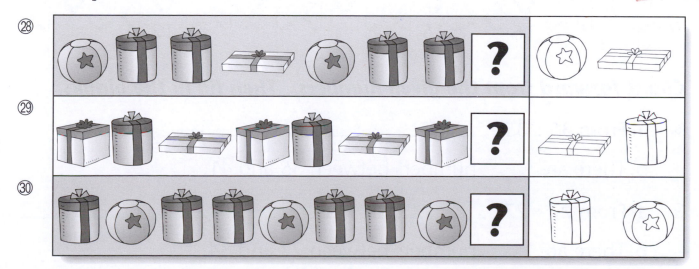

㉘

㉙

㉚

ISBN: 978-1-897164-12-9

Read what the children say. Then write the numbers in numerals and in words.

① The number on my T-shirt is 1 more than 17.

_____

② The number on my sweater is 1 less than 15.

_____

③ The number on my T-shirt is 2 less than 19.

_____

④ The number on my dress is 2 more than 14.

_____

Fill in the missing numbers.

⑤ 20 19 ___ ___ ___ 15 ___

⑥ 18 17 ___ ___ 14 ___ ___

⑦ ___ 16 15 ___ ___ 12 ___

Count forward from the given numbers. Then fill in the blanks.

⑧ a. From 35 : 35 , _____ , _____ , _____ , _____ , _____ , _____

b. There are _____ numbers between 35 and 41.

⑨ a. From 27 : 27 , _____ , _____ , _____ , _____ , _____ , _____

b. There are _____ numbers between 27 and 34.

ISBN: 978-1-897164-12-9

Write the numbers.

⑩ 53 = _____ tens and _____ ones

⑪ 47 = _____ tens and _____ ones

⑫ 85 = _____ tens and _____ ones

⑬ 60 = _____ tens and _____ ones

⑭ 39 = _____ tens and _____ ones

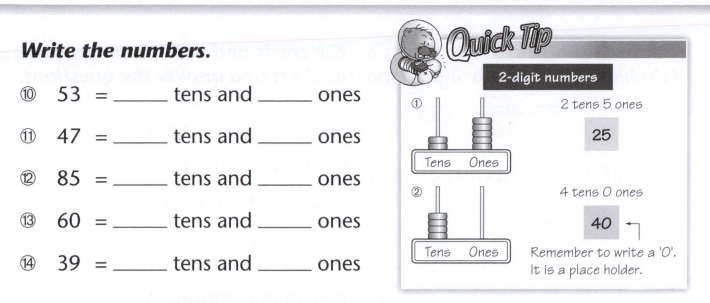

Quick Tip

2-digit numbers

① 2 tens 5 ones — 25

② 4 tens 0 ones — 40

Remember to write a '0'.
It is a place holder.

Sean puts his stickers in pairs. Colour the sticker with the greater number in each pair.

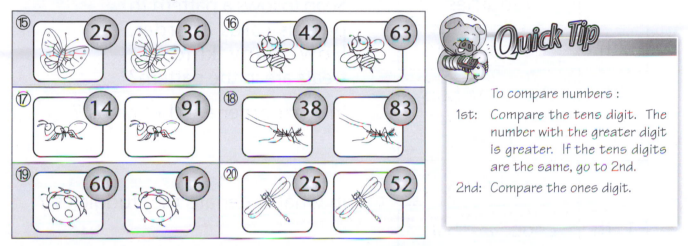

⑮ 25 36   ⑯ 42 63

⑰ 14 91   ⑱ 38 83

⑲ 60 16   ⑳ 25 52

Quick Tip

To compare numbers :

1st: Compare the tens digit. The number with the greater digit is greater. If the tens digits are the same, go to 2nd.

2nd: Compare the ones digit.

Help Sean label his stickers. Put the numbers in order from smallest to greatest.

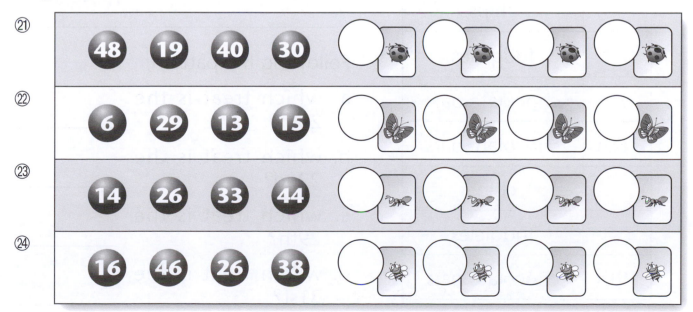

㉑ 48 19 40 30

㉒ 6 29 13 15

㉓ 14 26 33 44

㉔ 16 46 26 38

Sean writes his favourite treats on the cards and puts them in order. Help him write the missing ordinal numbers and answer the questions.

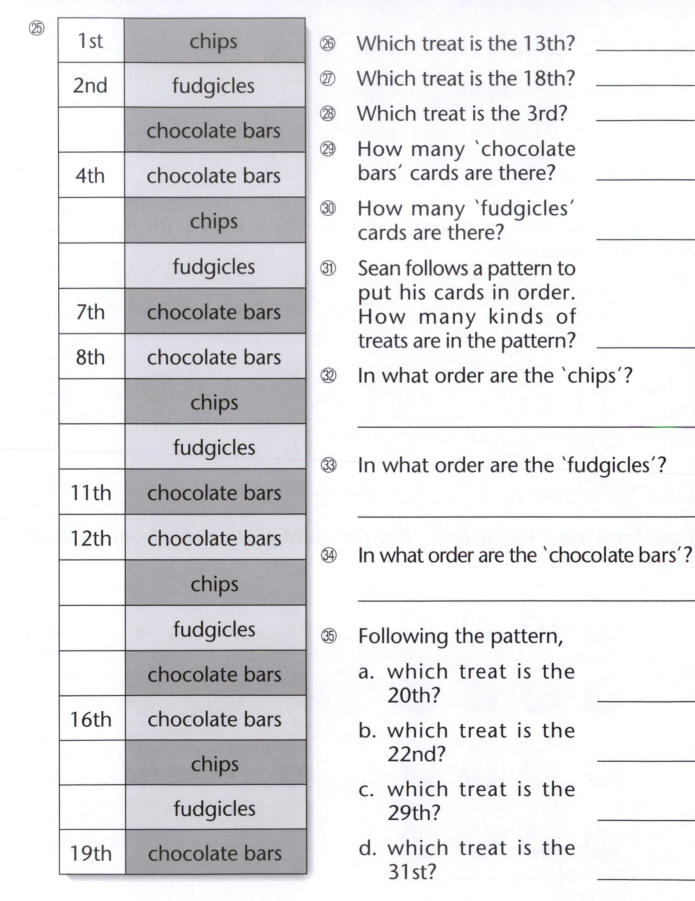

㉕

1st	chips
2nd	fudgicles
	chocolate bars
4th	chocolate bars
	chips
	fudgicles
7th	chocolate bars
8th	chocolate bars
	chips
	fudgicles
11th	chocolate bars
12th	chocolate bars
	chips
	fudgicles
	chocolate bars
16th	chocolate bars
	chips
	fudgicles
19th	chocolate bars

㉖ Which treat is the 13th? _____

㉗ Which treat is the 18th? _____

㉘ Which treat is the 3rd? _____

㉙ How many `chocolate bars' cards are there? _____

㉚ How many `fudgicles' cards are there? _____

㉛ Sean follows a pattern to put his cards in order. How many kinds of treats are in the pattern? _____

㉜ In what order are the `chips'?

_____

㉝ In what order are the `fudgicles'?

_____

㉞ In what order are the `chocolate bars'?

_____

㉟ Following the pattern,

a. which treat is the 20th? _____

b. which treat is the 22nd? _____

c. which treat is the 29th? _____

d. which treat is the 31st? _____

ISBN: 978-1-897164-12-9

① Count by 2's.

2 → 4 → 6 → 8 → 10 → 12

There are 12 🍒 .

② Count by 5's.

5 → 10 → 15 → 20

There are 20 🍌 .

③ Count by 10's.

10 → 20 → 30

There are 30 🍇 .

Count by 2's , 5's or 10's to connect the dots.

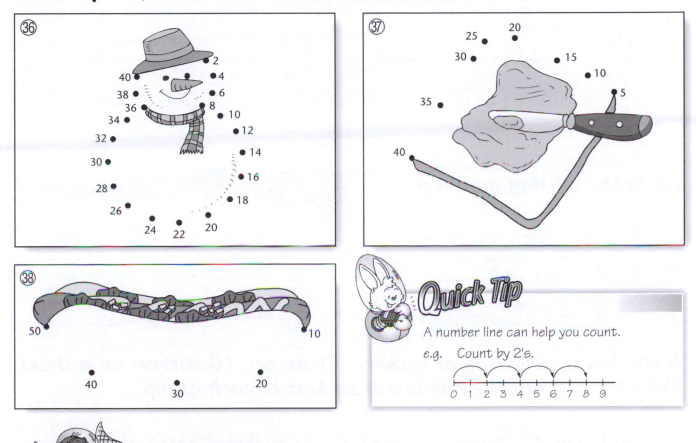

㊱

2
4
6
8
10
12
14
16
18
20
22
24
26
28
30
32
34
36
38
40

㊲

20
25
30
15
10
5
35
40

㊳

50
10
40
30
20

Quick Tip

A number line can help you count.

e.g.   Count by 2's.

0 1 2 3 4 5 6 7 8 9

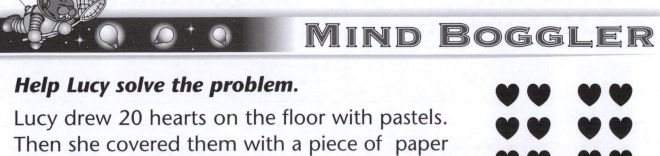

MIND BOGGLER

Help Lucy solve the problem.

Lucy drew 20 hearts on the floor with pastels. Then she covered them with a piece of paper and rubbed hard. How many hearts did she get in all?

She got _____ hearts in all.

ISBN: 978-1-897164-12-9

2 Addition

Write two addition sentences for each group of numbers.

① 9 16 7
_____ + _____ = _____
_____ + _____ = _____

② 3 11 8
_____ + _____ = _____
_____ + _____ = _____

③ 15 7 8
_____ + _____ = _____
_____ + _____ = _____

④ 13 9 4
_____ + _____ = _____
_____ + _____ = _____

Fill in the missing numbers.

⑤ $6 + 9 = 9 + $ _____ $ = $ _____

⑥ $5 + 7 = $ _____ $ + 5 = $ _____

⑦ $7 + 8 = 8 + $ _____ $ = $ _____

⑧ $3 + 9 = $ _____ $ + 3 = $ _____

Jayne has a collection of stickers. There are 10 stickers on a sheet. Help her find out the number of stickers in each group.

⑨
10
+ 20
_____

⑩
20
+ 30
_____

⑪
_____ + _____ = _____

⑫
_____ + _____ = _____

ISBN: 978-1-897164-12-9

Help Jayne complete the table to find how many stickers are in each group.

	1st group	2nd group	In all
⑬			+ _____
⑭			+ _____

Do the addition.

⑮
```
   2 3
 + 1 4
 _____
```

⑯
```
   3 6
 +   2
 _____
```

⑰
```
   1 2
 + 3 4
 _____
```

⑱
```
     7
 + 4 2
 _____
```

⑲ 15 + 33 = _____

⑳ 24 + 24 = _____

㉑ 20 + 17 = _____

㉒ 18 + 21 = _____

㉓ 43 + 6 = _____

㉔ 3 + 35 = _____

Solve the problems.

㉕ 15 boys and 12 girls go fishing. How many children go fishing?   _____ children

㉖ Amy has 23 red balloons and 14 blue balloons. How many balloons does Amy have in all?   _____ balloons

㉗ Lucy has 4 lollipops and Mabel has 30 lollipops. How many lollipops do they have in all?   _____ lollipops

㉘ Tim has 23 stamps. Peter has 25 stamps more than Tim. How many stamps does Peter have?   _____ stamps

Elaine is counting her stickers. Help her circle the stickers in groups of 10. Then calculate.

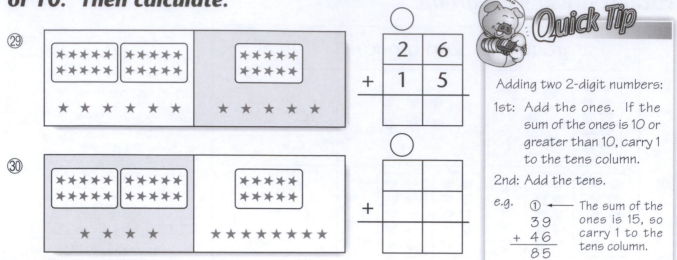

Do the addition.

③①
```
   2 9
 + 1 5
 ─────
```

③②
```
   2 8
 + 1 7
 ─────
```

③③
```
     9
 + 3 2
 ─────
```

③④
```
   3 6
 +   7
 ─────
```

③⑤
```
   2 9
 +   6
 ─────
```

③⑥
```
   1 6
 + 2 7
 ─────
```

③⑦
```
   3 8
 +   4
 ─────
```

③⑧
```
   1 7
 + 2 3
 ─────
```

③⑨
```
   3 5
 +   8
 ─────
```

④⓪
```
   1 2
 + 1 9
 ─────
```

④① 28 + 4 = _____

④② 39 + 8 = _____

④③ 41 + 9 = _____

④④ 18 + 26 = _____

④⑤ 15 + 16 = _____

④⑥ 25 + 25 = _____

④⑦ 17 + 17 = _____

④⑧ 34 + 6 = _____

Look at the stickers each girl has and solve the problems.

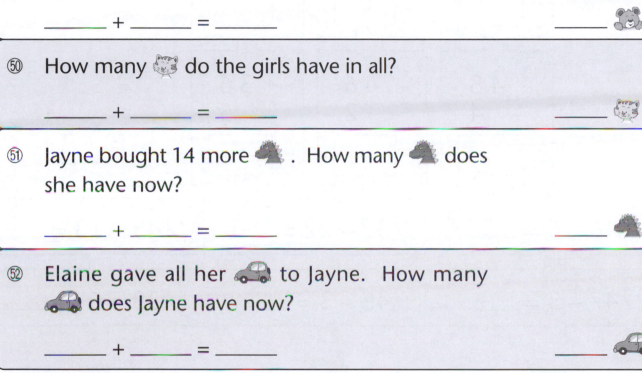

Jayne	14	26	27	8
Elaine	29	24	5	16

(49) How many [bear stickers] do the girls have in all?

_____ + _____ = _____   _____ [bear stickers]

(50) How many [cat stickers] do the girls have in all?

_____ + _____ = _____   _____ [cat stickers]

(51) Jayne bought 14 more [dinosaur stickers]. How many [dinosaur stickers] does she have now?

_____ + _____ = _____   _____ [dinosaur stickers]

(52) Elaine gave all her [car stickers] to Jayne. How many [car stickers] does Jayne have now?

_____ + _____ = _____   _____ [car stickers]

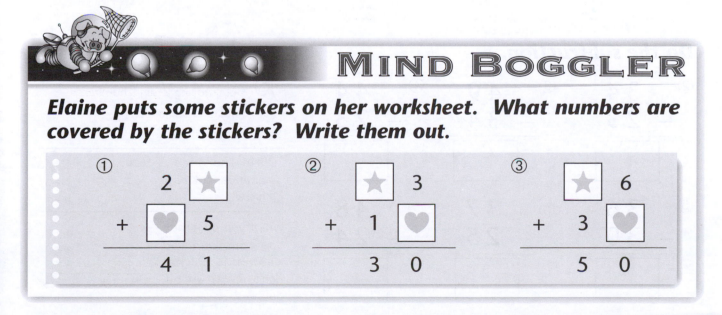

MIND BOGGLER

Elaine puts some stickers on her worksheet. What numbers are covered by the stickers? Write them out.

① $\begin{array}{r} 2\,\bigstar \\ +\ \heartsuit\,5 \\ \hline 4\,1 \end{array}$

② $\begin{array}{r} \bigstar\,3 \\ +\ 1\,\heartsuit \\ \hline 3\,0 \end{array}$

③ $\begin{array}{r} \bigstar\,6 \\ +\ 3\,\heartsuit \\ \hline 5\,0 \end{array}$

ISBN: 978-1-897164-12-9

3 Subtraction

Help Jason the frog find the way to get his food. Do the subtraction. Then colour the circles for the answers smaller than 35.

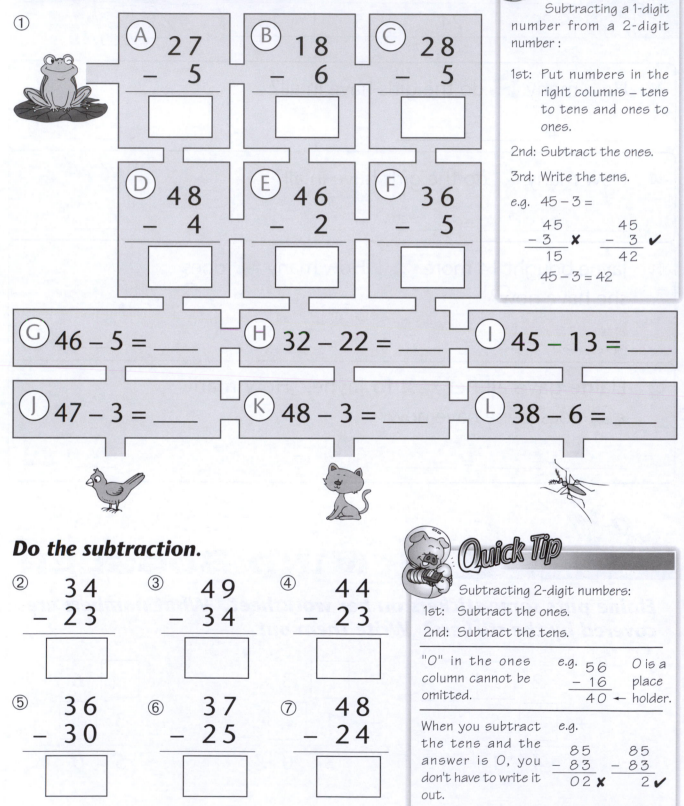

①

A) 27 − 5 = ☐

B) 18 − 6 = ☐

C) 28 − 5 = ☐

D) 48 − 4 = ☐

E) 46 − 2 = ☐

F) 36 − 5 = ☐

G) 46 − 5 = ____

H) 32 − 22 = ____

I) 45 − 13 = ____

J) 47 − 3 = ____

K) 48 − 3 = ____

L) 38 − 6 = ____

Quick Tip

Subtracting a 1-digit number from a 2-digit number :

1st: Put numbers in the right columns — tens to tens and ones to ones.

2nd: Subtract the ones.

3rd: Write the tens.

e.g. 45 − 3 =

$$\begin{array}{r} 45 \\ -\ 3 \\ \hline 15 \end{array} \text{✗}
\qquad
\begin{array}{r} 45 \\ -\ 3 \\ \hline 42 \end{array} \text{✔}$$

45 − 3 = 42

Do the subtraction.

②
$$\begin{array}{r} 34 \\ -\ 23 \\ \hline \end{array}$$

③
$$\begin{array}{r} 49 \\ -\ 34 \\ \hline \end{array}$$

④
$$\begin{array}{r} 44 \\ -\ 23 \\ \hline \end{array}$$

⑤
$$\begin{array}{r} 36 \\ -\ 30 \\ \hline \end{array}$$

⑥
$$\begin{array}{r} 37 \\ -\ 25 \\ \hline \end{array}$$

⑦
$$\begin{array}{r} 48 \\ -\ 24 \\ \hline \end{array}$$

Quick Tip

Subtracting 2-digit numbers:
1st: Subtract the ones.
2nd: Subtract the tens.

"O" in the ones column cannot be omitted.	e.g. $\begin{array}{r} 56 \\ -\ 16 \\ \hline 40 \end{array}$	O is a place holder. ← holder.
When you subtract the tens and the answer is 0, you don't have to write it out.	e.g. $\begin{array}{r} 85 \\ -\ 83 \\ \hline 02 \end{array}$ ✗	$\begin{array}{r} 85 \\ -\ 83 \\ \hline 2 \end{array}$ ✔

ISBN: 978-1-897164-12-9

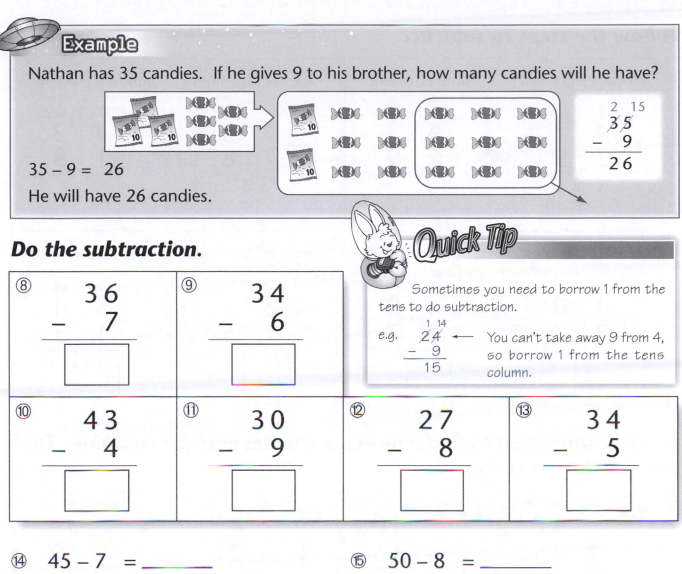

Example

Nathan has 35 candies. If he gives 9 to his brother, how many candies will he have?

$35 - 9 = 26$

He will have 26 candies.

$$\begin{array}{r} {\scriptstyle 2\ \ 15} \\ \cancel{3}\cancel{5} \\ -\ \ \ 9 \\ \hline 2\,6 \end{array}$$

Do the subtraction.

Quick Tip

Sometimes you need to borrow 1 from the tens to do subtraction.

e.g.
$$\begin{array}{r} {\scriptstyle 1\ \ 14} \\ \cancel{2}\cancel{4} \\ -\ \ \ 9 \\ \hline 1\,5 \end{array}$$
← You can't take away 9 from 4, so borrow 1 from the tens column.

⑧
$$\begin{array}{r} 36 \\ -\ \ 7 \\ \hline \end{array}$$

⑨
$$\begin{array}{r} 34 \\ -\ \ 6 \\ \hline \end{array}$$

⑩
$$\begin{array}{r} 43 \\ -\ \ 4 \\ \hline \end{array}$$

⑪
$$\begin{array}{r} 30 \\ -\ \ 9 \\ \hline \end{array}$$

⑫
$$\begin{array}{r} 27 \\ -\ \ 8 \\ \hline \end{array}$$

⑬
$$\begin{array}{r} 34 \\ -\ \ 5 \\ \hline \end{array}$$

⑭ $45 - 7 =$ _____

⑮ $50 - 8 =$ _____

⑯ $21 - 4 =$ _____

⑰ $32 - 7 =$ _____

See how many candies are in each jar. Solve the problems.

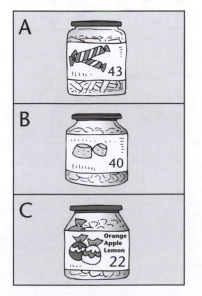

A ... 43

B ... 40

C Orange Apple Lemon 22

⑱ Lucy takes 5 🍬 from jar A. _____ 🍬 are left in jar A.

⑲ Douglas takes 9 🍬 from jar B. _____ 🍬 are left in jar B.

⑳ 8 🍬 in jar C are orange flavoured. _____ 🍬 in jar C are not orange flavoured.

㉑ 9 🍬 in jar C are apple flavoured. _____ 🍬 in jar C are lemon flavoured.

ISBN: 978-1-897164-12-9

Follow the steps to subtract.

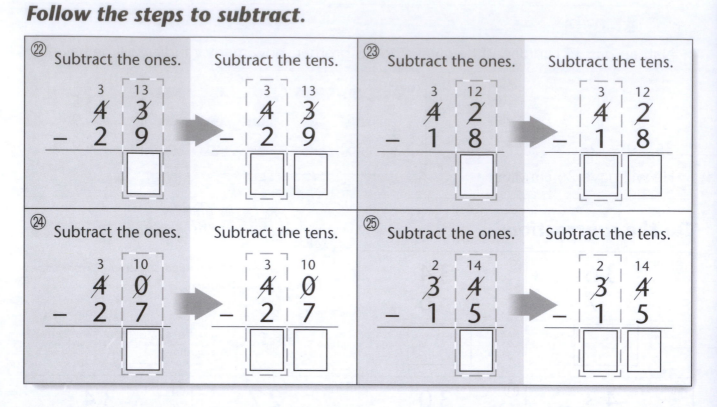

22 Subtract the ones. | Subtract the tens.

$$\begin{array}{c} \overset{3}{\cancel{4}}\ \overset{13}{\cancel{3}} \\ -\ 2\ \ 9 \\ \hline \end{array}$$

➡

$$\begin{array}{c} \overset{3}{\cancel{4}}\ \overset{13}{\cancel{3}} \\ -\ 2\ \ 9 \\ \hline \end{array}$$

23 Subtract the ones. | Subtract the tens.

$$\begin{array}{c} \overset{3}{\cancel{4}}\ \overset{12}{2} \\ -\ 1\ \ 8 \\ \hline \end{array}$$

➡

$$\begin{array}{c} \overset{3}{\cancel{4}}\ \overset{12}{2} \\ -\ 1\ \ 8 \\ \hline \end{array}$$

24 Subtract the ones. | Subtract the tens.

$$\begin{array}{c} \overset{3}{\cancel{4}}\ \overset{10}{\cancel{0}} \\ -\ 2\ \ 7 \\ \hline \end{array}$$

➡

$$\begin{array}{c} \overset{3}{\cancel{4}}\ \overset{10}{\cancel{0}} \\ -\ 2\ \ 7 \\ \hline \end{array}$$

25 Subtract the ones. | Subtract the tens.

$$\begin{array}{c} \overset{2}{\cancel{3}}\ \overset{14}{\cancel{4}} \\ -\ 1\ \ 5 \\ \hline \end{array}$$

➡

$$\begin{array}{c} \overset{2}{\cancel{3}}\ \overset{14}{\cancel{4}} \\ -\ 1\ \ 5 \\ \hline \end{array}$$

Do the subtraction to find how many candies each jar contains. Then answer the questions.

26

A
$$\begin{array}{r} 42 \\ -\ 25 \\ \hline \end{array}$$

B
$$\begin{array}{r} 40 \\ -\ 35 \\ \hline \end{array}$$

C
$$\begin{array}{r} 43 \\ -\ 26 \\ \hline \end{array}$$

D
$$\begin{array}{r} 34 \\ -\ 17 \\ \hline \end{array}$$

E
$$\begin{array}{r} 50 \\ -\ 46 \\ \hline \end{array}$$

F
$$\begin{array}{r} 33 \\ -\ 24 \\ \hline \end{array}$$

G
$$\begin{array}{r} 45 \\ -\ 26 \\ \hline \end{array}$$

H
$$\begin{array}{r} 48 \\ -\ 9 \\ \hline \end{array}$$

I
$$\begin{array}{r} 37 \\ -\ 19 \\ \hline \end{array}$$

J
$$\begin{array}{r} 46 \\ -\ 38 \\ \hline \end{array}$$

K
$$\begin{array}{r} 50 \\ -\ 36 \\ \hline \end{array}$$

L
$$\begin{array}{r} 44 \\ -\ 7 \\ \hline \end{array}$$

27 Which jar contains the most candies? _____

28 Which jar contains the fewest candies? _____

ISBN: 978-1-897164-12-9

Count and write how many tickets are needed to trade each toy in the box. Then help the children solve their problems.

㉙

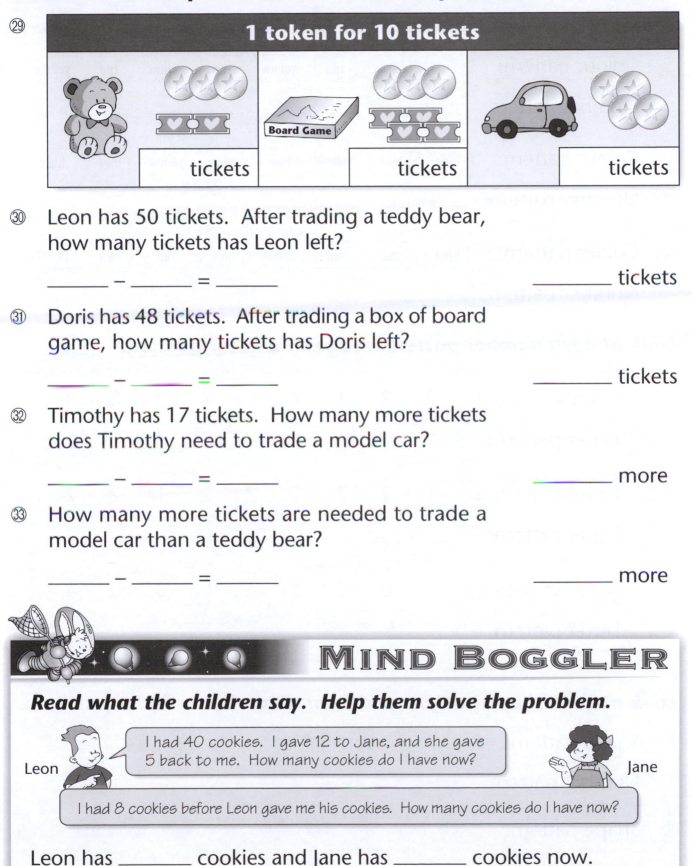

1 token for 10 tickets

tickets   tickets   tickets

㉚ Leon has 50 tickets. After trading a teddy bear, how many tickets has Leon left?

_____ – _____ = _____   _____ tickets

㉛ Doris has 48 tickets. After trading a box of board game, how many tickets has Doris left?

_____ – _____ = _____   _____ tickets

㉜ Timothy has 17 tickets. How many more tickets does Timothy need to trade a model car?

_____ – _____ = _____   _____ more

㉝ How many more tickets are needed to trade a model car than a teddy bear?

_____ – _____ = _____   _____ more

MIND BOGGLER

Read what the children say. Help them solve the problem.

Leon: I had 40 cookies. I gave 12 to Jane, and she gave 5 back to me. How many cookies do I have now?

Jane

I had 8 cookies before Leon gave me his cookies. How many cookies do I have now?

Leon has _____ cookies and Jane has _____ cookies now.

ISBN: 978-1-897164-12-9

4 Patterning

Colour each group of blocks as labelled. Then form a number pattern.

① Colour pattern:

| red | yellow | red | yellow | red | yellow | red | yellow |

Number pattern: ___ ___ ___ ___ ___ ___ ___ ___

② Colour pattern:

| blue | blue | yellow | blue | blue | yellow | blue | blue |

Number pattern: ___ ___ ___ ___ ___ ___ ___ ___

③ Colour pattern:

| blue | red | red | green | blue | red | red | green |

Number pattern: ___ ___ ___ ___ ___ ___ ___ ___

Look at each number pattern and form a letter pattern.

④ Number pattern: 7   8   4   7   8   4   7   8   4

Letter pattern: ___ ___ ___ ___ ___ ___ ___ ___ ___

⑤ Number pattern: 1   2   2   1   2   2   1   2   2

Letter pattern: ___ ___ ___ ___ ___ ___ ___ ___ ___

⑥ Number pattern: 4   0   0   5   4   0   0   5   4

Letter pattern: ___ ___ ___ ___ ___ ___ ___ ___ ___

Look at each shape pattern and form a number or letter pattern.

⑦ Shape pattern: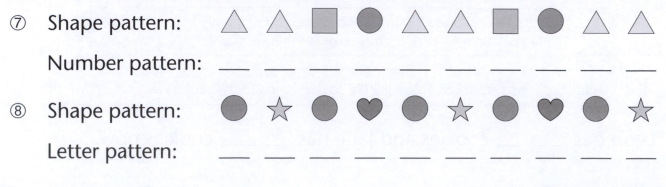

Number pattern: ___ ___ ___ ___ ___ ___ ___ ___ ___ ___

⑧ Shape pattern:

Letter pattern: ___ ___ ___ ___ ___ ___ ___ ___ ___ ___

   ISBN: 978-1-897164-12-9

Look at each pattern. Form a number pattern.

⑨ △ ▲ ▲ △ ▲ ▲ △ ▲ ▲

Number pattern: __ __ __ __ __ __ __ __ __

⑩ • • ○ • • ○ • • ○

Number pattern: __ __ __ __ __ __ __ __ __

⑪

Number pattern: __ __ __ __ __ __ __ __ __

⑫

Number pattern: __ __ __ __ __ __ __ __ __

Follow each pattern and draw the next 2 diagrams.

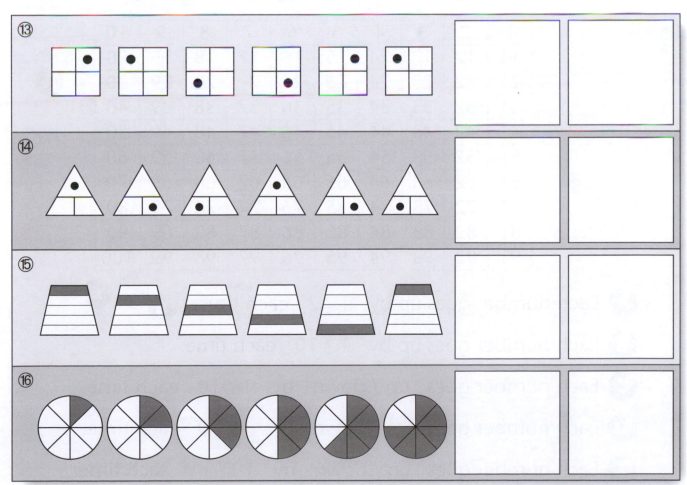

Monica is making music with her hands. Write each sound pattern with numbers or letters.

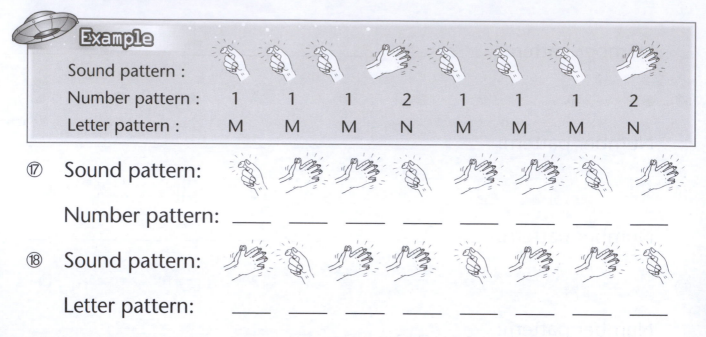

Example

Sound pattern :								
Number pattern :	1	1	1	2	1	1	1	2
Letter pattern :	M	M	M	N	M	M	M	N

⑰ Sound pattern:

Number pattern: ____ ____ ____ ____ ____ ____ ____ ____

⑱ Sound pattern:

Letter pattern: ____ ____ ____ ____ ____ ____ ____ ____

Look at the number chart. Circle the correct answers.

⑲

1	2	3	4	5	6	7	8	9	10
11	12	13	14	15	16	17	18	19	20
21	22	23	24	25	26	27	28	29	30
31	32	33	34	35	36	37	38	39	40
41	42	43	44	45	46	47	48	49	50
51	52	53	54	55	56	57	58	59	60
61	62	63	64	65	66	67	68	69	70
71	72	73	74	75	76	77	78	79	80
81	82	83	84	85	86	87	88	89	90
91	92	93	94	95	96	97	98	99	100

A Each number goes up by 1 / 2 each time.

B Each number goes up by 1 / 10 each time.

C Each number goes up / down by 1 / 10 each time.

D Each number goes up / down by 1 / 10 each time.

E Each number goes up / down by 10 / 11 each time.

ISBN: 978-1-897164-12-9

Look at each number pattern. Circle the correct word or number to complete the description. Then write the next 2 numbers.

⑳ 1 , 3 , 5 , 7 , 9 , 11

  a. Each number goes up by   2 / 3   each time.

  b. The next 2 numbers are _____ and _____ .

㉑ 5 , 10 , 15 , 20 , 25 , 30

  a. Each number goes   up / down   by 5 each time.

  b. The next 2 numbers are _____ and _____ .

㉒ 90 , 80 , 70 , 60 , 50 , 40

  a. Each number goes   up / down   by   5 / 10   each time.

  b. The next 2 numbers are _____ and _____ .

㉓ 6 , 16 , 26 , 36 , 46 , 56

  a. Each number goes   up / down   by   6 / 10   each time.

  b. The next 2 numbers are _____ and _____ .

㉔ 60 , 58 , 56 , 54 , 52 , 50

  a. Each number goes   up / down   by   2 / 4   each time.

  b. The next 2 numbers are _____ and _____ .

MIND BOGGLER

Use a calculator to discover the patterns.

① 15 + _____ = 21   ② 21 − _____ = 15

  16 + _____ = 21   21 − _____ = 16

  17 + _____ = 21   21 − _____ = 17

  18 + _____ = 21   21 − _____ = 18

  19 + _____ = 21   21 − _____ = 19

Mario wants to measure some of the things that he finds at home. Help him choose the best units to do the measurement. Check ✔ the correct answers.

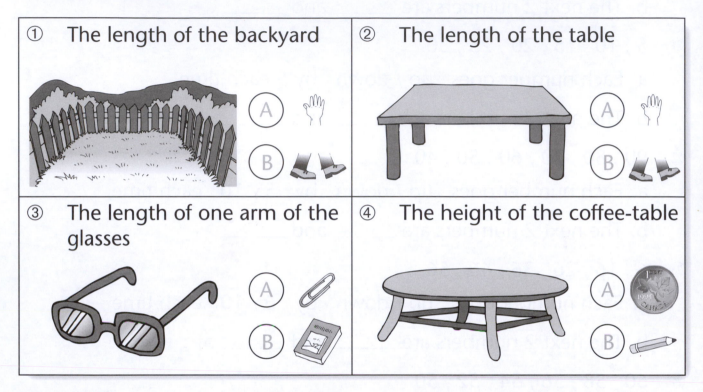

① The length of the backyard

A 🖐
B 👟

② The length of the table

A 🖐
B 👟

③ The length of one arm of the glasses

A 📎
B 📖

④ The height of the coffee-table

A 🪙
B ✏️

Use a ruler to measure the length and width of each ribbon.

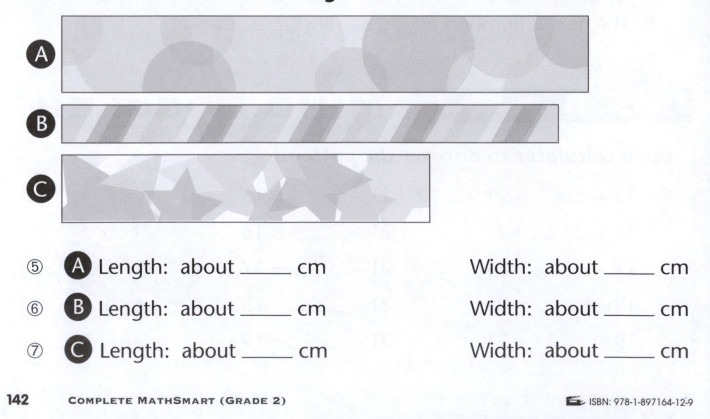

A

B

C

⑤ **A** Length: about _____ cm   Width: about _____ cm

⑥ **B** Length: about _____ cm   Width: about _____ cm

⑦ **C** Length: about _____ cm   Width: about _____ cm

ISBN: 978-1-897164-12-9

Mario measures with a metre stick. Help him choose the best description for each picture. Circle the correct words.

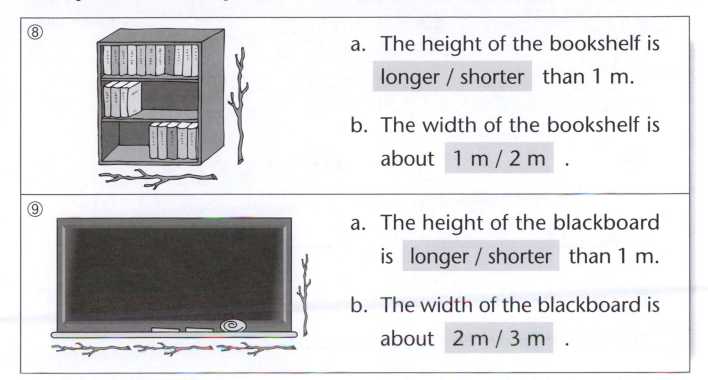

⑧
a. The height of the bookshelf is longer / shorter than 1 m.

b. The width of the bookshelf is about 1 m / 2 m .

⑨
a. The height of the blackboard is longer / shorter than 1 m.

b. The width of the blackboard is about 2 m / 3 m .

Look at the pictures. Help Mario choose the best units to do the measurement. Circle the correct units.

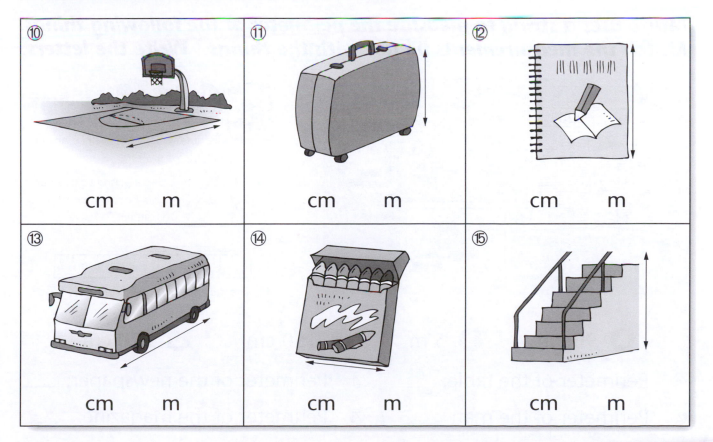

⑩ cm   m

⑪ cm   m

⑫ cm   m

⑬ cm   m

⑭ cm   m

⑮ cm   m

Mario traces some cookies on the grid paper. Help him find the area of each cookie to the nearest square units.

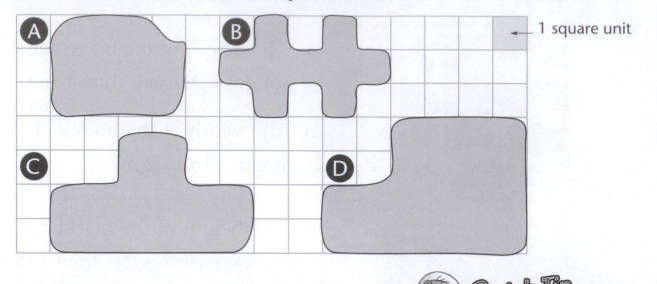

1 square unit

⑯ The area of cookie A is about _____ ⬜ .

⑰ The area of cookie B is about _____ ⬜ .

⑱ The area of cookie C is about _____ ⬜ .

⑲ The area of cookie D is about _____ ⬜ .

Quick Tip

Area – the number of square units of a surface

e.g.

The area of the sticker is 16 ⬛ .

Mario uses a string to measure the perimeter of the following things. Match the measurements he got with the things. Write the letters.

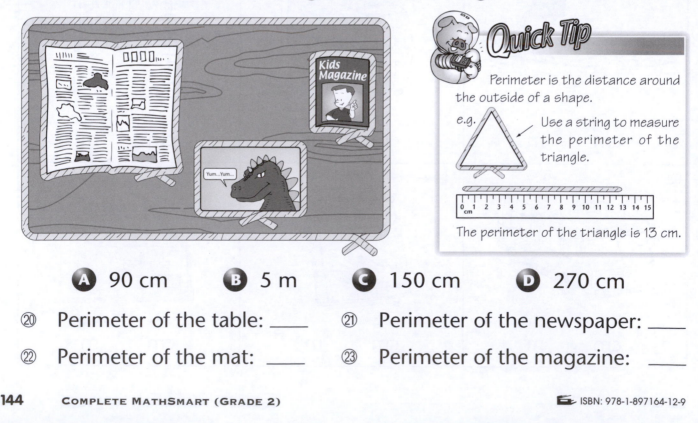

Quick Tip

Perimeter is the distance around the outside of a shape.

e.g.

Use a string to measure the perimeter of the triangle.

The perimeter of the triangle is 13 cm.

Ⓐ 90 cm   Ⓑ 5 m   Ⓒ 150 cm   Ⓓ 270 cm

⑳ Perimeter of the table: ____   ㉑ Perimeter of the newspaper: ____

㉒ Perimeter of the mat: ____   ㉓ Perimeter of the magazine: ____

ISBN: 978-1-897164-12-9

Put the fruits in order from the lightest to the heaviest. Write the numbers 1 - 4 to show their order.

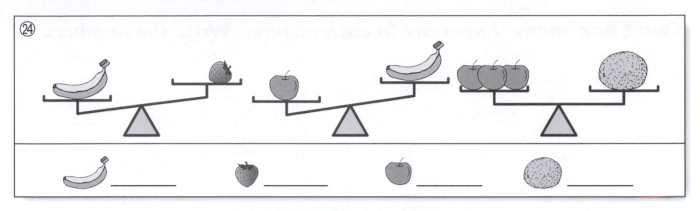

Mario uses his juice boxes to measure things. See how many boxes he needs and help him record the results.

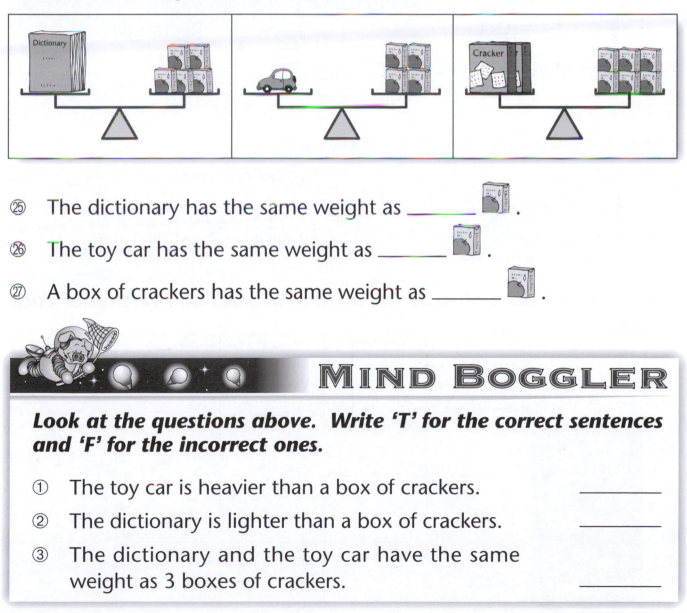

㉕ The dictionary has the same weight as _____ .

㉖ The toy car has the same weight as _____ .

㉗ A box of crackers has the same weight as _____ .

MIND BOGGLER

Look at the questions above. Write 'T' for the correct sentences and 'F' for the incorrect ones.

① The toy car is heavier than a box of crackers.   _____

② The dictionary is lighter than a box of crackers.   _____

③ The dictionary and the toy car have the same weight as 3 boxes of crackers.   _____

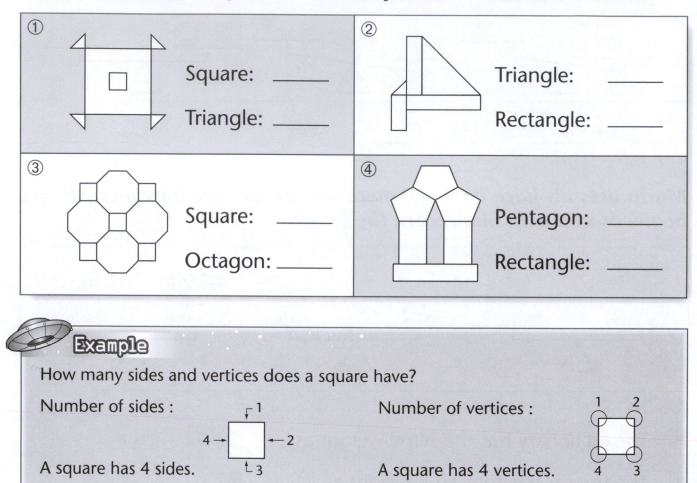

6 Geometry I

Count how many shapes are in each picture. Write the numbers.

① Square: _____
Triangle: _____

② Triangle: _____
Rectangle: _____

③ Square: _____
Octagon: _____

④ Pentagon: _____
Rectangle: _____

Example

How many sides and vertices does a square have?

Number of sides :
A square has 4 sides.

Number of vertices :
A square has 4 vertices.

Name the shapes and write the number of sides and vertices of each shape.

⑤ Name					
⑥ Number of sides					
⑦ Number of vertices					

   ISBN: 978-1-897164-12-9

Find the similarities and differences in each group of shapes. Write the numbers or circle the correct letters to complete the sentences.

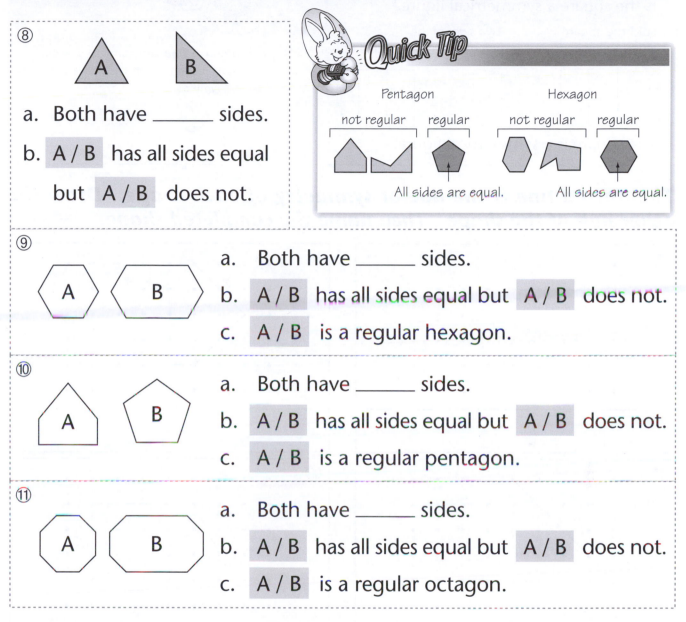

⑧

a. Both have _____ sides.

b. A / B has all sides equal but A / B does not.

Quick Tip

Pentagon   Hexagon

not regular   regular   not regular   regular

All sides are equal.   All sides are equal.

⑨

a. Both have _____ sides.

b. A / B has all sides equal but A / B does not.

c. A / B is a regular hexagon.

⑩

a. Both have _____ sides.

b. A / B has all sides equal but A / B does not.

c. A / B is a regular pentagon.

⑪

a. Both have _____ sides.

b. A / B has all sides equal but A / B does not.

c. A / B is a regular octagon.

Look at the patterns on the quilts and write the two kinds of shapes in each of them.

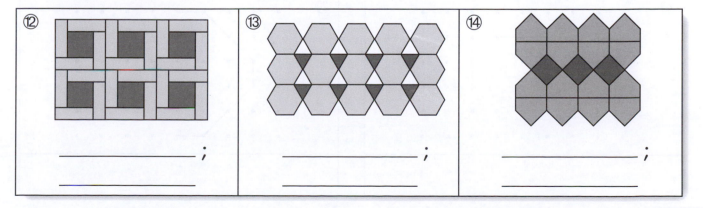

⑫ _____ ;
_____

⑬ _____ ;
_____

⑭ _____ ;
_____

Is the square a symmetrical figure?

Fold the square along the line.

Two sides of the line match.

line of symmetry

The square is a symmetrical figure.

Quick Tip

When you fold the shape along a line and the two sides match each other, the line is a line of symmetry.

e.g.

line of symmetry

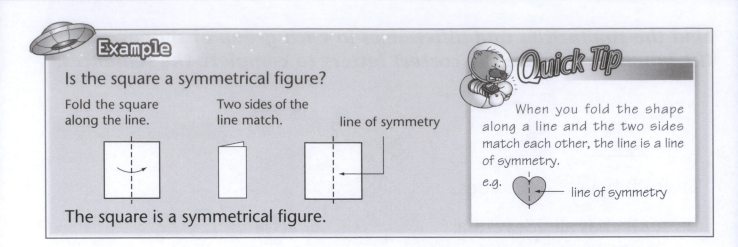

The dotted line is the line of symmetry of each shape. Draw the other half of the shape. Then name the completed shape.

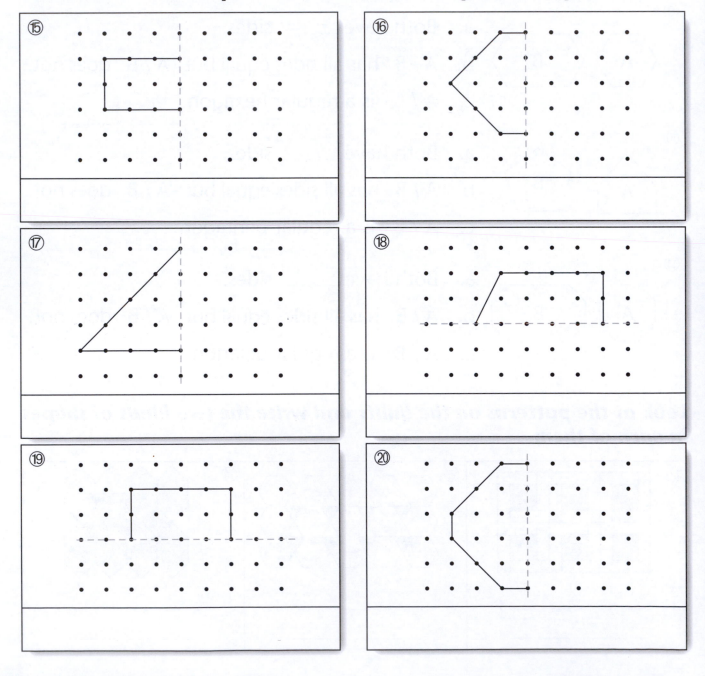

⑮

⑯

⑰

⑱

⑲

⑳

ISBN: 978-1-897164-12-9

Look at the figures on the grid. Follow the arrows to translate the figures. Circle the correct words.

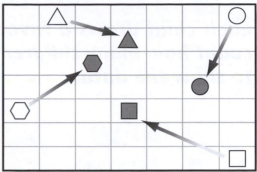

㉑ Translation of △ :

go left / right and move up / down

㉒ Translation of ⬡ :

go left / right and move up / down

㉓ Translation of □ :

go left / right and move up / down

㉔ Translation of ○ :

go left / right and move up / down

Quick Tip

Translation : E ⟶ E

Reflection : B ⟶ ᗺ

Rotation : A ⟶ ⋗

Look how each shape is transformed. Write 'translation', 'reflection' or 'rotation'.

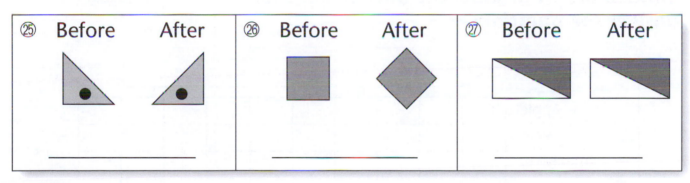

㉕ Before   After

㉖ Before   After

㉗ Before   After

MIND BOGGLER

Cut the folded circle along the dotted line. What two shapes can you get ? Check ✔ the correct letters.

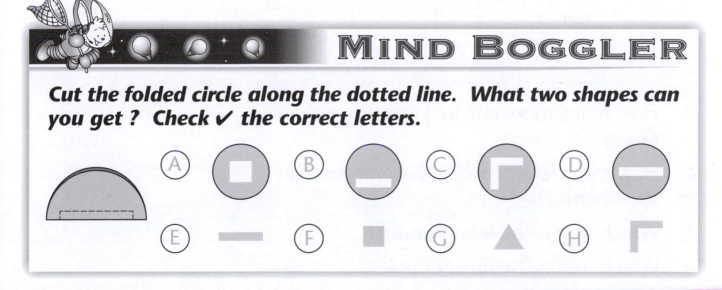

A   B   C   D

E   F   G   H

ISBN: 978-1-897164-12-9

Each child draws a favourite fruit on the blackboard. Help Louis count how many children like each kind of fruit and use tally marks to show the data.

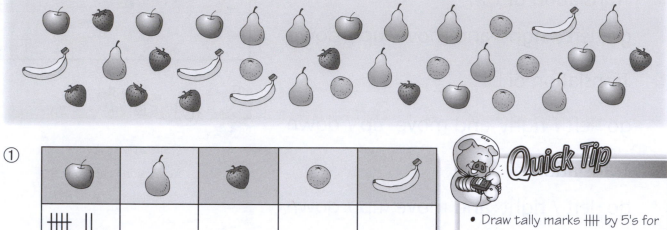

①

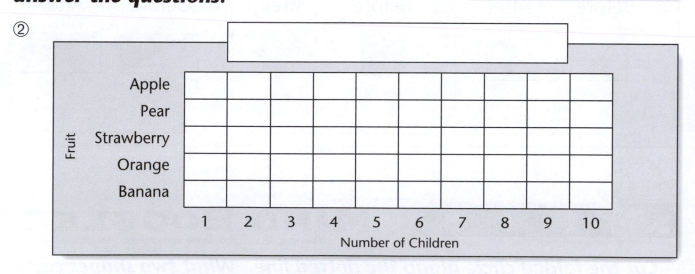				

Quick Tip

- Draw tally marks ||||| by 5's for each tally.
  e.g. ||||| ||| 5 and 3 is 8.
- The title of the graph tells what the graph is about.

Make a graph to show the data in ①. Then answer the questions.

②

Fruit	1	2	3	4	5	6	7	8	9	10
Apple										
Pear										
Strawberry										
Orange										
Banana										

Number of Children

③ How many more children like apples than oranges?

_____ more

④ How many fewer children like oranges than strawberries?

_____ fewer

⑤ Which fruit is the least popular? _____

⑥ Which fruit is the most popular? _____

 ISBN: 978-1-897164-12-9

Uncle Mike has an ice cream stall. See how many ice cream cones he sold yesterday. Look at the graph and complete the table with tally marks. Then answer the questions.

⑦

Chocolate	Vanilla	Strawberry	Cherry

⑧ What is the title of the graph ?

_____

⑨ How many flavours were there?   _____ flavours

⑩ Which flavour was the most popular?   _____

⑪ Which flavour was the least popular?   _____

⑫ How many chocolate ice cream cones were sold?   _____ cones

⑬ How many cherry and strawberry ice cream cones were sold?   _____ cones

⑭ How many more vanilla ice cream cones were sold than cherry ice cream cones?   _____ more

⑮ How many ice cream cones were sold in all?   _____ cones

Hannah has a collection of hats. Some have dots, some have stripes, and some have both. Look at her hats and use tally marks to complete the table.

⑯

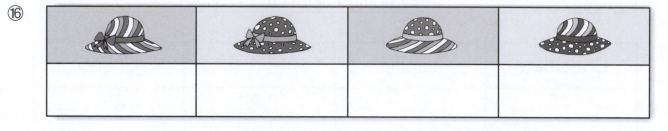

Use the table above to colour the graph. Then answer the questions.

⑰

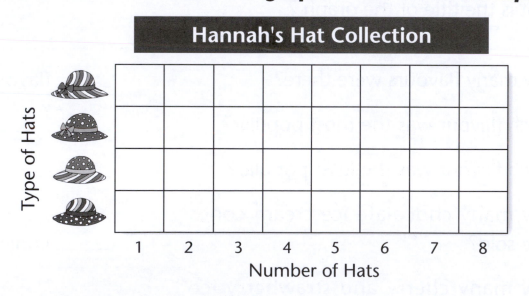

⑱ What is the title of the graph?   _____

⑲ How many hats have stripes?   _____ hats

⑳ How many hats have dots?   _____ hats

㉑ How many hats have both stripes and dots?   _____ hats

㉒ How many hats does Hannah have in all?   _____ hats

The Green family are dining out. Record their selections with tally marks and colour the graph. Then answer the questions.

Dad	Mom	Evan	Kim	Andrew	Cathy
Chicken Baked potato Salad	Chicken Fries Salad	Beef Baked potato Salad	Beef Baked potato Salad	Chicken Baked potato Cheese-cake	Beef Fries Salad

㉓

Chicken	Beef	Baked potato	Fries	Salad	Cheese-cake

㉔

The Greens' Food Selections

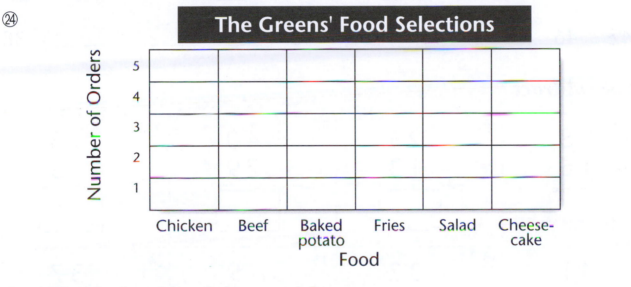

㉕ What is the title of the graph? _____

㉖ How many orders of chicken are there? _____ orders

㉗ How many orders of salad are there? _____ orders

㉘ How many people are in the Green family? _____ people

MIND BOGGLER

Look at the graph above. Answer the questions.

① Do you know what kind of salad the Greens ordered? _____

② Does everyone in the Green family order cheese-cake? _____

ISBN: 978-1-897164-12-9

Follow the patterns. Fill in the missing words, numbers or pictures.

① thirteen   fourteen   _____   _____   seventeen   _____

② 32   33   _____   35   _____   37   _____   40

③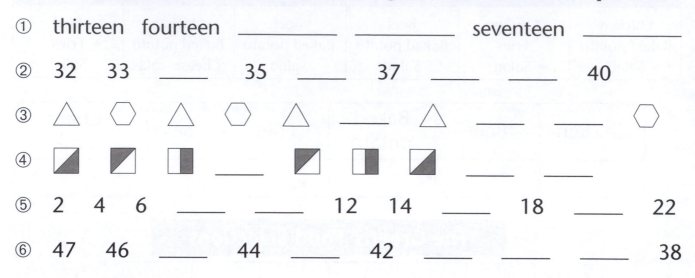

④

⑤ 2   4   6   _____   _____   12   14   _____   18   _____   22

⑥ 47   46   _____   44   _____   42   _____   _____   38

Add or subtract.

⑦ $\begin{array}{r} 18 \\ + 16 \\ \hline \end{array}$	⑧ $\begin{array}{r} 25 \\ - 13 \\ \hline \end{array}$	⑨ $\begin{array}{r} 40 \\ - 29 \\ \hline \end{array}$	⑩ $\begin{array}{r} 45 \\ + 5 \\ \hline \end{array}$
⑪ $\begin{array}{r} 41 \\ - 27 \\ \hline \end{array}$	⑫ $\begin{array}{r} 32 \\ + 9 \\ \hline \end{array}$	⑬ $\begin{array}{r} 9 \\ + 38 \\ \hline \end{array}$	⑭ $\begin{array}{r} 37 \\ - 27 \\ \hline \end{array}$

⑮ 50 − 44 = _____   ⑯ 27 + 23 = _____

⑰ Joe has 19 green marbles and 28 red marbles.

    a. How many marbles does Joe have in all? _____ marbles

    b. How many more red marbles does Joe have
       than green marbles? _____ more

    c. If Joe gives 15 green marbles to his sister,
       how many green marbles will he have? _____ marbles

 ISBN: 978-1-897164-12-9

Circle the best unit for measuring each of the following.

⑱ The length of a house   cm   m

⑲ The width of your shoulders   cm   m

⑳ The length of your leg   cm   m

㉑ The height of a building   cm   m

Look at the leaves. Fill in the blanks and answer the questions.

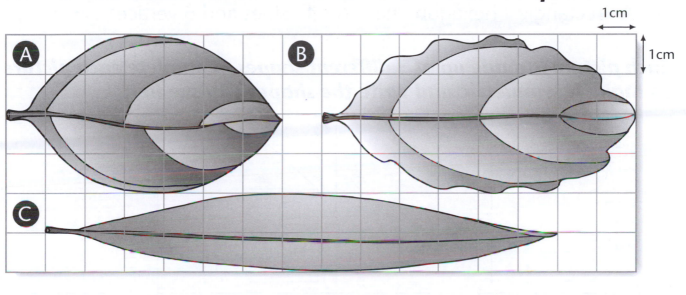

1cm

1cm

㉒ Leaf A is _____ cm long; the area of leaf A is about _____ ▢ .

㉓ Leaf B is _____ cm long; the area of leaf B is about _____ ▢ .

㉔ Leaf C is _____ cm long; the area of leaf C is about _____ ▢ .

㉕ Which leaf is the longest?   Leaf _____

㉖ Which leaf has the greatest area?   Leaf _____

㉗ Which is the correct method to measure the perimeter of a leaf with
   a string? Check ✔ the correct letter.

Ⓐ   Ⓑ   Ⓒ

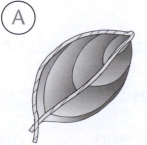 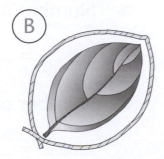 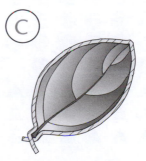

ISBN: 978-1-897164-12-9   **COMPLETE MATHSMART (GRADE 2)**

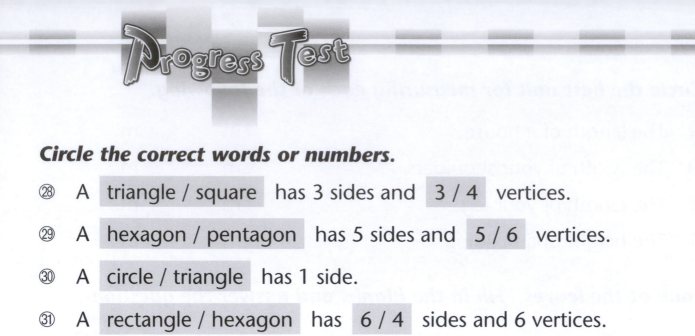

Circle the correct words or numbers.

㉘ A triangle / square has 3 sides and 3 / 4 vertices.

㉙ A hexagon / pentagon has 5 sides and 5 / 6 vertices.

㉚ A circle / triangle has 1 side.

㉛ A rectangle / hexagon has 6 / 4 sides and 6 vertices.

Each picture is made up of 3 different shapes. Complete each picture to make it symmetric and write the shapes you see in it.

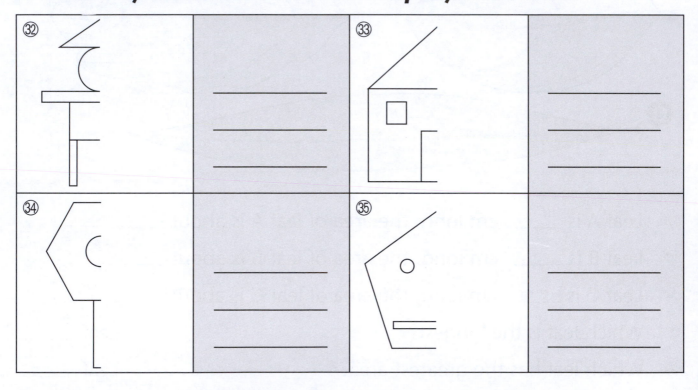

㉜

㉝

㉞

㉟

Count and write the numbers.

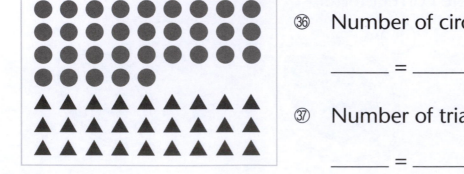

㊱ Number of circles :

_____ = _____ tens and _____ ones

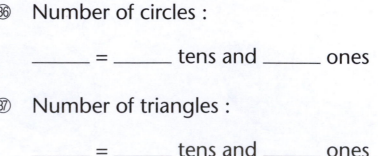

㊲ Number of triangles :

_____ = _____ tens and _____ ones

ISBN: 978-1-897164-12-9

Jacob and Bruce are counting their toy cars. Use their records to make a tally chart. Then complete the graph and fill in the blanks.

Number of Toy Cars Jacob and Bruce have

1 ✔ for 1 car

Red ✔✔✔✔✔✔ ✔✔✔✔✔

Blue ✔✔✔

Green ✔✔✔ ✔✔✔

Yellow ✔✔✔✔✔ ✔✔✔✔

38.

Colour of Toy Cars	Red	Blue	Green	Yellow
Number of Toy Cars				

39.

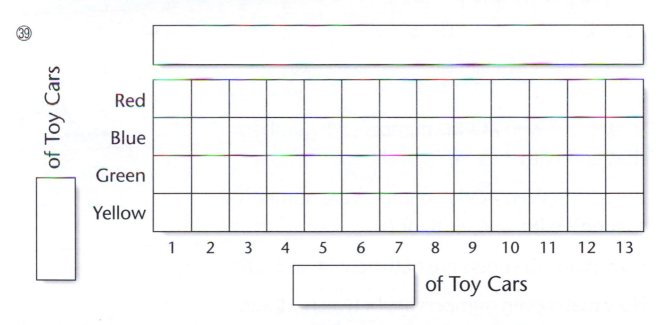

of Toy Cars

Red
Blue
Green
Yellow

1 2 3 4 5 6 7 8 9 10 11 12 13

_____ of Toy Cars

40. Jacob and Bruce have _____ blue and red toy cars altogether.

41. They have _____ more green toy cars than blue toy cars.

42. Jacob has 5 yellow toy cars; Bruce has _____ yellow toy cars.

43. They have _____ toy cars in all.

44. If they give 26 toy cars to their neighbours, they still have _____ toy cars.

⑧ Numbers to 100

Fill in the missing numbers in the 100-chart. Then fill in the blanks and answer the questions.

①

1	2	3	4	5			8	9	
11				15	16	17		19	20
	22	23	24			27			30
31	32			35		37	38		
		43	44		46			49	50
	52	53	54				58	59	60
61		63			66	67			70
	72	73		75		77			
81	82				86	87	88		
			94	95	96			99	100

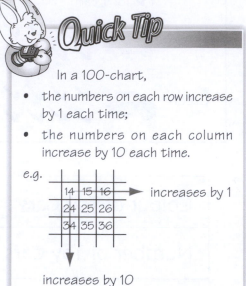

Quick Tip

In a 100-chart,
- the numbers on each row increase by 1 each time;
- the numbers on each column increase by 10 each time.

e.g.

14	15	16	→ increases by 1
24	25	26	
34	35	36	

↓ increases by 10

② _____ Even / Odd numbers are numbers that end with 1, 3, 5, 7, or 9.

③ _____ Even / Odd numbers are numbers that end with 2, 4, 6, 8, or 0.

④ How many numbers are between 34 and 40?   _____ numbers

⑤ How many even numbers are between 71 and 85?

_____ even numbers

⑥ What numbers are between 94 and 98?   _____

⑦ Which number is 1 more than 60?   _____

⑧ Which number is 10 less than 77?   _____

⑨ Which number is greater, 19 or 91?   _____

⑩ Write 3 numbers that are smaller than 80.   _____

ISBN: 978-1-897164-12-9

Help Sam count the crackers. Write the numbers.

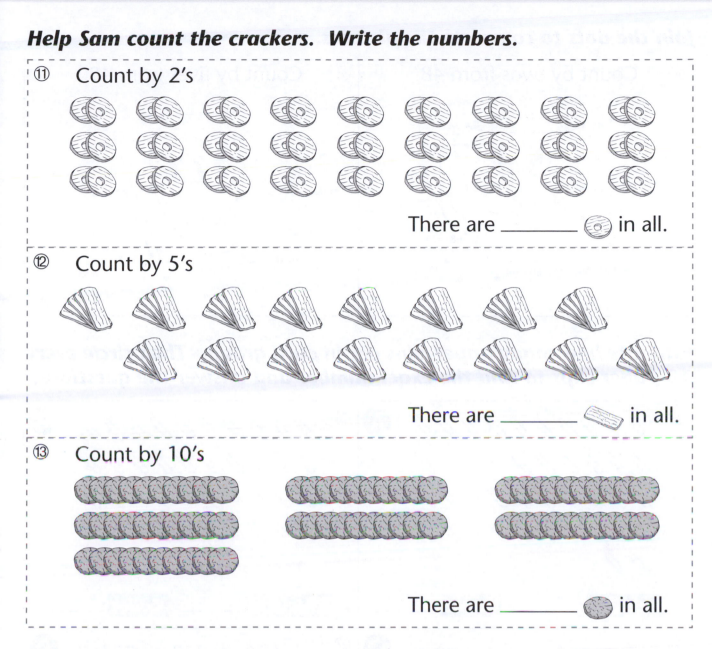

⑪ Count by 2's

There are _____ 🍩 in all.

⑫ Count by 5's

There are _____ in all.

⑬ Count by 10's

There are _____ in all.

Help Sam give each cracker a number. Write the missing numbers.

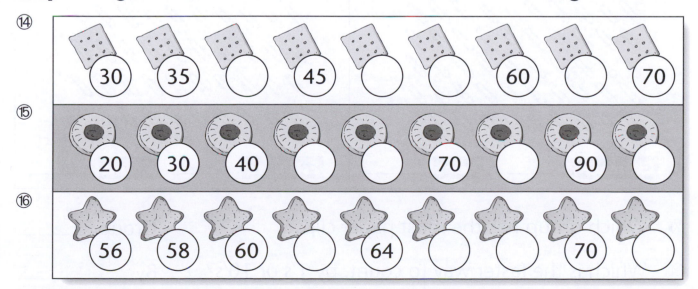

⑭ 30 35 ◯ 45 ◯ ◯ 60 ◯ 70

⑮ 20 30 40 ◯ ◯ 70 ◯ 90 ◯

⑯ 56 58 60 ◯ 64 ◯ ◯ 70 ◯

ISBN: 978-1-897164-12-9

Join the dots to complete the pictures.

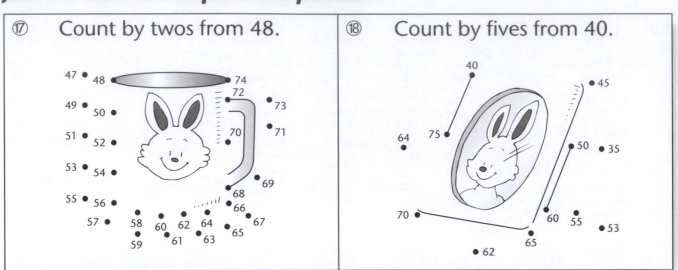

⑰ Count by twos from 48.

47 • 48   74 •
            72 •
49 • 50 •   • 73
51 • 52 •   70 •   • 71
53 • 54 •
                • 69
55 • 56 •   68 •
            66 • • 67
57 • 58 60 62 64 • 65
      59 61 63

⑱ Count by fives from 40.

40 •
        • 45
64 • 75 •   • 50 • 35
70 •   60 55 • 53
      65   65
• 62

Estimate how many paper clips are in each group. Then circle every 10 paper clips to find the exact number and answer the questions.

⑲ **A**

Estimate : _____   Count : _____

⑳ **B**

Estimate : _____   Count : _____

㉑ **C**

Estimate : _____   Count : _____

㉒ **D**

Estimate : _____   Count : _____

㉓ Which group has the most paper clips?   Group _____

㉔ Which is the faster way to count, by 1's or 10's?   By _____

ISBN: 978-1-897164-12-9

Put the numbers in order from greatest to smallest.

㉕ 92, 58, 64, 70   ____ , ____ , ____ , ____

㉖ 40, 29, 53, 50   ____ , ____ , ____ , ____

㉗ 32, 63, 60, 49   ____ , ____ , ____ , ____

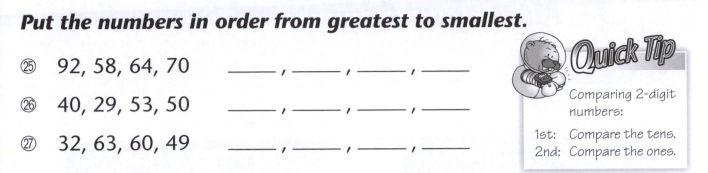

See how many flowers each girl has. Solve the problems.

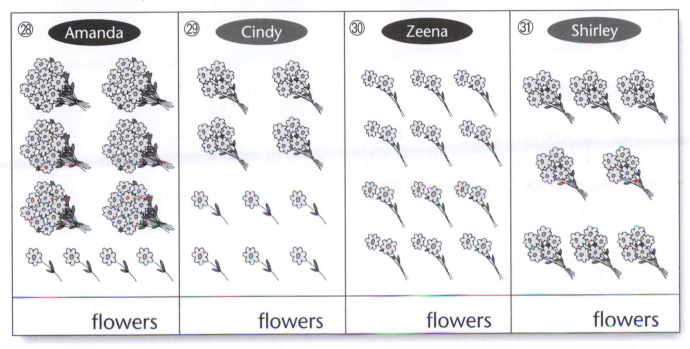

㉘ Amanda	㉙ Cindy	㉚ Zeena	㉛ Shirley
_____ flowers	_____ flowers	_____ flowers	_____ flowers

㉜ Who has the most flowers?   _____

㉝ Who has the fewest flowers?   _____

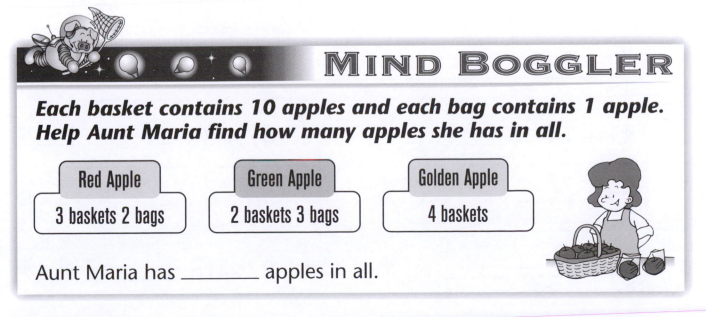

MIND BOGGLER

Each basket contains 10 apples and each bag contains 1 apple. Help Aunt Maria find how many apples she has in all.

Red Apple	Green Apple	Golden Apple
3 baskets 2 bags	2 baskets 3 bags	4 baskets

Aunt Maria has _____ apples in all.

9 More about Addition and Subtraction

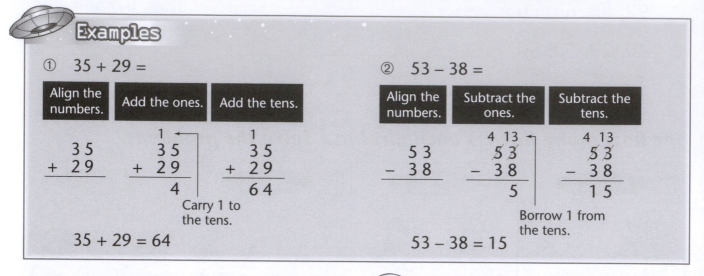

Examples

① 35 + 29 =

Align the numbers.	Add the ones.	Add the tens.

```
                  1 ←          1
   3 5          3 5          3 5
 + 2 9        + 2 9        + 2 9
                  4          6 4
```

Carry 1 to the tens.

35 + 29 = 64

② 53 – 38 =

Align the numbers.	Subtract the ones.	Subtract the tens.

```
                4 13 ←       4 13
   5 3          5 3          5 3
 – 3 8        – 3 8        – 3 8
                  5          1 5
```

Borrow 1 from the tens.

53 – 38 = 15

Add or subtract. Then match each notebook with the pencil that has the same answer. Write the letters in the circles.

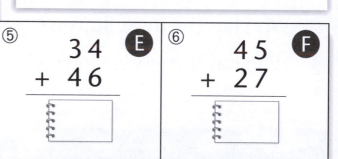

Quick Tip

You can make use of 10 to do addition or subtraction.

e.g. 8 + 9 = 8 + 2 + 7 ← Break 9 into
= 10 + 7   2 + 7.
= 17

15 – 6 = 10 + 5 – 6 ← Break 15 into
= 10 – 6 + 5   10 + 5.
= 4 + 5
= 9

①
```
   3 6
 + 2 5
```
A

②
```
   7 1
 – 1 6
```
B

③
```
   3 2
 + 4 9
```
C

④
```
   8 5
 – 4 6
```
D

⑤
```
   3 4
 + 4 6
```
E

⑥
```
   4 5
 + 2 7
```
F

⑦ 41 + 14 = _____ ◯

⑧ 47 + 33 = _____ ◯

⑨ 52 – 13 = _____ ◯

⑩ 70 – 9 = _____ ◯

⑪ 36 + 36 = _____ ◯

⑫ 97 – 16 = _____ ◯

ISBN: 978-1-897164-12-9

Uncle Raymond has a pizza store. See how many pizzas were sold yesterday. Help him complete the table and solve the problems.

⑬

	Canadian	Pepperoni	Vegetarian
Number of pizzas sold in the afternoon	49	39	
Number of pizzas sold in the evening		28	17
Number of pizzas sold in all	63		50

⑭ How many Canadian and pepperoni pizzas were sold in the afternoon?

_____ Canadian and pepperoni pizzas were sold.

⑮ How many more pepperoni pizzas were sold than vegetarian pizzas?

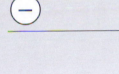

_____ more pepperoni pizzas were sold than vegetarian pizzas.

⑯ 17 medium Canadian pizzas were sold in the afternoon. How many Canadian pizzas sold in the afternoon were not medium?

◯

_____ Canadian pizzas were not medium.

⑰ 23 vegetarian pizzas were delivered to the customers yesterday. How many vegetarian pizzas were eaten in the store?

◯

_____ vegetarian pizzas were eaten in the store.

ISBN: 978-1-897164-12-9

Nicholas works in a convenience store. Look at his work schedule and help him solve the problems.

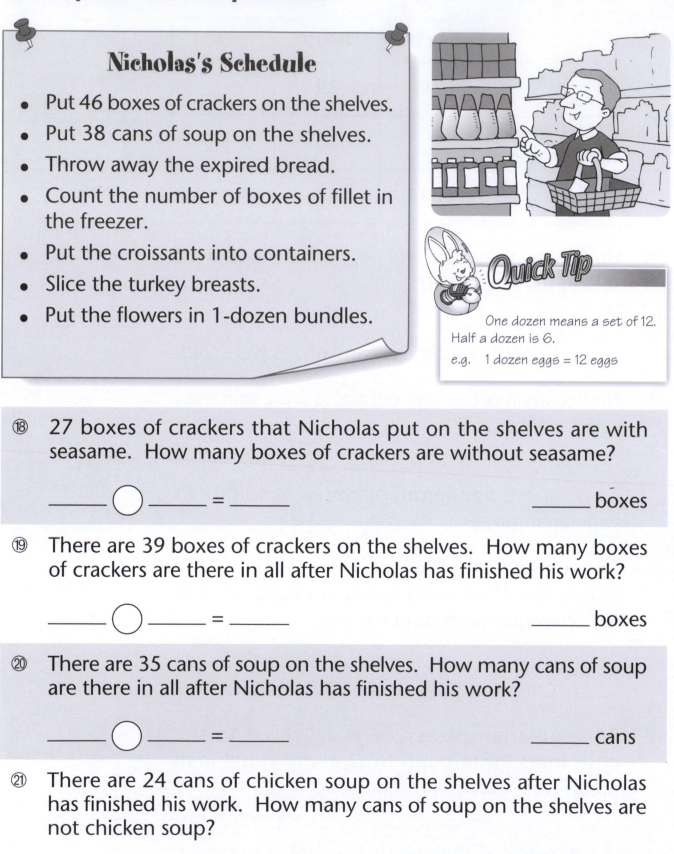

Nicholas's Schedule

- Put 46 boxes of crackers on the shelves.
- Put 38 cans of soup on the shelves.
- Throw away the expired bread.
- Count the number of boxes of fillet in the freezer.
- Put the croissants into containers.
- Slice the turkey breasts.
- Put the flowers in 1-dozen bundles.

Quick Tip

One dozen means a set of 12. Half a dozen is 6.

e.g.   1 dozen eggs = 12 eggs

⑱ 27 boxes of crackers that Nicholas put on the shelves are with seasame. How many boxes of crackers are without seasame?

_____ ◯ _____ = _____   _____ boxes

⑲ There are 39 boxes of crackers on the shelves. How many boxes of crackers are there in all after Nicholas has finished his work?

_____ ◯ _____ = _____   _____ boxes

⑳ There are 35 cans of soup on the shelves. How many cans of soup are there in all after Nicholas has finished his work?

_____ ◯ _____ = _____   _____ cans

㉑ There are 24 cans of chicken soup on the shelves after Nicholas has finished his work. How many cans of soup on the shelves are not chicken soup?

_____ ◯ _____ = _____   _____ cans

ISBN: 978-1-897164-12-9

㉒ There are 70 bags of bread. 14 bags of them have expired. How many bags of bread are still on the shelves after Nicholas has finished his work?

_____ ◯ _____ = _____   _____ bags

㉓ There are 15 boxes of sole fillet and 29 boxes of breaded fillet in the freezer. How many boxes of fillet are there in all?

_____ ◯ _____ = _____   _____ boxes

㉔ Every container can hold 6 croissants. There are 50 croissants. After Nicholas has packed 1 container of croissants, how many more croissants does he need to pack?

_____ ◯ _____ = _____   _____ more

㉕ Nicholas cuts each pack of turkey breast into 45 slices. How many slices of turkey breast can he get by cutting 2 packs?

_____ ◯ _____ = _____   _____ slices

㉖ Nicholas has 2 bundles of carnations. How many carnations are there in all?

_____ ◯ _____ = _____   _____ carnations

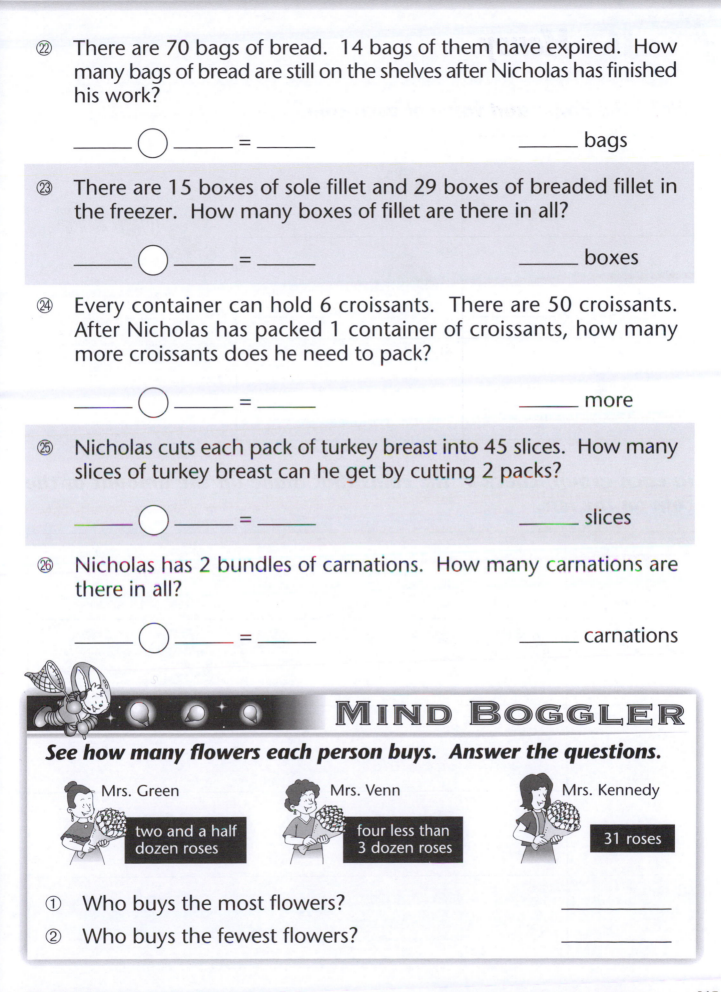

MIND BOGGLER

See how many flowers each person buys. Answer the questions.

Mrs. Green — two and a half dozen roses

Mrs. Venn — four less than 3 dozen roses

Mrs. Kennedy — 31 roses

① Who buys the most flowers? _____

② Who buys the fewest flowers? _____

10 Money

Write the name and value of each coin.

① 5 cents coin — _____

_____ ¢

② 1 cent coin — _____

_____ ¢

③ 2 dollars coin — _____

$ _____

④ 1 dollar coin — _____

$ _____

⑤ 25 cents coin — _____

_____ ¢

⑥ 10 cents coin — _____

_____ ¢

In each group, check ✔ the coins that make up the amount of the coin on the left.

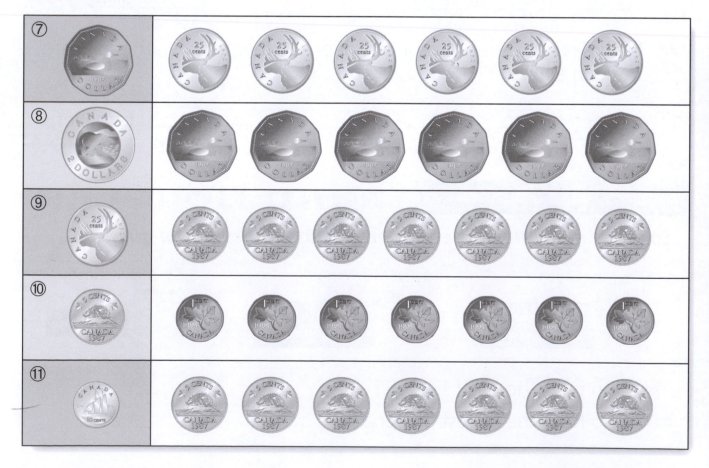

⑦

⑧

⑨

⑩

⑪

Count the coins. Then estimate and find the exact amount of money each child has. Answer the questions.

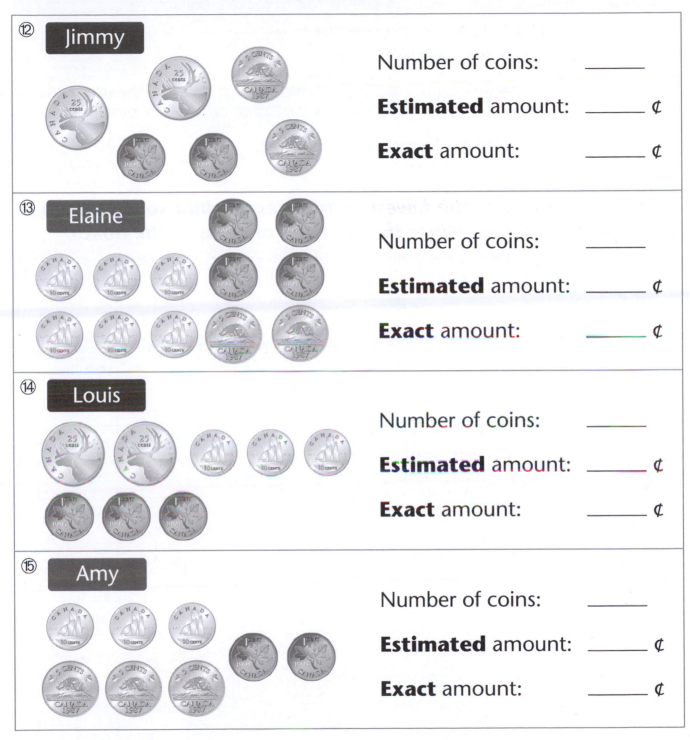

⑫ Jimmy

Number of coins: _____

Estimated amount: _____ ¢

Exact amount: _____ ¢

⑬ Elaine

Number of coins: _____

Estimated amount: _____ ¢

Exact amount: _____ ¢

⑭ Louis

Number of coins: _____

Estimated amount: _____ ¢

Exact amount: _____ ¢

⑮ Amy

Number of coins: _____

Estimated amount: _____ ¢

Exact amount: _____ ¢

⑯ Who has the most money? _____

⑰ Who has the fewest coins? _____

⑱ Jimmy says that the one with the greatest number of coins has the most money. Is he right? _____

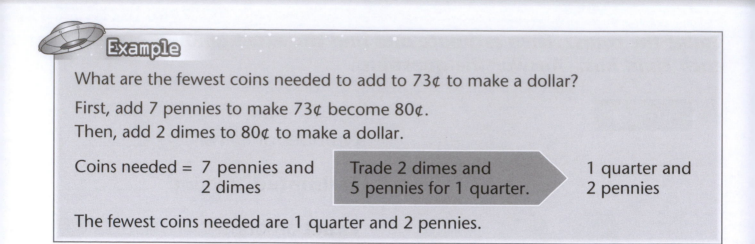

Example

What are the fewest coins needed to add to 73¢ to make a dollar?

First, add 7 pennies to make 73¢ become 80¢.

Then, add 2 dimes to 80¢ to make a dollar.

Coins needed = 7 pennies and 2 dimes → Trade 2 dimes and 5 pennies for 1 quarter. → 1 quarter and 2 pennies

The fewest coins needed are 1 quarter and 2 pennies.

Help Uncle Tom give the fewest coins to each child so that each of them has one dollar. Write the numbers of coins in the boxes.

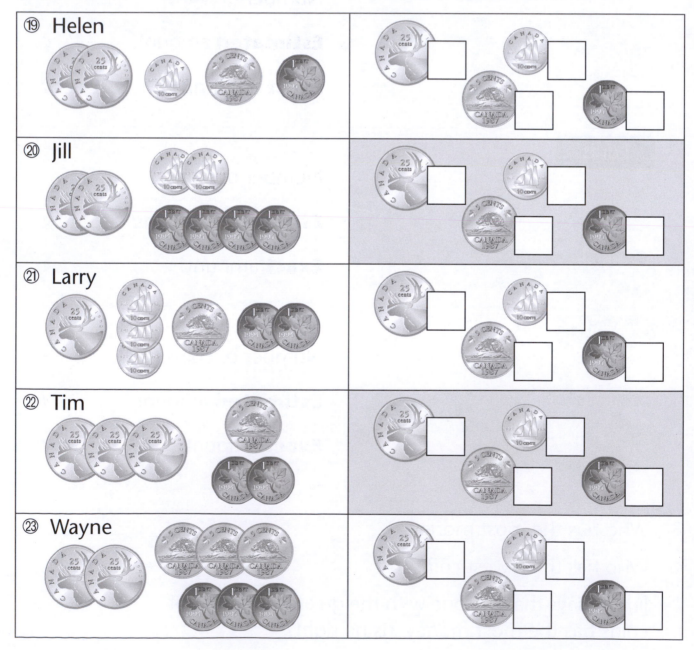

⑲ Helen

⑳ Jill

㉑ Larry

㉒ Tim

㉓ Wayne

ISBN: 978-1-897164-12-9

Write how much money each child has. Then solve the problems.

㉔ Minnie had _____ ¢ . She bought a 〈65¢〉.

She has _____ ¢ left.

㉕ Tom had _____ ¢. He bought a 〈38¢〉. He has _____ ¢ left.

㉖ Louis has _____ ¢. He wants to buy a 〈90¢〉. He needs _____ ¢ more.

㉗ Peter has _____ ¢. He wants to buy a 〈85¢〉. He needs _____ ¢ more.

MIND BOGGLER

Read what the children say. Fill in the blanks with the names of the coins.

① I have 2 different coins. Their total value is 35¢.

Patrick has a _____ and a _____ .

② I have 3 coins. 2 of them are the same. Their total value is 35¢.

Jacky has 2 _____ and 1 _____ .

③ I have 4 coins. 2 of them are the same. Their total value is 26¢.

Molly has 2 _____ , 1 _____ and 1 _____ .

Circle the best measuring units.

① The time you spend in school every day — Year / Week / Hour

② The time between 2 Olympics — Year / Month / Second

③ The time to clap your hands 10 times — Day / Month / Second

④ The time in each season — Year / Month / Minute

⑤ The time between today and next Sunday — Month / Day / Second

Look at Joe's calendar and answer the questions.

June						
SUN	MON	TUE	WED	THU	FRI	SAT
	①1	2	3	4	5	6
7	⑧8	9	10	11	12	13
14	⑮15	16	17	18	19	20
21	㉒22	23	24	25	26	27
28	㉙29	30				
○ To library						

July						
SUN	MON	TUE	WED	THU	FRI	SAT
				1	2	3	④4
5	6	⑦7	8	9	10	11
12	13	14	15	⑯16	17	18
19	20	21	22	23	24	㉕25
26	27	28	29	30	31	
○ To library						

Quick Tip

How to read a calendar:

first day of a week   last day of a week

Feb						
SUN	MON	TUE	WED	THU	FRI	SAT
	1	2	3	4	5	6
7	8	9	10	11	12	13
14	15	⑯16	17	18	19	20
21	22	23	24	25	26	27
28						

↳ Feb 16, on Tuesday

⑥ How many days are there in a week? _____ days

⑦ What day of the week is June 1? _____

⑧ What day of the week is July 31? _____

⑨ How many days will Joe go to the library in June? What are the dates?

_____ days; _____

⑩ How many days will Joe go to the library in July? What are the dates?

_____ days; _____

⑪ How many days are there between the last day Joe goes to the library in June and the first day he goes there in July? _____ days

ISBN: 978-1-897164-12-9

Help Joe fill in the missing months and answer his questions.

Quick Tip

31 days

January   March   May   July   August   October   December

    February   April   June   September   November

Normal year - 28 days
Leap year - 29 days   30 days

⑫ January, _____ , March, _____ , May

⑬ July, _____ , _____ , October, November

⑭ August, _____ , October, November, _____

⑮ Which month comes just after July?   _____

⑯ What is the 6th month of a year?   _____

⑰ How many days are there in August?   _____ days

⑱ How many months have 31 days?   _____ months

⑲ How many days are there in a leap year?   _____ days

You can use a calculator to add the days of each month. Press
3 1 + 2 9 + ... + 3 1 = to find the answer.

If the last day of September falls on Tuesday, help Joe write the dates on the calendar. Then answer the questions.

⑳

October						
Sun	Mon	Tue	Wed	Thu	Fri	Sat

㉑ What day of the week is Oct 26?

_____

㉒ What day of the week is the last day of October?

_____

㉓ What day of the week is Nov 1?

_____

Jenny and Jimmy are talking about times. Help them circle the correct answers.

㉔ There are 7 / 14 / 5 days in a week.

㉕ There are 12 / 13 / 14 months in a year.

㉖ There are 15 / 30 / 60 minutes in one hour.

㉗ There are 12 / 14 / 24 hours in a day.

Write the times on the digital clocks or draw the hands to show the times on the clock faces. Then answer the questions.

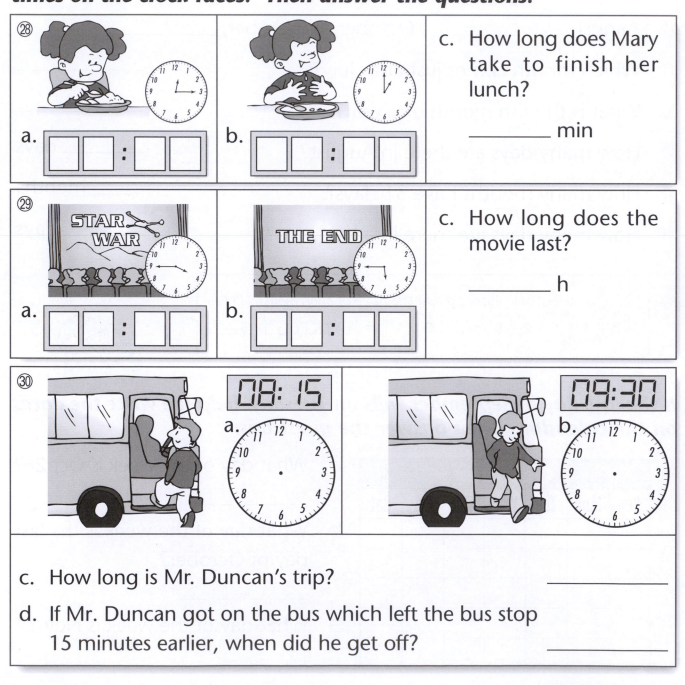

㉘ a. [ ][ ] : [ ][ ]

b. [ ][ ] : [ ][ ]

c. How long does Mary take to finish her lunch?

_____ min

㉙ a. [ ][ ] : [ ][ ]

b. [ ][ ] : [ ][ ]

c. How long does the movie last?

_____ h

㉚ a. 08:15

b. 09:30

c. How long is Mr. Duncan's trip? _____

d. If Mr. Duncan got on the bus which left the bus stop 15 minutes earlier, when did he get off? _____

ISBN: 978-1-897164-12-9

See where Nathan puts the thermometers. Check ✔ the correct thermometers and circle the correct answers.

 **Quick Tip**

The liquid in the thermometer rises as the temperature goes up.

Temperature is measured in degree Celcius (°C).

③① Nathan puts a thermometer which shows 20°C into a freezer.
a. What will the reading be after 2 hours?

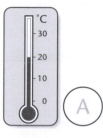 A   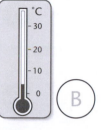 B   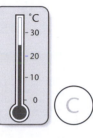 C

b. The reading will show a higher / lower temperature .

c. The temperature rises / drops 5°C / 10°C / 15°C .

③② He puts another thermometer which shows 15°C beside a furnace.
a. What will the reading be after 1 hour?

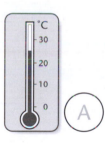 A    B   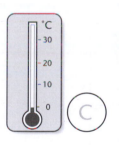 C

b. The reading will show a higher / lower temperature.

c. The temperature rises / drops 5°C / 10°C / 15°C .

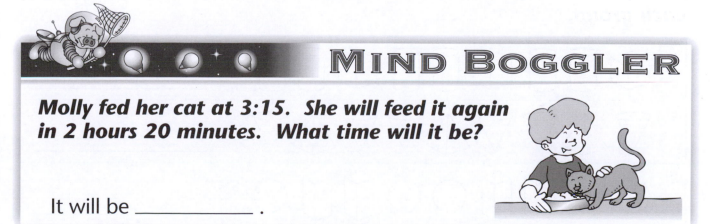

MIND BOGGLER

Molly fed her cat at 3:15. She will feed it again in 2 hours 20 minutes. What time will it be?

It will be _____ .

12 Geometry II

Write the names beside the solids. Then match the solids with the things that Jeffrey finds in his house. Write the letters.

Cylinder   Pyramid   Cone   Rectangular prism   Cube   Sphere

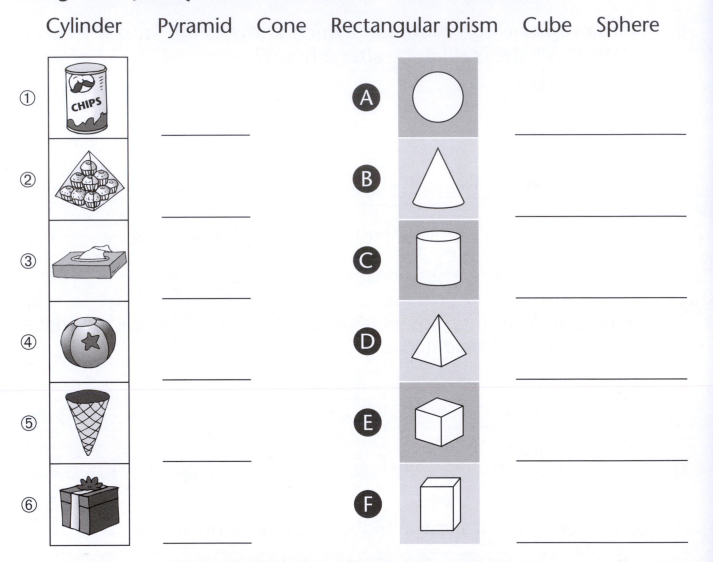

① CHIPS _____

A _____

② _____

B _____

③ _____

C _____

④ _____

D _____

⑤ _____

E _____

⑥ _____

F _____

Jeffrey puts the solids in order. Name the solid that comes next in each group.

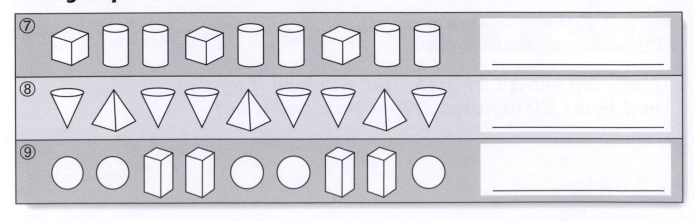

⑦ _____

⑧ _____

⑨ _____

ISBN: 978-1-897164-12-9

Jeffrey is making a record of his solids. Help him complete the table and answer the questions.

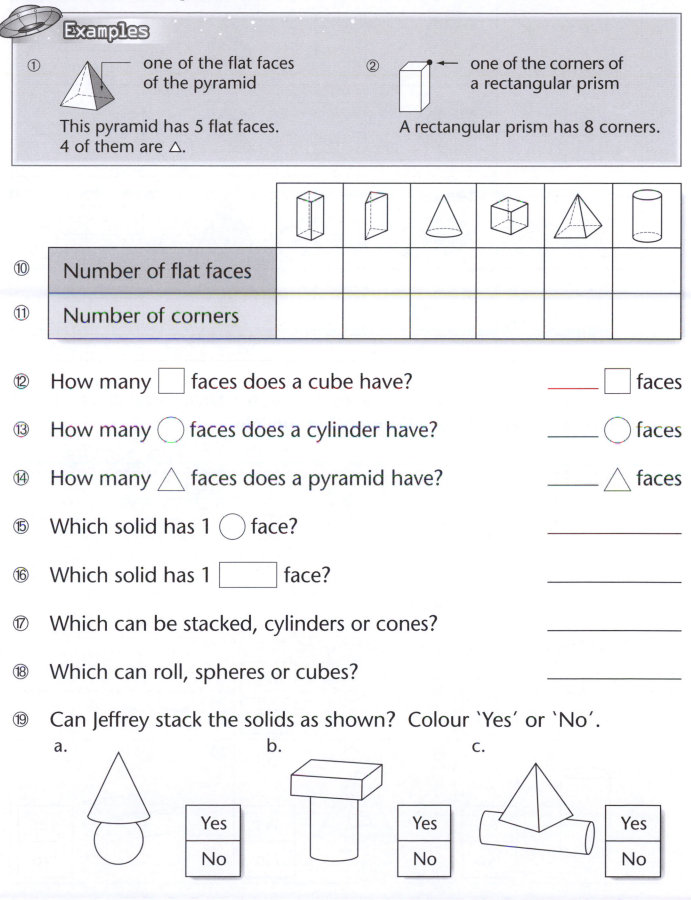

Examples

① one of the flat faces of the pyramid

This pyramid has 5 flat faces. 4 of them are △.

② one of the corners of a rectangular prism

A rectangular prism has 8 corners.

⑩ Number of flat faces						
⑪ Number of corners						

⑫ How many ☐ faces does a cube have? ____ ☐ faces

⑬ How many ◯ faces does a cylinder have? ____ ◯ faces

⑭ How many △ faces does a pyramid have? ____ △ faces

⑮ Which solid has 1 ◯ face? _____

⑯ Which solid has 1 ☐ face? _____

⑰ Which can be stacked, cylinders or cones? _____

⑱ Which can roll, spheres or cubes? _____

⑲ Can Jeffrey stack the solids as shown? Colour 'Yes' or 'No'.

a.
Yes
No

b.
Yes
No

c.
Yes
No

Jeffrey traced the solids. Check ✔ the correct shapes he traced.

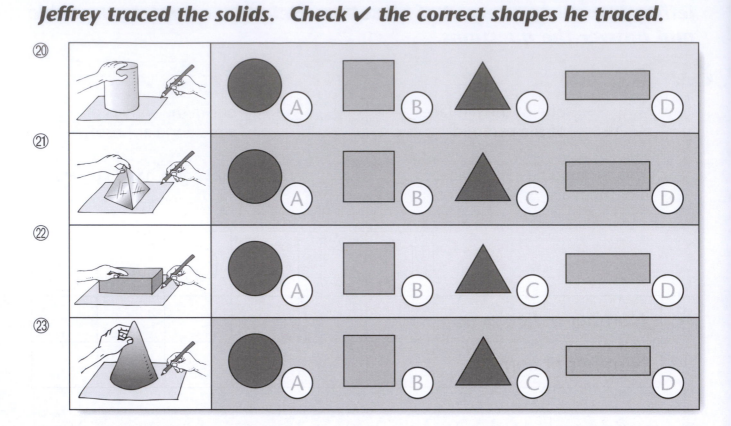

20   A   B   C   D

21   A   B   C   D

22   A   B   C   D

23   A   B   C   D

Jeffrey traced the shaded 2 faces of each solid. Are these faces congruent to each other? Colour 'Yes' or 'No'.

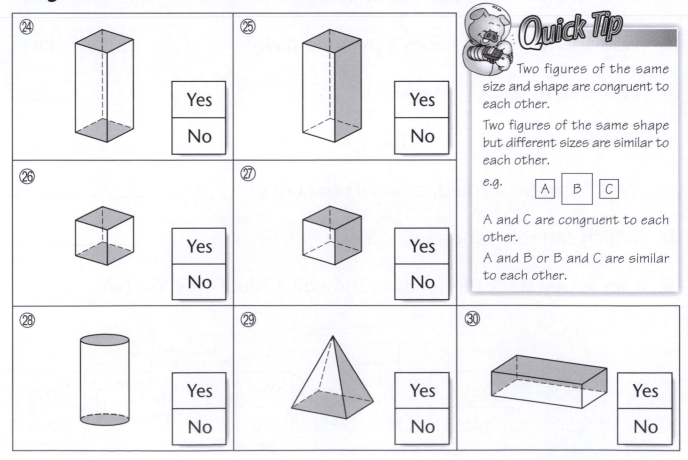

24   Yes / No

25   Yes / No

26   Yes / No

27   Yes / No

28   Yes / No

29   Yes / No

30   Yes / No

Quick Tip

Two figures of the same size and shape are congruent to each other.

Two figures of the same shape but different sizes are similar to each other.

e.g.   A   B   C

A and C are congruent to each other.

A and B or B and C are similar to each other.

ISBN: 978-1-897164-12-9

See how Jeffrey makes the solids. Name the solids for him.

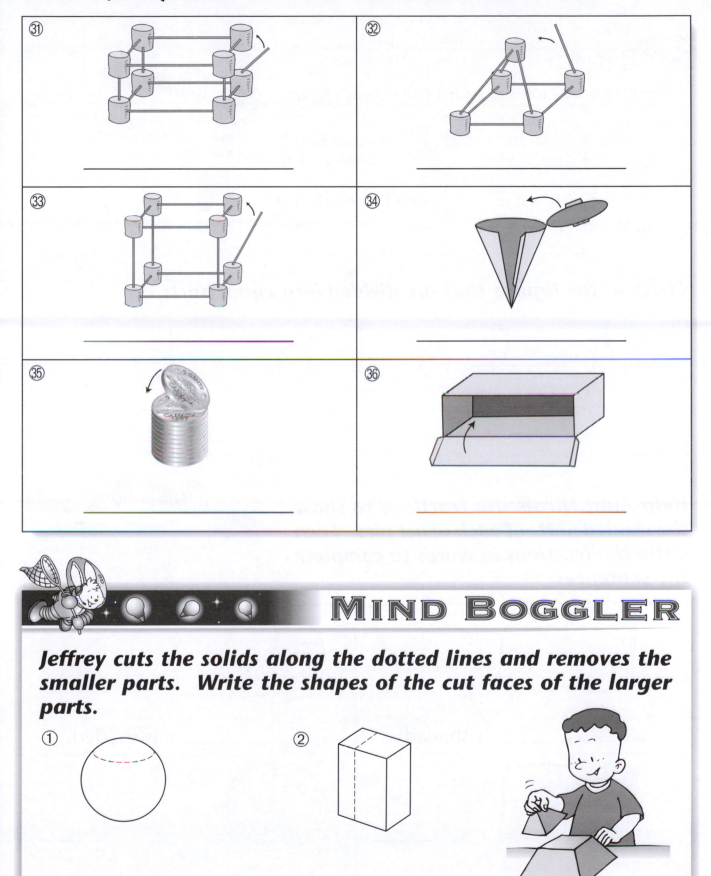

㉛ _____

㉜ _____

㉝ _____

㉞ _____

㉟ _____

㊱ _____

Jeffrey cuts the solids along the dotted lines and removes the smaller parts. Write the shapes of the cut faces of the larger parts.

① _____

② _____

ISBN: 978-1-897164-12-9

13 Fractions

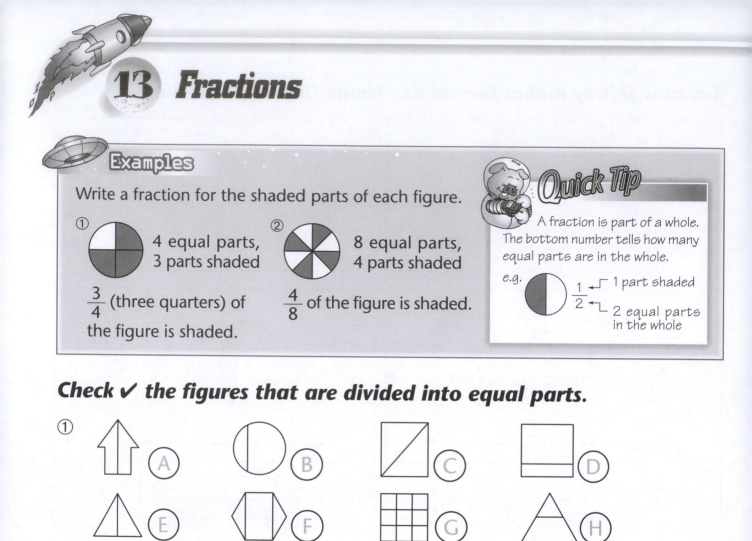

Examples

Write a fraction for the shaded parts of each figure.

① 4 equal parts, 3 parts shaded

$\frac{3}{4}$ (three quarters) of the figure is shaded.

② 8 equal parts, 4 parts shaded

$\frac{4}{8}$ of the figure is shaded.

Quick Tip

A fraction is part of a whole. The bottom number tells how many equal parts are in the whole.

e.g. $\frac{1}{2}$ ⌐ 1 part shaded
⌐ 2 equal parts in the whole

Check ✔ the figures that are divided into equal parts.

① A   B   C   D

E   F   G   H

Help Aunt Nicole use fractions to show the shaded parts of each of her pies. Then write the fractions in words to complete the sentences.

Quick Tip

Fractions in words:

$\frac{1}{3}$ one third $\frac{1}{4}$ one quarter

$\frac{1}{5}$ one fifth

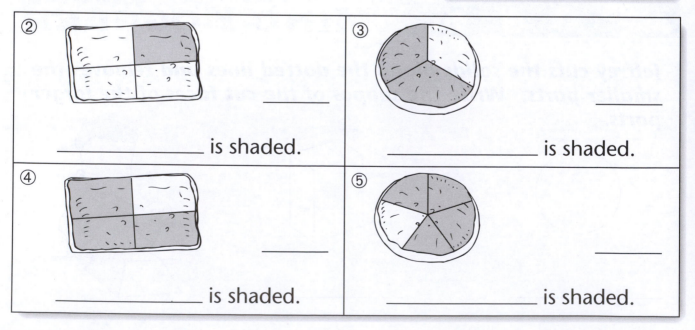

② _____ _____ is shaded.

③ _____ _____ is shaded.

④ _____ _____ is shaded.

⑤ _____ _____ is shaded.

ISBN: 978-1-897164-12-9

Colour the shapes to show each fraction.

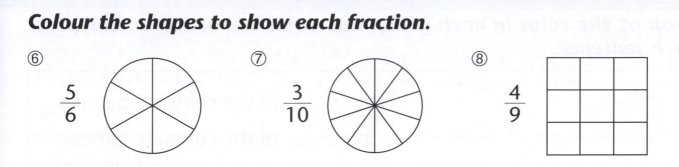

⑥ $\dfrac{5}{6}$

⑦ $\dfrac{3}{10}$

⑧ $\dfrac{4}{9}$

Write a fraction for the shaded parts of each shape. Then circle the correct words.

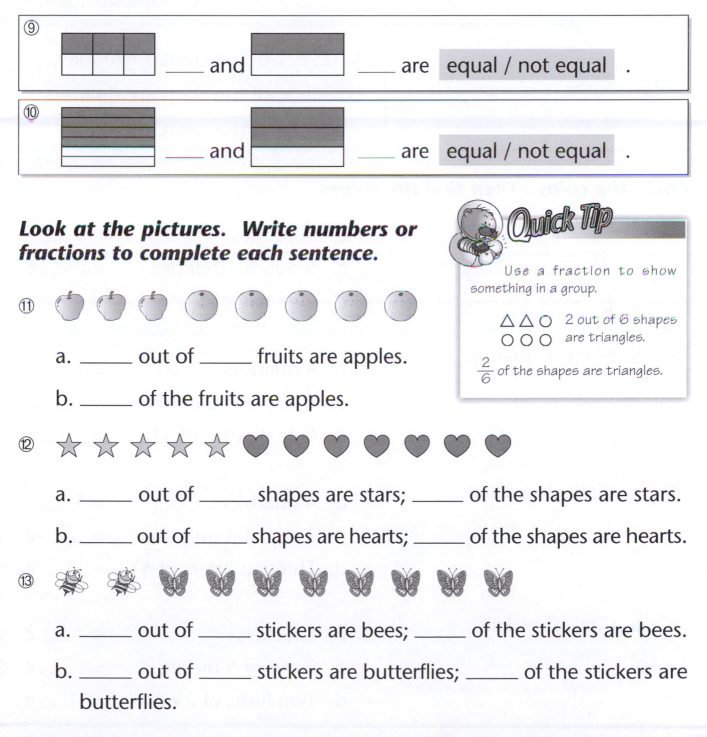

⑨ _____ and _____ are equal / not equal .

⑩ _____ and _____ are equal / not equal .

Look at the pictures. Write numbers or fractions to complete each sentence.

> ### Quick Tip
> Use a fraction to show something in a group.
>
> △ △ ○ 2 out of 6 shapes
> ○ ○ ○ are triangles.
>
> $\dfrac{2}{6}$ of the shapes are triangles.

⑪

a. _____ out of _____ fruits are apples.

b. _____ of the fruits are apples.

⑫

a. _____ out of _____ shapes are stars; _____ of the shapes are stars.

b. _____ out of _____ shapes are hearts; _____ of the shapes are hearts.

⑬

a. _____ out of _____ stickers are bees; _____ of the stickers are bees.

b. _____ out of _____ stickers are butterflies; _____ of the stickers are butterflies.

Look at the coins in each group and write a fraction to complete each sentence.

⑭

a. _____ of the coins are pennies.

b. _____ of the coins are dimes.

⑮

a. _____ of the coins are nickels.

b. _____ of the coins are quarters.

⑯

a. _____ of the coins are loonies.

b. _____ of the coins are quarters.

c. _____ of the coins are dimes.

Circle the coins. Then find the values.

⑰ a. Circle 5 dimes.

b. 10 dimes   = $ _____

c. 5 out of 10 dimes   = _____ ¢

d One half of $1   = _____ ¢

⑱ a. Circle 1 quarter.

b. 4 quarters   = $ _____

c. 1 out of 4 quarters   = _____ ¢

d. One quarter of $1   = _____ ¢

⑲ a. Circle 3 quarters.

b. 4 quarters   = $ _____

c. 3 out of 4 quarters   = _____ ¢

d. Three quarters of $1   = _____ ¢

⑳ a. Circle 2 nickels.

b. 5 nickels   = _____ ¢

c. 2 out of 5 nickels   = _____ ¢

d. Two fifths of 25 ¢   = _____ ¢

ISBN: 978-1-897164-12-9

Look at the clock faces. Fill in the blanks and circle the correct answers.

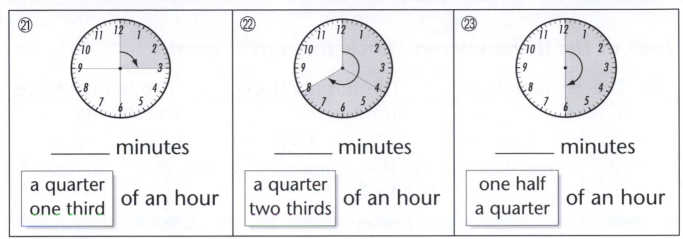

㉑ _____ minutes

a quarter
one third of an hour

㉒ _____ minutes

a quarter
two thirds of an hour

㉓ _____ minutes

one half
a quarter of an hour

Write how long the children take to do their homework in minutes. Then answer the question.

㉔ I take three quarters of an hour to do my homework.   Joe   _____ minutes

㉕ I take half an hour to do my homework.   Daisy   _____ minutes

㉖ I take one third of an hour to do my homework.   David   _____ minutes

㉗ Who spends the most time doing homework?   _____

MIND BOGGLER

Write a fraction to show the shaded parts of each shape.

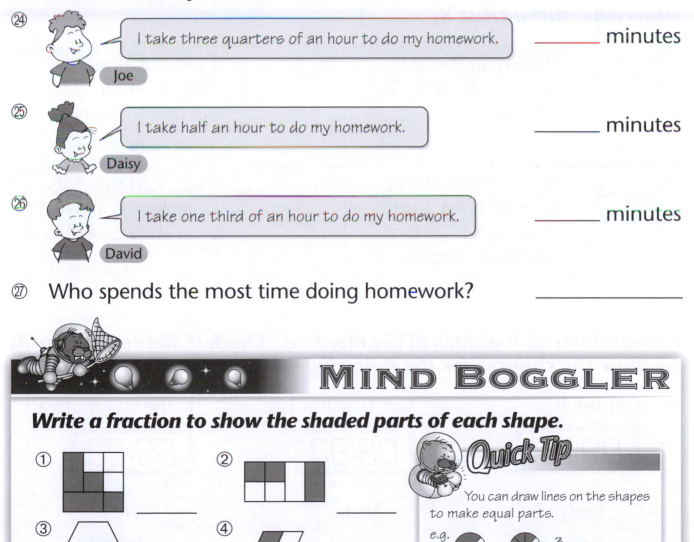

① _____

② _____

③ _____

④ _____

Quick Tip

You can draw lines on the shapes to make equal parts.

e.g. → $\frac{3}{8}$ is shaded.

ISBN: 978-1-897164-12-9

14 Probability

Look at the thermometers. Circle the correct words.

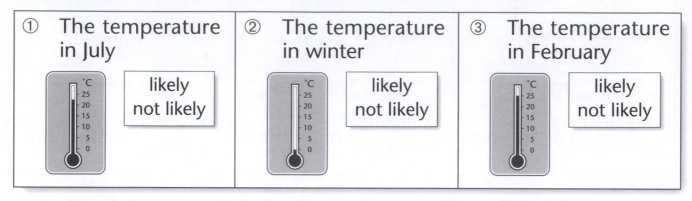

① The temperature in July

°C
25
20
15
10
5
0

likely
not likely

② The temperature in winter

°C
25
20
15
10
5
0

likely
not likely

③ The temperature in February

°C
25
20
15
10
5
0

likely
not likely

Put a check mark ✔ in the circle if the answer is probably true; otherwise, put a cross ✗.

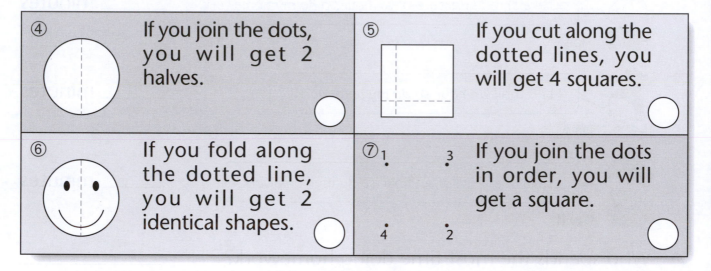

④ If you join the dots, you will get 2 halves. ◯

⑤ If you cut along the dotted lines, you will get 4 squares. ◯

⑥ If you fold along the dotted line, you will get 2 identical shapes. ◯

⑦ 1   3
   4   2
If you join the dots in order, you will get a square. ◯

School starts at 9 o'clock in the morning. Check ✔ the correct words to show the chances for the following events to happen.

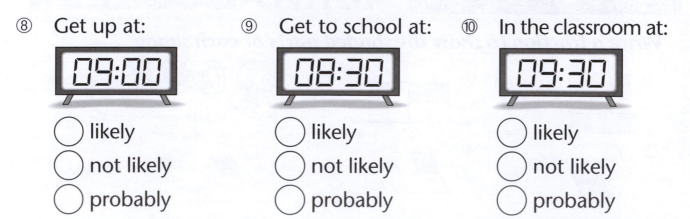

⑧ Get up at:

09:00

◯ likely
◯ not likely
◯ probably

⑨ Get to school at:

08:30

◯ likely
◯ not likely
◯ probably

⑩ In the classroom at:

09:30

◯ likely
◯ not likely
◯ probably

ISBN: 978-1-897164-12-9

Use the words given to describe the chances.

never   **sometimes**   **often**

⑪ Coco the clown juggles 6 balls. What is the chance of

   a. a ◯ ball dropping? _____

   b. a ◯ ball dropping? _____

   c. a ★ ball dropping? _____

⑫ Dad closes his eyes and picks a tie for himself. What is his chance of

   a. picking a tie with stripes? _____

   b. picking a tie with dots? _____

   c. picking a tie with checks? _____

⑬ Maria takes a popsicle from the box. What is her chance of

   a. picking a cherry popsicle? _____

   b. picking a strawberry popsicle? _____

   c. picking a grape popsicle? _____

Cherry 2
Grape 12

⑭ There are 9 pepperoni pizzas and 2 Canadian pizzas on the table. Bruce is going to pick a pizza. What is his chance of

   a. picking a pepperoni pizza? _____

   b. picking a Canadian pizza? _____

   c. picking a vegetarian pizza? _____

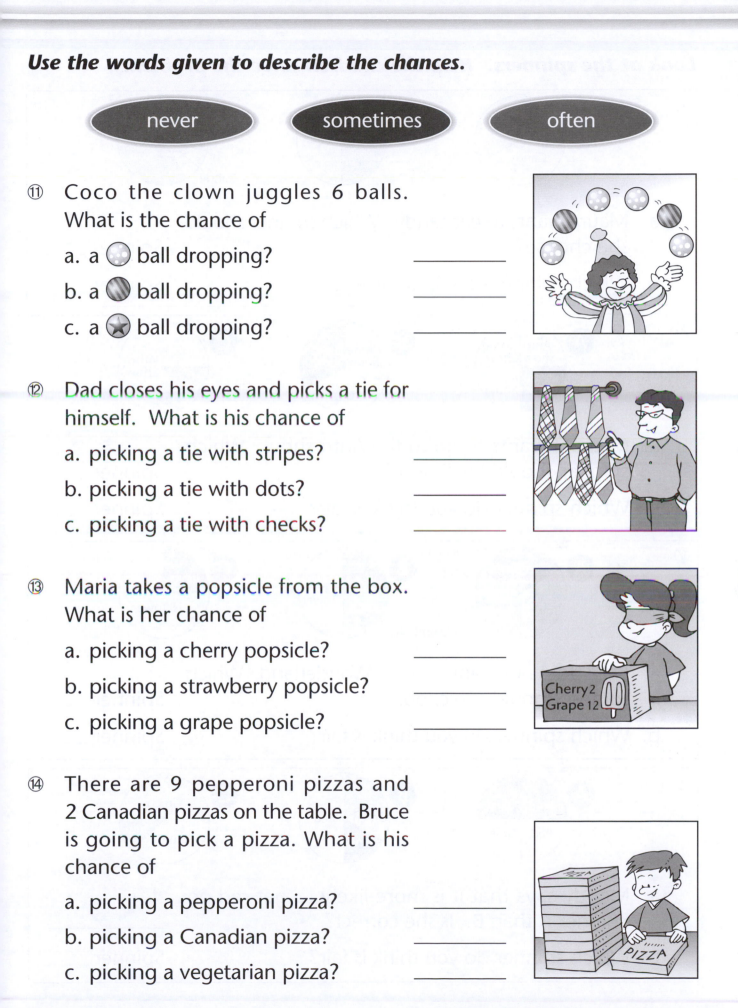

Look at the spinners. Help the children solve the problems.

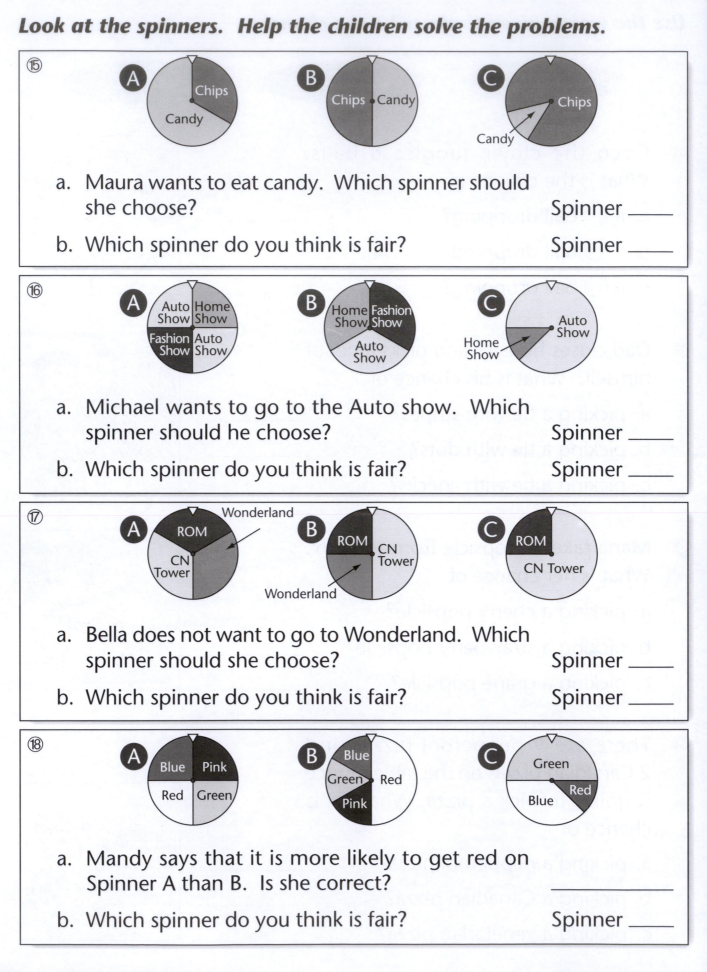

⑮

a. Maura wants to eat candy. Which spinner should
   she choose?   Spinner ____

b. Which spinner do you think is fair?   Spinner ____

⑯

a. Michael wants to go to the Auto show. Which
   spinner should he choose?   Spinner ____

b. Which spinner do you think is fair?   Spinner ____

⑰

a. Bella does not want to go to Wonderland. Which
   spinner should she choose?   Spinner ____

b. Which spinner do you think is fair?   Spinner ____

⑱

a. Mandy says that it is more likely to get red on
   Spinner A than B. Is she correct?   _____

b. Which spinner do you think is fair?   Spinner ____

ISBN: 978-1-897164-12-9

Tommy spins each spinner 20 times and records how many times the pointer lands on each section. Help him match the tables with the spinners. Draw ©, ☼, ☆, or ☺ in the boxes and answer the questions.

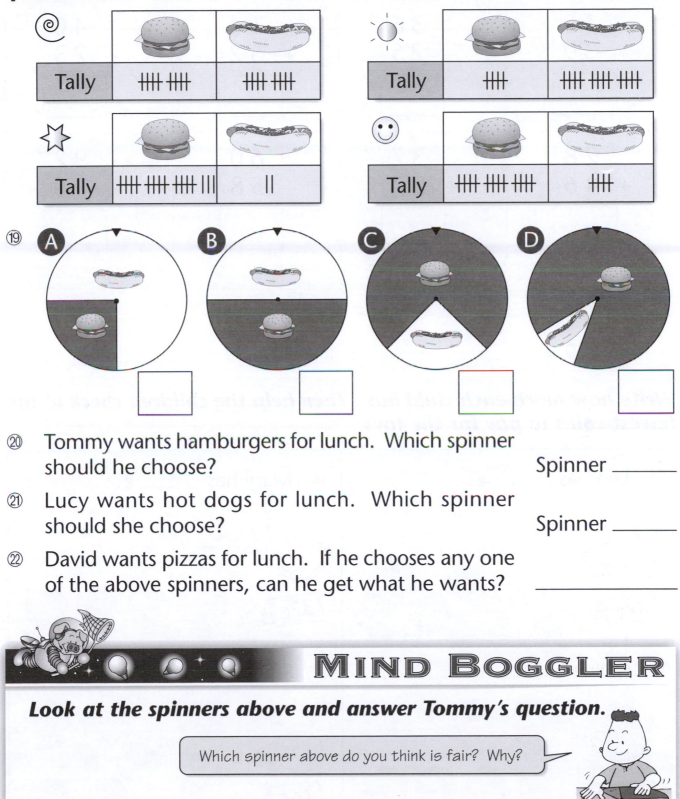

⑲ A □   B □   C □   D □

⑳ Tommy wants hamburgers for lunch. Which spinner should he choose?   Spinner _____

㉑ Lucy wants hot dogs for lunch. Which spinner should she choose?   Spinner _____

㉒ David wants pizzas for lunch. If he chooses any one of the above spinners, can he get what he wants?   _____

MIND BOGGLER

Look at the spinners above and answer Tommy's question.

Which spinner above do you think is fair? Why?

_____

Add or subtract.

①	②	③	④
12 + 39	36 − 25	14 + 52	40 − 23

⑤	⑥	⑦	⑧
28 + 46	37 + 37	60 − 58	92 − 6

⑨ 25 + 26 = _____   ⑩ 77 − 23 = _____

⑪ 47 − 19 = _____   ⑫ 24 + 59 = _____

Write how much each child has. Then help the children check ✔ the fewest coins to pay for the toys.

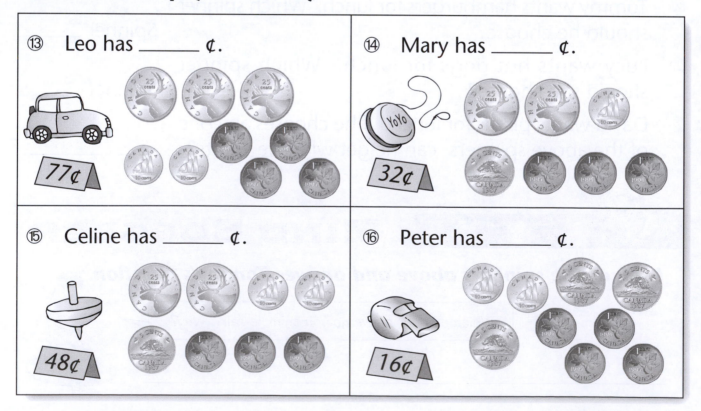

⑬ Leo has _____ ¢.   77¢

⑭ Mary has _____ ¢.   32¢

⑮ Celine has _____ ¢.   48¢

⑯ Peter has _____ ¢.   16¢

Write a fraction to show the shaded parts of each shape.

⑰ 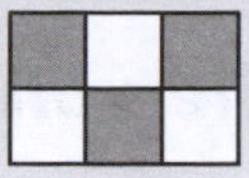 ______	⑱ 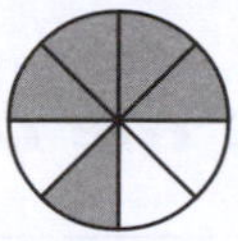 ______	⑲ 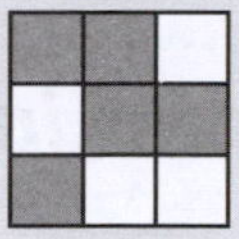 ______
⑳ 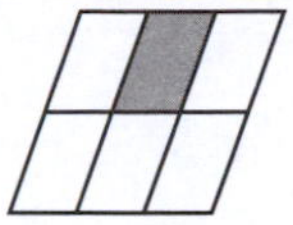 ______	㉑ 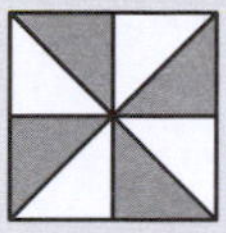 ______	㉒ 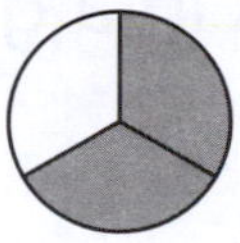 ______

Look at the shapes and complete the table.

	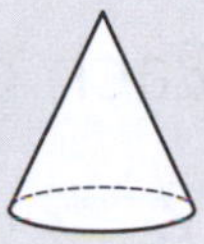	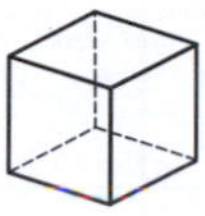	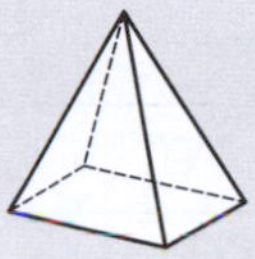	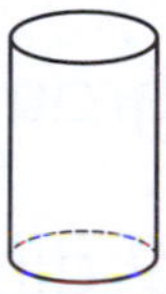	
㉓ Name of shape					
㉔ Number of flat faces					
㉕ Number of △ faces					
㉖ Number of corners					
㉗ Can it roll? (✔ / ✘)					

Count by fives to join the dots to complete the picture. Then answer the questions.

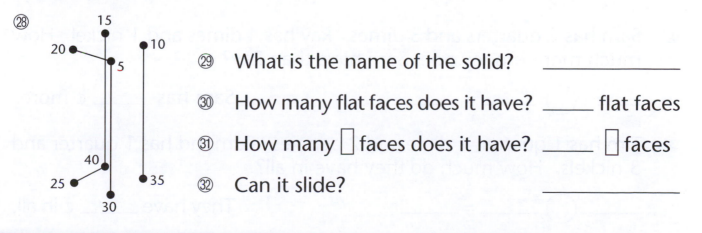

㉘

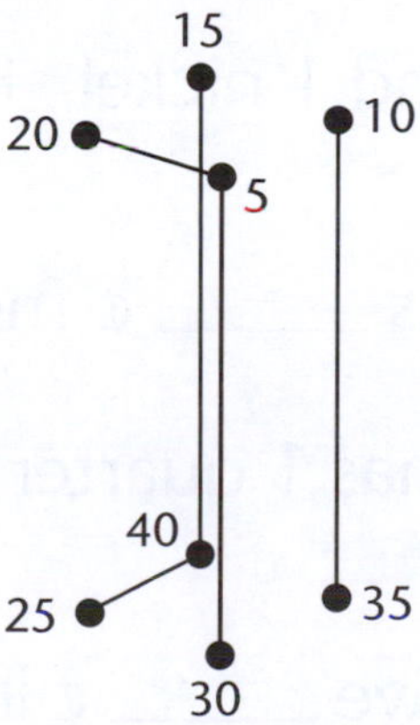
15
20
5
10
40
25
35
30

㉙ What is the name of the solid? ______________

㉚ How many flat faces does it have? ______ flat faces

㉛ How many ▯ faces does it have? ______ ▯ faces

㉜ Can it slide? ______________

ISBN: 978-1-897164-12-9

Divide the coins into groups. Circle the coins and write the values.

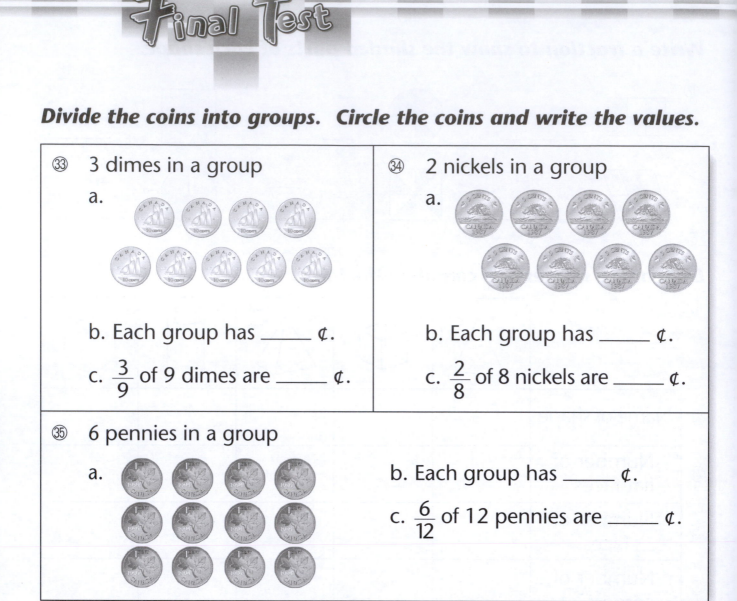

③③ 3 dimes in a group

a.

b. Each group has _____ ¢.

c. $\frac{3}{9}$ of 9 dimes are _____ ¢.

③④ 2 nickels in a group

a.

b. Each group has _____ ¢.

c. $\frac{2}{8}$ of 8 nickels are _____ ¢.

③⑤ 6 pennies in a group

a.

b. Each group has _____ ¢.

c. $\frac{6}{12}$ of 12 pennies are _____ ¢.

Help the children solve the problems.

③⑥ Lucy has 3 quarters and 2 pennies. She pays 56¢ for her toy. How much has she left?

_____ ◯ _____ = _____   She has _____ ¢ left.

③⑦ Sam has 2 quarters and 3 dimes. Ray has 4 dimes and 1 nickel. How much more money does Sam have than Ray?

_____ ◯ _____ = _____   Sam has _____ ¢ more.

③⑧ Tim has 1 quarter, 1 dime and 2 pennies. Edmond has 1 quarter and 3 nickels. How much do they have in all?

_____ ◯ _____ = _____   They have _____ ¢ in all.

ISBN: 978-1-897164-12-9

Complete the following.

③⑨ Draw a square and divide it into 5 equal parts. Then colour 2 parts.

_____ of the square is shaded.

④⓪ Draw a rectangle and divide it into 3 equal parts. Then colour 2 parts.

_____ of the rectangle is shaded.

④① Draw lines to complete the hexagon and divide it into 6 equal parts. Then colour 3 parts.

_____ of the hexagon is shaded.

④② Draw lines to complete the octagon and divide it into 8 equal parts. Then colour 7 parts.

_____ of the octagon is shaded.

Circle the correct words to show the chances.

④③ The chance of winning a lottery

Often   Sometimes   Never

④④ The chance of drawing a 3 from 2 2 4 5 6

Often   Sometimes   Never

④⑤ The chance of getting a 5 by rolling a dice with numbers 1 - 6

Often   Sometimes   Never

④⑥ The chance of getting a green marble from a box of 20 green and 5 yellow marbles

Often   Sometimes   Never

Check ✔ the spinner each child spun.

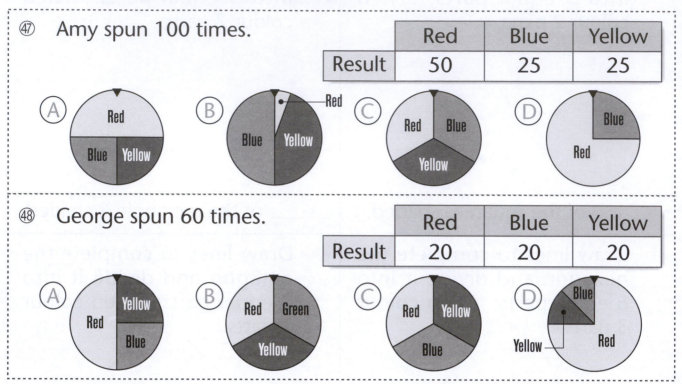

⑦ Amy spun 100 times.

Result	Red	Blue	Yellow
	50	25	25

Ⓐ   Ⓑ   Ⓒ   Ⓓ

⑱ George spun 60 times.

Result	Red	Blue	Yellow
	20	20	20

Ⓐ   Ⓑ   Ⓒ   Ⓓ

Draw the clock hands to show the times and fill in the blanks.

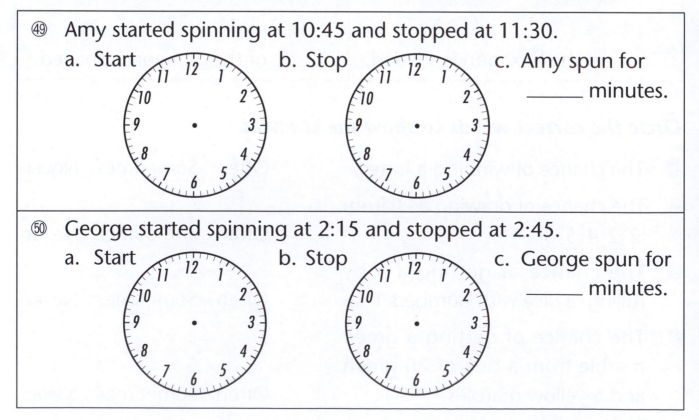

⑲ Amy started spinning at 10:45 and stopped at 11:30.
  a. Start   b. Stop   c. Amy spun for
                                     _____ minutes.

⑳ George started spinning at 2:15 and stopped at 2:45.
  a. Start   b. Stop   c. George spun for
                                     _____ minutes.

Make a tally for the number of juice boxes on each shelf. Then colour the graph and answer the questions.

(51)

	Number of Juice Boxes
1st shelf	
2nd shelf	
3rd shelf	
4th shelf	
5th shelf	
6th shelf	

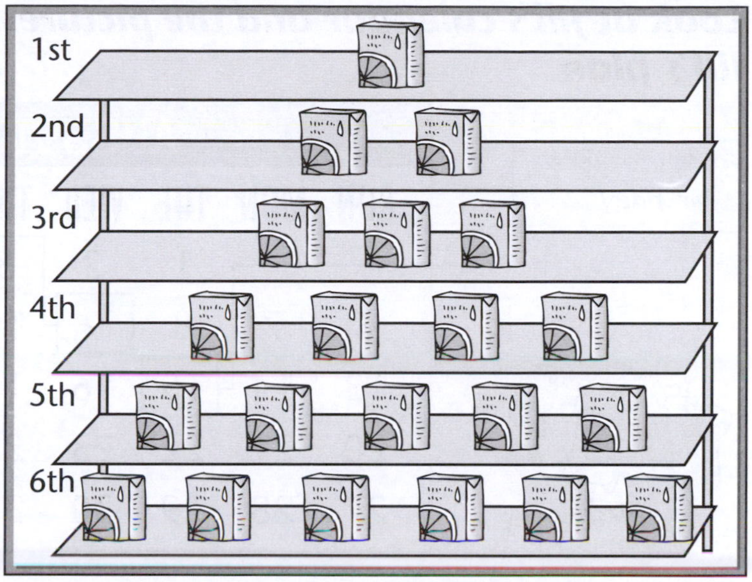

(52)

Number of Juice Boxes on Each Shelf

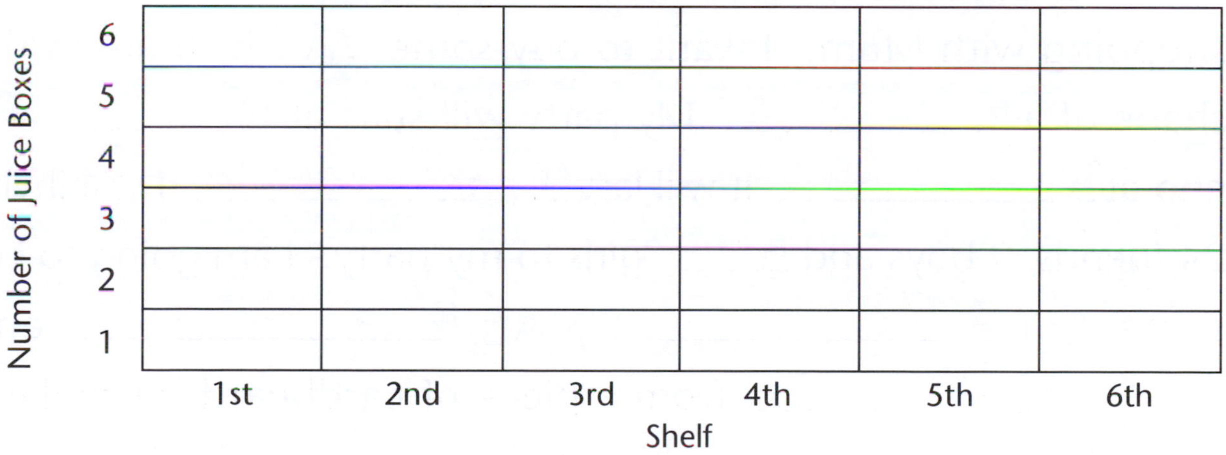

(53) What is the title of the graph?

____

(54) How many juice boxes are there in all? ______ juice boxes

(55) From the top shelf to the bottom, does the number of juice boxes go up or down? By how many each time? ______ ; ______

(56) If the pattern continues, how many juice boxes will there be on the 7th shelf? ______ juice boxes

ISBN: 978-1-897164-12-9

Look at Jill's calendar and the pictures. Fill in the blanks to complete Jill's plan.

My brother's birthday

AUGUST

SUN	MON	TUE	WED	THU	FRI	SAT
		1	2	3	4	5
6	7	8	9	10	11	12
13	14	15	16	17	18	19
20	21	22	23	24	25	26
27	28	29	30	31		

My birthday party

Start

End

There are ⑤⑦_____ days in August. My birthday is on August ⑤⑧_____ .
Two days before my birthday, that is, August ⑤⑨_____ , I will go
shopping with Mom. I want to buy some ⊱ which are in the
shape of a ⑥⓪_____ . My party will start at ⑥①_____ and
end at ⑥②_____ . It will last ⑥③_____ . I will invite
24 friends, 9 boys and ⑥④_____ girls to my party. I am going to cut
some ▱ ⑥⑤_____ , ◭ ⑥⑥_____ and
⬡ ⑥⑦_____ from a piece of cardboard for making
invitation cards.

My brother's birthday is ⑥⑧_____ days after my birthday. I am
going to buy him a small box of 🧩 , which is in the shape of a
⑥⑨_____ .

My sister's birthday is on the first day of the month following
August, that is, ⑦⓪_____ 1. On that day, I will help Mom bake
a birthday cake for my sister. It will take me three quarters of an
hour or ⑦①_____ minutes to finish.

Section IV

Overview

In Section III, children were encouraged to connect ideas from numbers, measurement, geometry, patterning and graphs, as they were introduced to the different strands of mathematics. They had the basic concepts of using addition, subtraction, multiplication and division in simple problem-solving activities.

In this section, integrated activities in the form of story problems involve children in the applications of arithmetic, graphing and measurement skills as described in the Grade 2 curriculum and beyond.

While calculators may be used where necessary, children should be encouraged to do calculations mentally whenever possible.

The children estimate the number of jelly beans in a jar. Answer the questions.

	Stella	Peggy	Sam	Max	Craig
Estimated number of jelly beans	178	193	145	180	213

① Who estimates the smallest number? _____

② Who estimates the largest number? _____

③ What is the smallest estimated number? Write the number in words.

_____

④ What is the largest estimated number? Write the number in words.

_____

⑤ Put the numbers in order, from the smallest to the largest.

_____

⑥ How many of the estimated numbers are smaller than 190? _____

⑦ How many of the estimated numbers are larger than 190? _____

There are 190 jelly beans in the jar. The winner is the one who gives the estimated number closest to 190. Help the children answer the questions.

⑧ Who is the winner? _____

⑨ Who is the second winner? _____

Matthew kept a record of the number of ice cream cones sold each month in summer at his store. Use his table to answer the questions.

	May	June	July	August	September
Number of 🍦 sold	774	810	988	910	780

⑩ In which month did he sell the most 🍦 ?

_____

⑪ In which month did he sell the fewest 🍦 ?

_____

⑫ In which months did he sell more than 900 🍦 ?

_____

⑬ In which months did he sell fewer than 900 🍦 ?

_____

⑭ What is the difference between the number of 🍦 sold in June and in August?   _____ 🍦

⑮ How many more 🍦 did he sell in September than in May?   _____ 🍦

⑯ Put the months in order, from the one which sold the most 🍦 to the one which sold the fewest.

_____

⑰ Matthew sold 100 fewer 🍦 in April than in May. How many 🍦 were sold in April? Write the number in words.

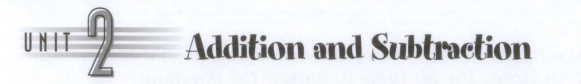

UNIT 2 — Addition and Subtraction

Peggy, Sue and Sarah use beads to make necklaces and bracelets. See how many beads they use. Then answer the questions.

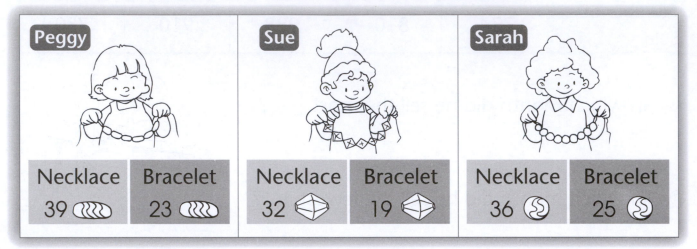

① How many 🫘 does Peggy use in all?

_____ = _____   _____ 🫘

② How many ◇ does Sue use in all?

_____ = _____   _____ ◇

③ How many Ⓢ does Sarah use in all?

_____ = _____   _____ Ⓢ

④ How many more 🫘 does Peggy use for her necklace than her bracelet?

_____ = _____   _____ more 🫘

⑤ How many more ◇ does Sue use for her necklace than her bracelet?

_____ = _____   _____ more ◇

⑥ How many beads do the girls use to make their bracelets?

_____ = _____   _____ beads

ISBN: 978-1-897164-12-9

Many people took part in a race to raise money for Heart Research. See how they participated in the race. Use the table to answer the questions.

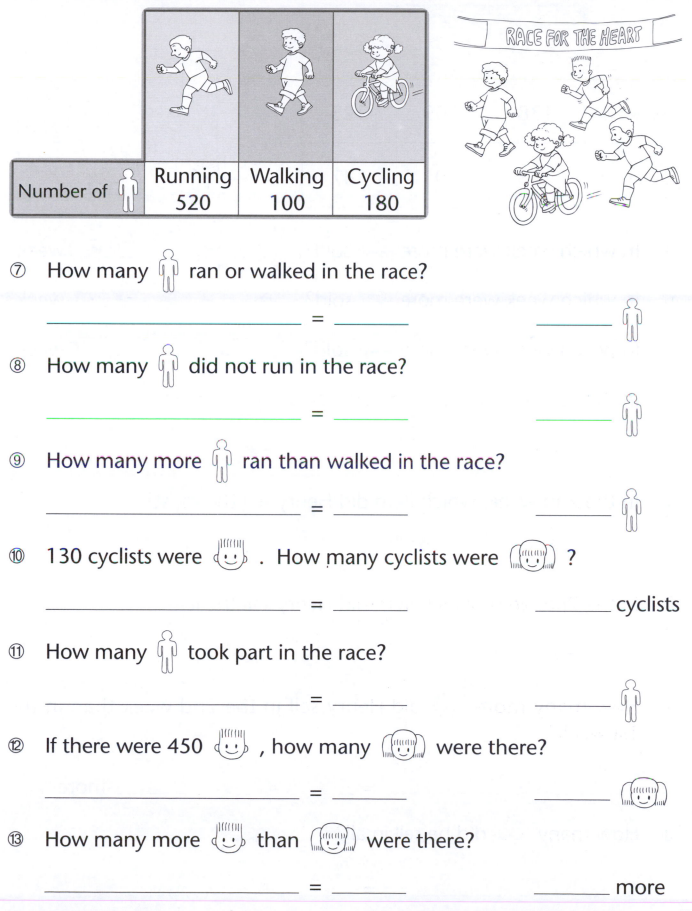

Number of 👤	Running 520	Walking 100	Cycling 180

⑦ How many 👤 ran or walked in the race?

_____ = _____   _____ 👤

⑧ How many 👤 did not run in the race?

_____ = _____   _____ 👤

⑨ How many more 👤 ran than walked in the race?

_____ = _____   _____ 👤

⑩ 130 cyclists were 🙂 . How many cyclists were 👧 ?

_____ = _____   _____ cyclists

⑪ How many 👤 took part in the race?

_____ = _____   _____ 👤

⑫ If there were 450 🙂 , how many 👧 were there?

_____ = _____   _____ 👧

⑬ How many more 🙂 than 👧 were there?

_____ = _____   _____ more

ISBN: 978-1-897164-12-9

See how many hamburgers, hot dogs and sandwiches Henry sold in the past two weeks. Answer the questions and check ✔ the correct answers.

1st week	138	109	123
2nd week	158	105	147

⑭ In which week were more 🍔 sold?   _____ week

⑮ In which week were more 🌭 sold?   _____ week

⑯ In which week were more 🥪 sold?   _____ week

⑰ In the 1st week, which item did Henry sell the most?

    Ⓐ 🍔   Ⓑ 🌭   Ⓒ 🥪

⑱ In the 2nd week, which item did Henry sell the most?

    Ⓐ 🍔   Ⓑ 🌭   Ⓒ 🥪

⑲ In the 2nd week, which item did Henry sell the least?

    Ⓐ 🍔   Ⓑ 🌭   Ⓒ 🥪

⑳ How many more 🍔 did Henry sell in the 2nd week than in the 1st week?

_____ = _____   _____ more 🍔

㉑ How many 🍔 did he sell in all?

_____ = _____   🍔

ISBN: 978-1-897164-12-9

㉒ How many more 🌭 did Henry sell in the 1st week than in the 2nd week?

_____ = _____   _____ more 🌭

㉓ How many 🌭 did he sell in all?

_____ = _____   _____ 🌭

㉔ How many more 🥪 did Henry sell in the 2nd week than in the 1st week?

_____ = _____   _____ more 🥪

㉕ How many 🥪 did he sell in all?

_____ = _____   _____ 🥪

㉖ What is the total number of the three items sold in the 1st week?

_____ = _____   _____

㉗ What is the total number of the three items sold in the 2nd week?

_____ = _____   _____

㉘ In the 1st week, 75 of the 🍔 sold were with cheese. How many 🍔 sold were without cheese?

_____ = _____   _____ 🍔

㉙ In the 2nd week, 89 of the 🥪 sold were with ham. How many 🥪 sold were without ham?

_____ = _____   _____ 🥪

UNIT 3 Multiplication

See how Graham lays the tiles. Then fill in the blanks.

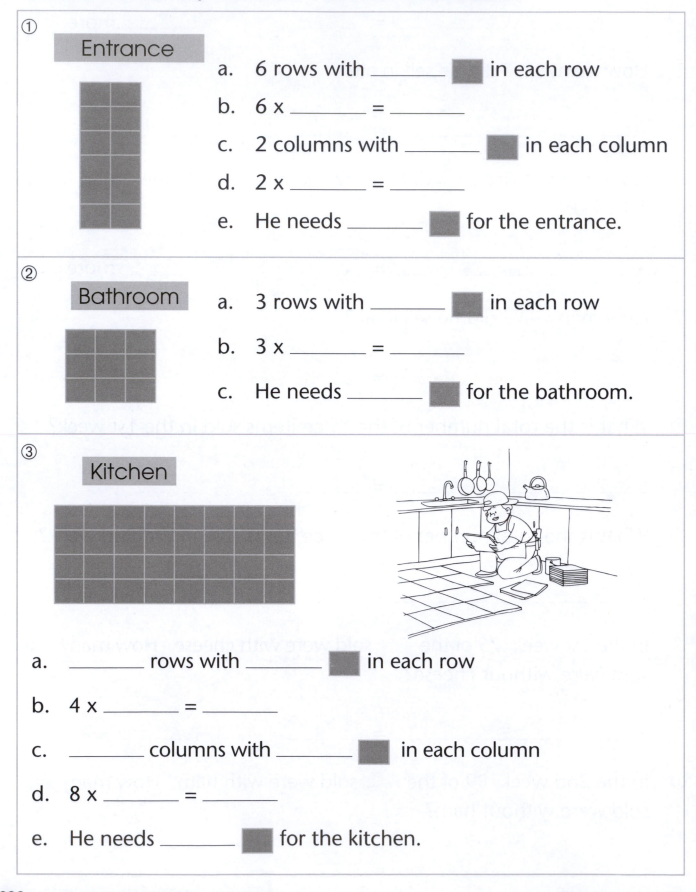

① **Entrance**

a. 6 rows with _____ ⬜ in each row

b. 6 x _____ = _____

c. 2 columns with _____ ⬜ in each column

d. 2 x _____ = _____

e. He needs _____ ⬜ for the entrance.

② **Bathroom**

a. 3 rows with _____ ⬜ in each row

b. 3 x _____ = _____

c. He needs _____ ⬜ for the bathroom.

③ **Kitchen**

a. _____ rows with _____ ⬜ in each row

b. 4 x _____ = _____

c. _____ columns with _____ ⬜ in each column

d. 8 x _____ = _____

e. He needs _____ ⬜ for the kitchen.

ISBN: 978-1-897164-12-9

Help Ted the farmer solve the problems.

④
a. One dog has _____ legs.

b. How many legs do 3 dogs have?

3 x _____ = _____   _____ legs

⑤
a. One cat has _____ ears.

b. How many ears do 5 cats have?

_____ x _____ = _____   _____ ears

⑥
a. One hen lays _____ eggs.

b. How many eggs do 2 hens lay?

_____ x _____ = _____   _____ eggs

⑦
a. One spider has _____ legs.

b. How many legs do 4 spiders have?

_____ x _____ = _____   _____ legs

⑧
a. One basket holds _____ carrots.

b. How many carrots do 3 baskets hold?

_____ x _____ = _____   _____ carrots

⑨
a. One bag holds _____ corn cobs.

b. How many corn cobs do 6 bags hold?

_____ x _____ = _____   _____ corn cobs

ISBN: 978-1-897164-12-9

It is Laura's birthday. Help her check ✔ the correct answers and solve the problems.

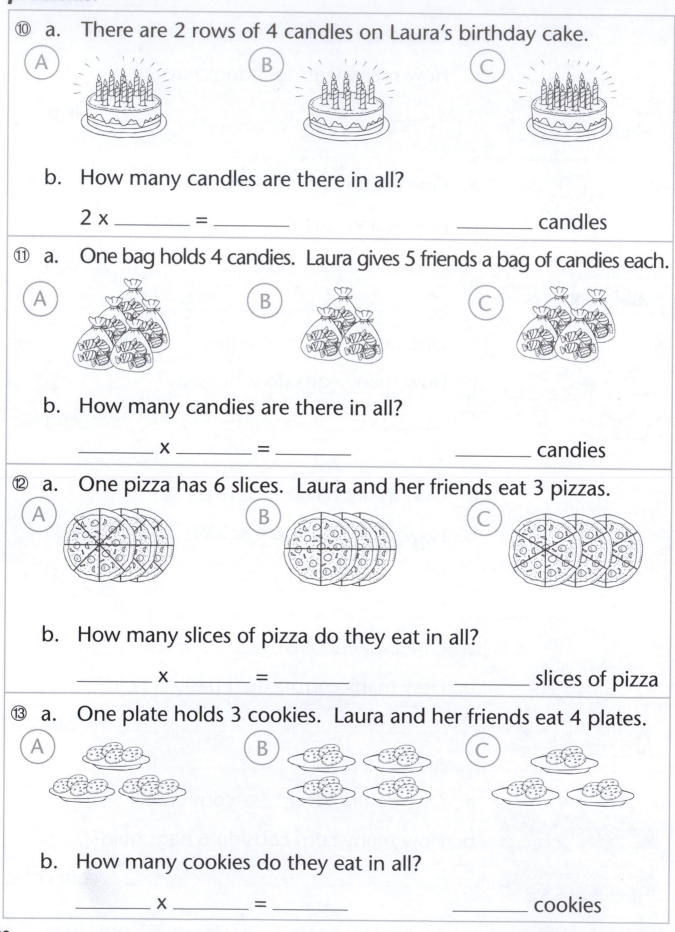

⑩ a. There are 2 rows of 4 candles on Laura's birthday cake.

A   B   C

b. How many candles are there in all?

2 x _____ = _____   _____ candles

⑪ a. One bag holds 4 candies. Laura gives 5 friends a bag of candies each.

A   B   C

b. How many candies are there in all?

_____ x _____ = _____   _____ candies

⑫ a. One pizza has 6 slices. Laura and her friends eat 3 pizzas.

A   B   C

b. How many slices of pizza do they eat in all?

_____ x _____ = _____   _____ slices of pizza

⑬ a. One plate holds 3 cookies. Laura and her friends eat 4 plates.

A   B   C

b. How many cookies do they eat in all?

_____ x _____ = _____   _____ cookies

ISBN: 978-1-897164-12-9

⑭ Laura invites 8 friends. Each friend eats 6 chocolates.
How many chocolates do they eat in all?

_____ x _____ = _____   _____ chocolates

⑮ There are 6 straws in a box. How many straws are
there in 7 boxes?

_____ x _____ = _____   _____ straws

⑯ There are 2 balloons in a bag. How many balloons
are there in 9 bags?

_____ x _____ = _____   _____ balloons

⑰ There are 6 plates in a pile. How many plates are
there in 4 piles?

_____ x _____ = _____   _____ plates

⑱ There are 5 forks in a cup. How many forks are there
in 5 cups?

_____ x _____ = _____   _____ cups

⑲ One child eats 4 marshmallows. How many
marshmallows do 5 children eat in all?

_____ x _____ = _____   _____ marshmallows

⑳ One plate holds 3 brownies. How many brownies
are there on 2 plates?

_____ x _____ = _____   _____ brownies

Read what the children say. Then check ✔ the coins and write the amounts.

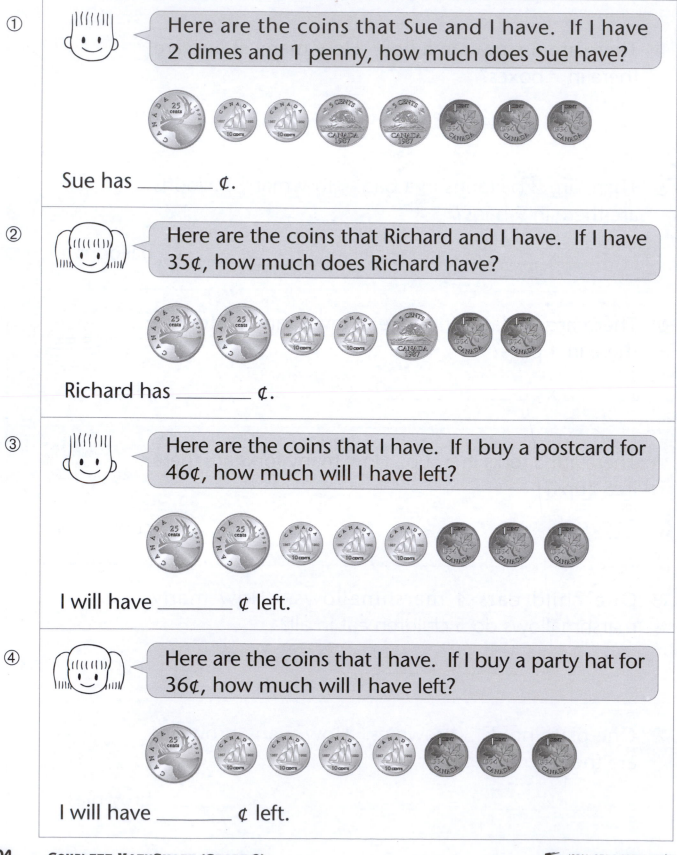

① Here are the coins that Sue and I have. If I have 2 dimes and 1 penny, how much does Sue have?

Sue has _____ ¢.

② Here are the coins that Richard and I have. If I have 35¢, how much does Richard have?

Richard has _____ ¢.

③ Here are the coins that I have. If I buy a postcard for 46¢, how much will I have left?

I will have _____ ¢ left.

④ Here are the coins that I have. If I buy a party hat for 36¢, how much will I have left?

I will have _____ ¢ left.

ISBN: 978-1-897164-12-9

Pat wants to buy some beads to make bracelets. See what kinds of beads she buys and answer the questions.

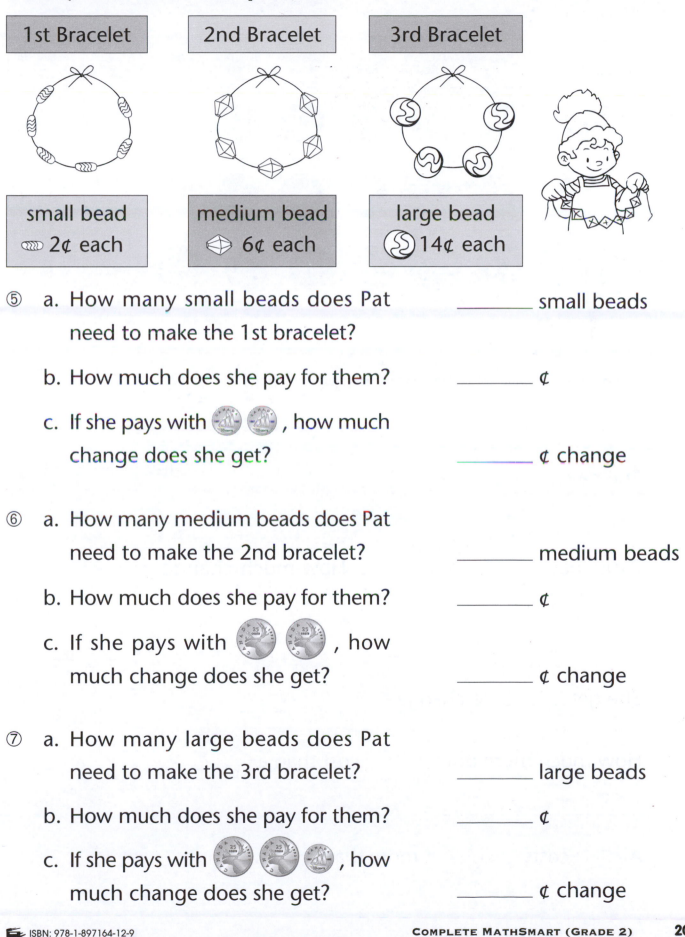

1st Bracelet	2nd Bracelet	3rd Bracelet

small bead	medium bead	large bead
2¢ each	6¢ each	14¢ each

⑤ a. How many small beads does Pat   _____ small beads
      need to make the 1st bracelet?

    b. How much does she pay for them?   _____ ¢

    c. If she pays with 🪙 🪙 , how much
       change does she get?   _____ ¢ change

⑥ a. How many medium beads does Pat
      need to make the 2nd bracelet?   _____ medium beads

    b. How much does she pay for them?   _____ ¢

    c. If she pays with 🪙 🪙 , how
       much change does she get?   _____ ¢ change

⑦ a. How many large beads does Pat
      need to make the 3rd bracelet?   _____ large beads

    b. How much does she pay for them?   _____ ¢

    c. If she pays with 🪙 🪙 🪙 , how
       much change does she get?   _____ ¢ change

Write how much each snack costs and see what the children buy. Help them solve the problems.

⑧ _____ ¢

⑨ _____ ¢

⑩ _____ ¢

⑪ _____ ¢

⑫ How much does Emma pays for a 🍪 and a 🧁 ?

_____ + _____ = _____

She pays _____ ¢.

⬚
+ ⬚
⬚

⑬ Paula pays 🪙🪙 for a 🥨. How much change does she get?

_____ − _____ = _____

She get _____ ¢ change.

⬚
⬚
− ⬚

⑭ How much more does a 🧀 cost than a 🧁 ?

_____ = _____

A 🧀 costs _____ ¢ more than a 🧁 .

COMPLETE MATHSMART (GRADE 2)

ISBN: 978-1-897164-12-9

⑮ How much do 2 🥨 cost?

_____ = _____

2 🥨 cost _____ ¢.

⑯ Jennifer buys a 🍪 and a 🥨. How much does she pay in all?

_____ = _____

She pays _____ ¢ in all.

⑰ Derek has 85¢. If he buys a 🧁, how much has he left?

_____ = _____

He has _____ ¢ left.

⑱ Molly buys 2 🍫 and 1 🍪. How much does she pay in all?

_____ = _____

She pays _____ ¢ in all.

⑲ Kevin gets 🪙 🪙 🪙 change from 🪙 🪙. What snack did he buy?

_____ = _____

He bought a _____ .

Pictographs

Look at the graph. Then answer the questions.

Favourite Footwear in Mrs Starkman's Class

Boots

Running shoes

Sandals

Dress shoes

Slippers

① Which type of footwear is the least popular? _____

② Which type of footwear is the most popular? _____

③ Which type of footwear is the next most popular? _____

④ Which type of footwear do fewer children like than slippers? _____

⑤ Which type of footwear is as popular as slippers? _____

⑥ How many more children like sandals than dress shoes? _____

⑦ How many children like running shoes or boots? _____

⑧ How many children are in Mrs Starkman's class? _____

   ISBN: 978-1-897164-12-9

Here are the records of the baseball teams. Look at the graph and answer the questions.

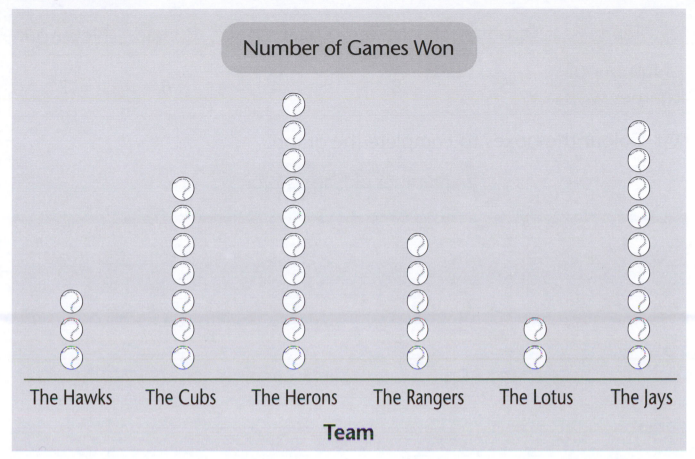

⑨ Which team has won 7 games?   _____

⑩ Which team has won 5 games?   _____

⑪ How many teams have won more than 6 games?   _____ teams

⑫ Which team has won 2 more games than The Cubs?   _____

⑬ Which team has the best record?   _____

⑭ Which team has the worst record?   _____

⑮ The Rangers have played 12 games. How many games did they lose?   _____ games

Ted has recorded the results of the hockey games. Use the table to complete the pictograph and answer the questions.

Team	Toronto	Rochester	Philadelphia	Buffalo	New York
Number of games won	5	8	4	6	7

⑯ Colour the boxes to complete the graph.

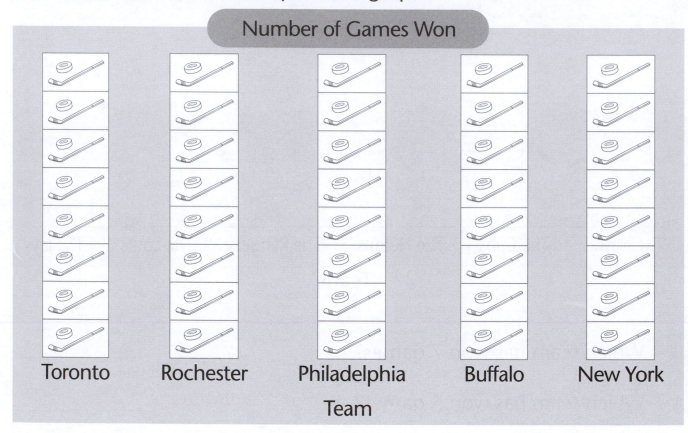

Number of Games Won

Toronto   Rochester   Philadelphia   Buffalo   New York

Team

⑰ Which team has the best record? _____

⑱ Which team has the worst record? _____

⑲ Which team has won 6 games? _____

⑳ How many teams have won 6 games or more? _____ teams

㉑ Buffalo has played 11 games. How many games did they lose? _____ games

㉒ Toronto has lost 7 games. How many games did they play in all? _____ games

ISBN: 978-1-897164-12-9

Uncle Jim has recorded his customers' favourite sandwiches. Use his record to complete the pictograph and answer the questions.

Sandwich	Ham	Corned Beef	Roast Beef	Egg Salad	Chicken	Tuna Salad
Number of customers	7	4	6	5	5	3

㉓   Colour the boxes to complete the graph.

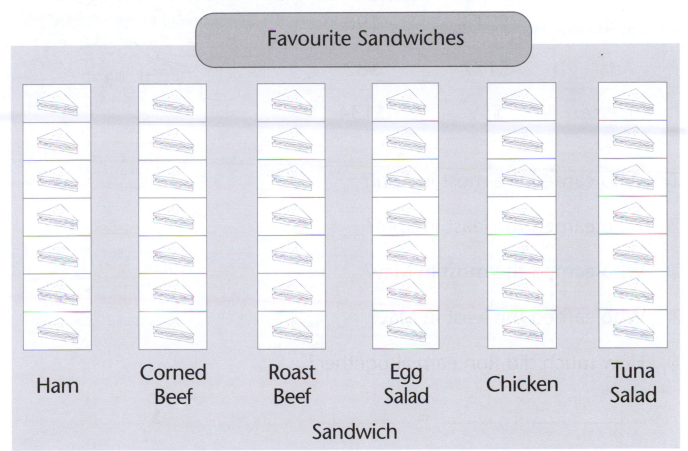

Favourite Sandwiches

Ham   Corned Beef   Roast Beef   Egg Salad   Chicken   Tuna Salad

Sandwich

㉔   Which is the most popular sandwich?   _____

㉕   Which is the least popular sandwich?   _____

㉖   How many customers like beef sandwiches?   _____

㉗   How many customers like salad sandwiches?   _____

㉘   How many more customers like ham sandwiches than chicken sandwiches?   _____

UNIT 6

More about Addition and Subtraction

See how much Ron and his friends earned in the past 2 months. Answer the questions.

	April	May
Ron	$145	$108
Dan	$213	$96
Ada	$177	$82
Roberta	$59	$134

① Who earned the most in April? _____

② Who earned the least in April? _____

③ Who earned the most in May? _____

④ Who earned the least in May? _____

⑤ How much did Ron earn altogether?

_____ = _____ $ _____

⑥ How much did Dan earn altogether?

_____ = _____ $ _____

⑦ How much more did Ada earn in April than in May?

_____ = _____ $ _____ more

⑧ How much more did Roberta earn in May than in April?

_____ = _____ $ _____ more

 ISBN: 978-1-897164-12-9

Scientists counted the number of Canada Geese and Mallard Ducks at different places along Lake Ontario. Use the table to answer the questions.

Place	Number of 	Number of
Hamilton	150	32
Oakville	165	64
Mississauga	178	45
Toronto	197	58

⑨ Where are the most 🦢 found? _____

⑩ Where are the most 🦆 found? _____

⑪ How many 🦢 and 🦆 were found in Hamilton?

_____ = _____   _____ 🦢 🦆

⑫ How many 🦢 and 🦆 were found in Oakville?

_____ = _____   _____ 🦢 🦆

⑬ How many 🦢 and 🦆 were found in Mississauga?

_____ = _____   _____ 🦢 🦆

⑭ How many 🦢 and 🦆 were found in Toronto?

_____ = _____   _____ 🦢 🦆

⑮ How many more 🦢 and 🦆 were found in Toronto than in Hamilton?

_____ = _____   _____ more 🦢 🦆

See how many students are in each school. Answer the questions.

Name of School	Number of Students
Cedar	154
Pine	326
Spruce	105
Maple	302

⑯ 72 students in Cedar School are 😊 . How many 🙂 are in Cedar school?

_____ = _____   _____ 🙂

⑰ 124 students in Maple School are 🙂 . How many 😊 are in Maple school?

_____ = _____   _____ 😊

⑱ 97 students in Pine School wear 👓 . How many students in Pine School do not wear 👓 ?

_____ = _____   _____ students

⑲ 35 students in Spruce School have blond hair. How many students in Spruce School do not have blond hair?

_____ = _____   _____ students

⑳ If Cedar School and Pine School have a joint Sports Day and all students participate, how many students will there be in all?

_____ = _____   _____ students

   ISBN: 978-1-897164-12-9

This year Simon's Sports Store sold a lot of bicycles, tricycles, skateboards and scooters. Help Simon solve the problems.

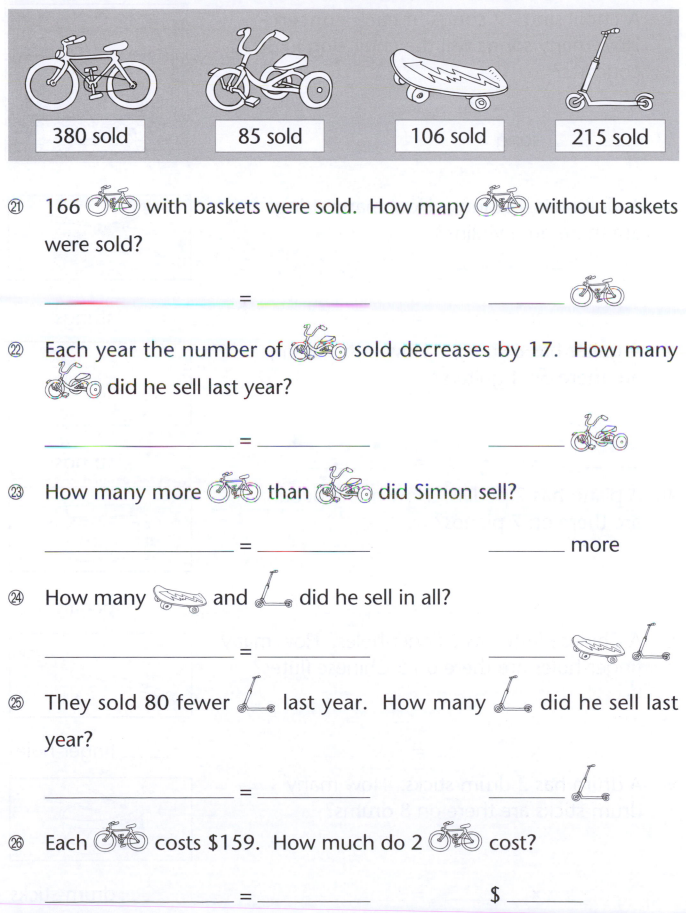

| 380 sold | 85 sold | 106 sold | 215 sold |

㉑ 166 🚲 with baskets were sold. How many 🚲 without baskets were sold?

_____ = _____   _____ 🚲

㉒ Each year the number of 🚲 sold decreases by 17. How many 🚲 did he sell last year?

_____ = _____   _____ 🚲

㉓ How many more 🚲 than 🚲 did Simon sell?

_____ = _____   _____ more

㉔ How many 🛹 and 🛴 did he sell in all?

_____ = _____   _____ 🛹 🛴

㉕ They sold 80 fewer 🛴 last year. How many 🛴 did he sell last year?

_____ = _____   _____ 🛴

㉖ Each 🚲 costs $159. How much do 2 🚲 cost?

_____ = _____ $ _____

Ivan goes to a music show. Help him solve the problems.

① A choir sings 9 songs in each concert. How many songs will the choir sing in 3 concerts?

3 x _____ = _____

_____ song

② A violin has 4 strings. How many strings are there on 5 violins?

_____ x _____ = _____   _____ strings

③ A guitar has 6 strings. How many strings are there on 4 guitars?

_____ x _____ = _____   _____ strings

④ A piano has 2 pedals. How many pedals are there on 7 pianos?

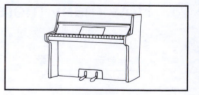
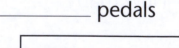

_____ x _____ = _____   _____ pedals

⑤ A Chinese flute has 6 finger-holes. How many finger-holes are there on 5 Chinese flutes?

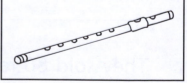

_____ x _____ = _____   _____ finger-holes

⑥ A drum has 2 drum-sticks. How many drum-sticks are there on 8 drums?

_____ x _____ = _____   _____ drum-sticks

   ISBN: 978-1-897164-12-9

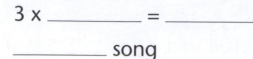

See how much money each girl has. Fill in the blanks and answer the questions.

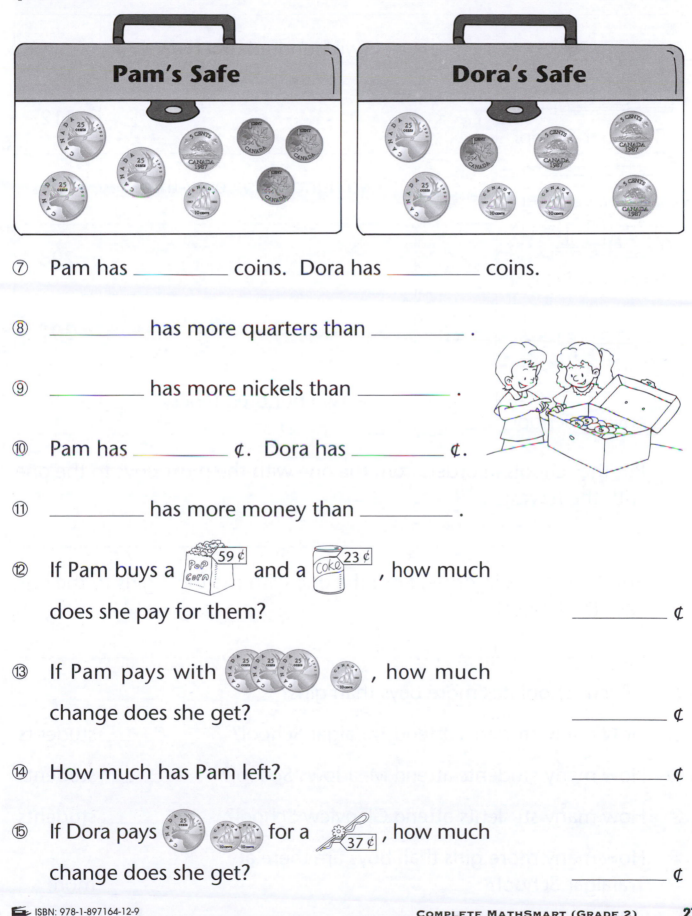

⑦ Pam has _____ coins. Dora has _____ coins.

⑧ _____ has more quarters than _____ .

⑨ _____ has more nickels than _____ .

⑩ Pam has _____ ¢. Dora has _____ ¢.

⑪ _____ has more money than _____ .

⑫ If Pam buys a PoP corn 59¢ and a Coke 23¢ , how much does she pay for them? _____ ¢

⑬ If Pam pays with 25¢ 25¢ 25¢ 10¢ , how much change does she get? _____ ¢

⑭ How much has Pam left? _____ ¢

⑮ If Dora pays 25¢ 10¢ 10¢ for a 37¢ , how much change does she get? _____ ¢

ISBN: 978-1-897164-12-9

The table shows the number of boys and girls at each school. Complete the table and answer the questions.

⑯ Trafalgar School	(boy)	Two hundred ninety-five	
	(girl)		312
⑰ Meadows School	(boy)	Two hundred seventy-three	
	(girl)		298
⑱ Glenview School	(boy)		301
	(girl)	Two hundred ninety	

⑲ Put the schools in order, from the one with the most boys to the one with the fewest.

_____ , _____ , _____

⑳ Put the schools in order, from the one with the most girls to the one with the fewest.

_____ , _____ , _____

㉑ Which school has more boys than girls?   _____

㉒ How many students attend Trafalgar School?   _____ students

㉓ How many students attend Meadows School?   _____ students

㉔ How many students attend Glenview School?   _____ students

㉕ How many more girls than boys are there at Trafalgar School?   _____ more

ISBN: 978-1-897164-12-9

Simon and his friends joined the Summer Reading Programme. See how many books they read. Answer the questions.

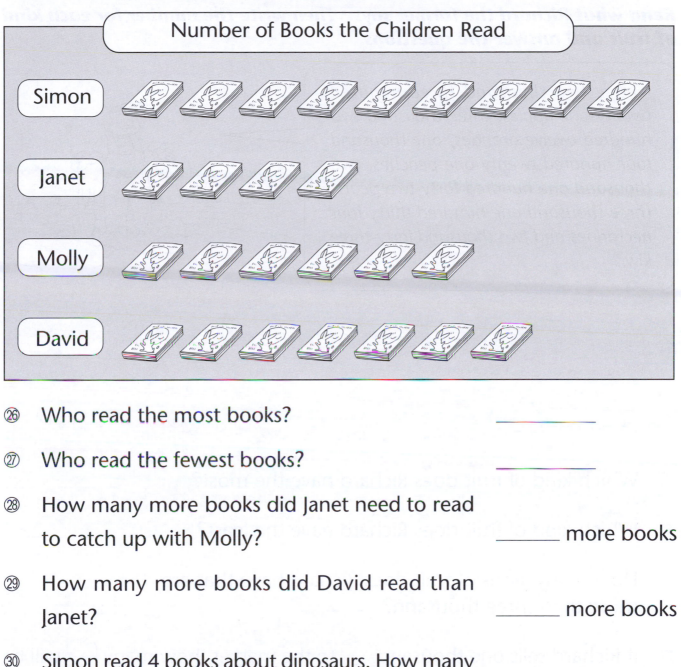

Number of Books the Children Read

Simon

Janet

Molly

David

㉖ Who read the most books? _____

㉗ Who read the fewest books? _____

㉘ How many more books did Janet need to read to catch up with Molly? _____ more books

㉙ How many more books did David read than Janet? _____ more books

㉚ Simon read 4 books about dinosaurs. How many of his books were not about dinosaurs? _____ books

㉛ Did the girls read more books than the boys? _____

㉜ For every 3 books each child read, he or she would get a prize. How many prizes would Simon get? _____ prizes

㉝ How many prizes would David get? _____ prizes

Read what Richard the farmer says. Then write the number for each kind of fruit and answer the questions.

I have two thousand three hundred twenty-one apples, three thousand two hundred twelve oranges, one thousand four hundred twenty-one peaches, two thousand one hundred forty-two pears, three thousand one hundred thirty-four nectarines and two thousand forty-three kiwi.

① _____ 🍎   ② _____ 🍊   ③ _____ 🍑

④ _____ 🍐   ⑤ _____ 🍎   ⑥ _____ 🥝

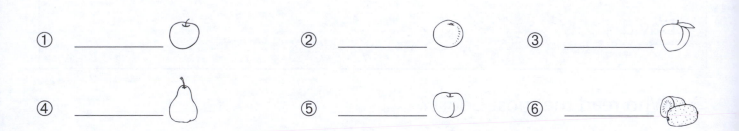

⑦ Which kind of fruit does Richard have the most?   _____

⑧ Which kind of fruit does Richard have the least?   _____

⑨ How many kinds of fruit does Richard have that are more than three thousand?   _____

⑩ If Richard sells one thousand 🍎 to the market, how many 🍎 will be left? Write the number in words.

_____

⑪ If Richard gets five hundred 🍑 from Tim, how many 🍑 will he have in all? Write the number in words.

_____

Dave went to the Royal Ontario Museum and learned all about dinosaurs. Look at the table and answer the questions.

Dinosaur	Length (cm)
Tyrannosarus	1200
Diplodocus	2600
Brachiosaurus	2200
Plesiosaurus	1800
Brontosaurus	2100
Triceratops	600
Giganotosaurus	1300

⑫ Which dinosaur was the longest? _____

⑬ Which dinosaur was the second longest? _____

⑭ How much longer was Brachiosaurus than Tyrannosaurus? _____ cm

⑮ What is the difference in length between Diplodocus and Triceratops? _____ cm

⑯ Which dinosaur was longer than Tyrannosaurus but shorter than Plesiosaurus? _____

⑰ How long was Brontosaurus? Write its length in words.

_____

⑱ How long was Giganotosaurus? Write its length in words.

Mrs Ling and Mrs Ford buy some lottery tickets to support the Canadian Cancer Society. Help them put the tickets in order and answer the questions.

⑲ Help Mrs Ling put the tickets in order, from the largest to the smallest.

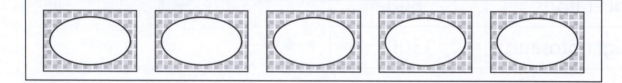

⑳ Help Mrs Ford put the tickets in order, from the largest to the smallest.

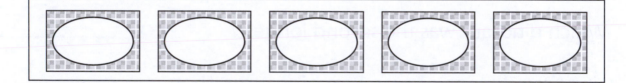

㉑ Write the smallest number of Mrs Ling's tickets in words.

_____

㉒ Write the largest number of Mrs Ford's tickets in words.

_____

㉓ How many tickets with 2 in the hundreds place does Mrs Ling have? What are they?

_____ tickets; _____

㉔ How many tickets with 5 in the tens place does Mrs Ford have? What are they?

_____ tickets; _____

ISBN: 978-1-897164-12-9

Sam's factory supplies markers to different stores. The markers come in boxes of different sizes. Complete the table and answer the questions.

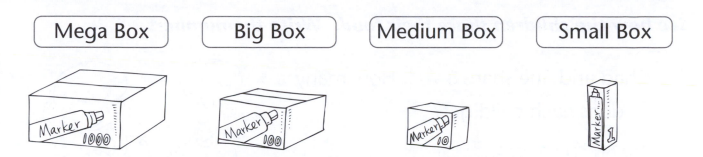

	Mega Box	Big Box	Medium Box	Small Box	Total Number of Markers
㉕ Max's Mart	2	3	1	4	
㉖ Toby's Shop	3	1	0	5	
㉗ Ranis Retail				0	1470
㉘ Tedd Depot			6		2069

㉙ Which store orders the most number of 🖊 ? _____

㉚ Which store orders the least number of 🖊 ? _____

㉛ Max's Mart sold 800 🖊 last month. How many big boxes of 🖊 did it sell in all? ____ big boxes

㉜ Toby's Shop sold 70 🖊 last week. How many medium boxes of 🖊 did it sell in all? ____ medium boxes

㉝ Ranis Retail sells 5 mega boxes of 🖊 a year. How many 🖊 does it sell in all? _____ 🖊

ISBN: 978-1-897164-12-9

Division

See how the children share their food. Write the numbers.

① Chad and Sue share 8 🍎 . How many 🍎 does each child get?

🍎 🍎 🍎 🍎 🍎 🍎 🍎 🍎

8 ÷ 2 = _____

Each child gets _____ 🍎 .

② 5 children share 15 🍬 . How many 🍬 does each child get?

🍬 🍬 🍬 🍬 🍬 🍬 🍬 🍬 🍬 🍬 🍬 🍬 🍬 🍬 🍬

15 ÷ 5 = _____   Each child gets _____ 🍬 .

③ 4 children share 12 🍪 . How many 🍪 does each child get?

🍪 🍪 🍪 🍪 🍪 🍪 🍪 🍪 🍪 🍪 🍪 🍪

12 ÷ 4 = _____   Each child gets _____ 🍪 .

④ 3 children share 18 🍭 . How many 🍭 does each child get?

🍭 🍭 🍭 🍭 🍭 🍭 🍭 🍭 🍭 🍭 🍭 🍭 🍭 🍭 🍭 🍭 🍭 🍭

18 ÷ 3 = _____   Each child gets _____ 🍭 .

⑤ 6 children share 12 🍓 . How many 🍓 does each child get?

🍓 🍓 🍓 🍓 🍓 🍓 🍓 🍓 🍓 🍓 🍓 🍓

12 ÷ 6 = _____   Each child gets _____ 🍓 .

    ISBN: 978-1-897164-12-9

Mrs Starkman wants to sew some buttons on the clothes. Help her draw the buttons and write the numbers.

⑥   Divide 25 ⊞ equally among 5 shirts.

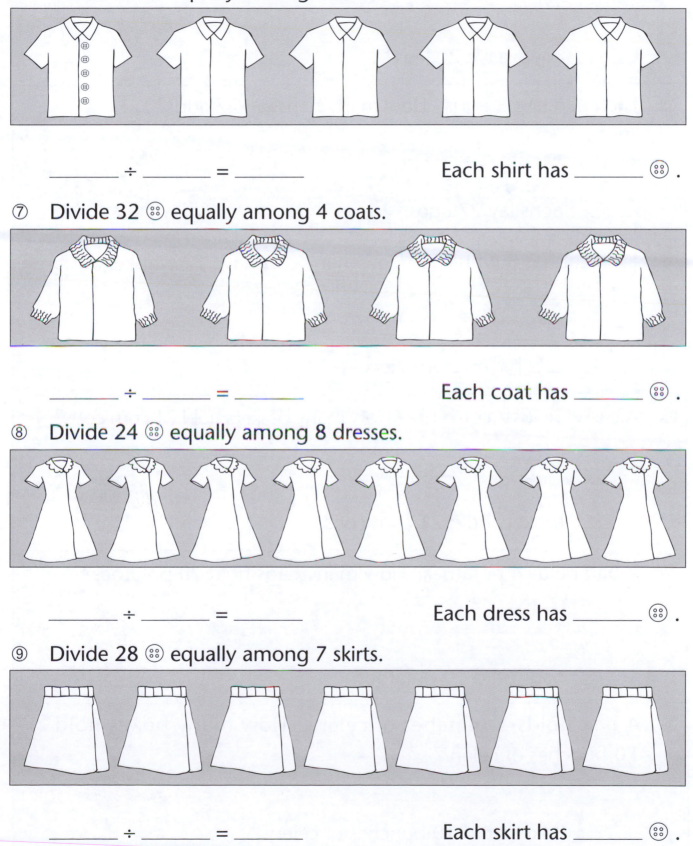

_____ ÷ _____ = _____   Each shirt has _____ ⊞ .

⑦   Divide 32 ⊞ equally among 4 coats.

_____ ÷ _____ = _____   Each coat has _____ ⊞ .

⑧   Divide 24 ⊞ equally among 8 dresses.

_____ ÷ _____ = _____   Each dress has _____ ⊞ .

⑨   Divide 28 ⊞ equally among 7 skirts.

_____ ÷ _____ = _____   Each skirt has _____ ⊞ .

Help Dale the farmer solve the problems.

⑩ A cow has 4 legs. How many cows have 20 legs?

_____ ÷ _____ = _____

_____ cows have 20 legs.

⑪ Each hen lays 3 eggs. How many hens lay 27 eggs?

_____ ÷ _____ = _____

_____ hens lay 27 eggs.

⑫ Each cat has 8 whiskers. How many cats have 72 whiskers?

_____ ÷ _____ = _____

_____ cats have 72 whiskers.

⑬ A basket holds 7 corn cobs. How many baskets hold 21 corn cobs?

_____ ÷ _____ = _____

_____ baskets hold 21 corn cobs.

⑭ A bag holds 4 potatoes. How many bags hold 20 potatoes?

_____ ÷ _____ = _____

_____ bags hold 20 potatoes.

⑮ A box holds 5 bunches of celery. How many boxes hold 10 bunches of celery?

_____ ÷ _____ = _____

_____ boxes hold 10 bunches of celery.

ISBN: 978-1-897164-12-9

5 girls go apple-picking. Help them solve the problems.

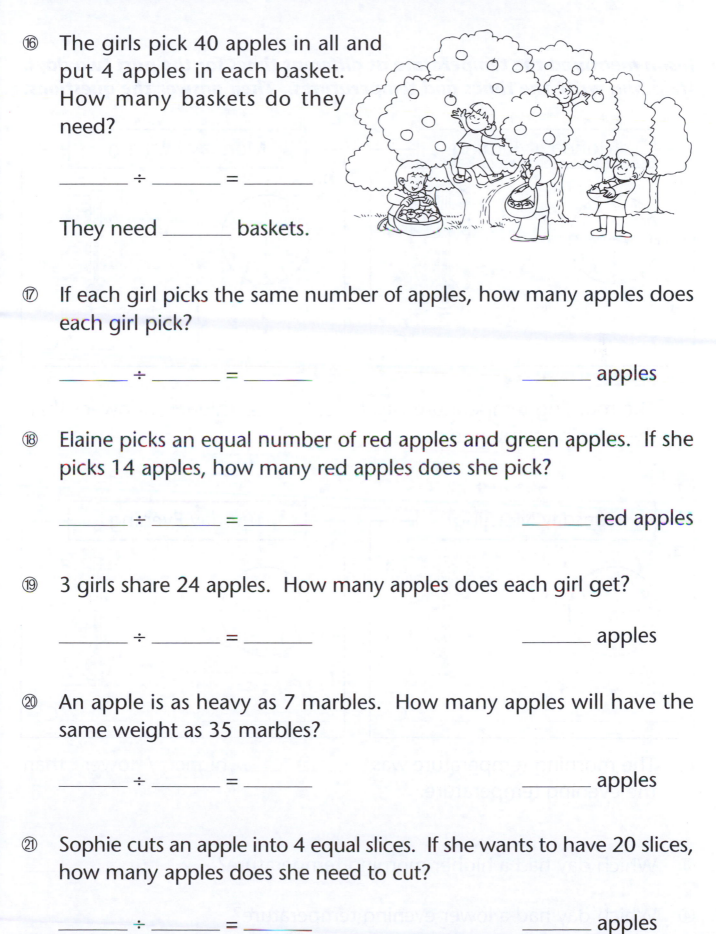

⑯ The girls pick 40 apples in all and put 4 apples in each basket. How many baskets do they need?

_____ ÷ _____ = _____

They need _____ baskets.

⑰ If each girl picks the same number of apples, how many apples does each girl pick?

_____ ÷ _____ = _____   _____ apples

⑱ Elaine picks an equal number of red apples and green apples. If she picks 14 apples, how many red apples does she pick?

_____ ÷ _____ = _____   _____ red apples

⑲ 3 girls share 24 apples. How many apples does each girl get?

_____ ÷ _____ = _____   _____ apples

⑳ An apple is as heavy as 7 marbles. How many apples will have the same weight as 35 marbles?

_____ ÷ _____ = _____   _____ apples

㉑ Sophie cuts an apple into 4 equal slices. If she wants to have 20 slices, how many apples does she need to cut?

_____ ÷ _____ = _____   _____ apples

ISBN: 978-1-897164-12-9

Jason measured the temperature at different times for the past two days.
Help him write the times and temperatures. Then answer the questions.

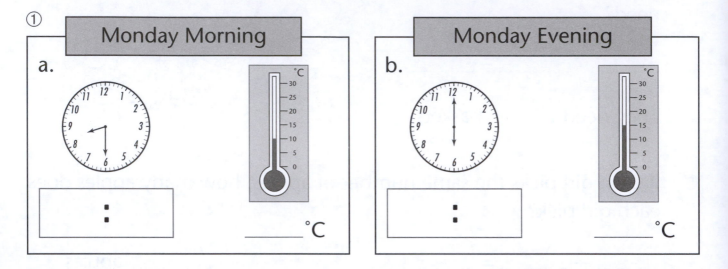

c. The morning temperature was _____ higher / lower than the evening temperature.

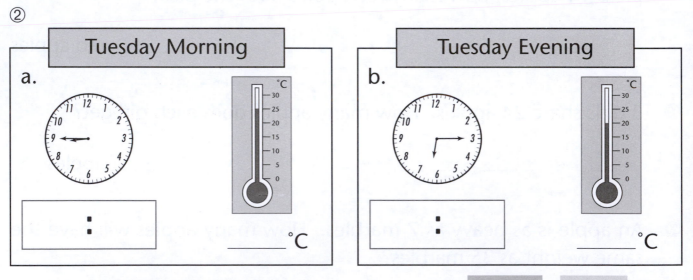

c. The morning temperature was _____ higher / lower than the evening temperature.

③ Which day had a higher morning temperature? _____

④ Which day had a lower evening temperature? _____

Mr Richards organized a track event at Riverview School. Look at the 6 best times for the 400-m race and answer the questions.

The 6 Best Times	
Adam	2 min 50 s
Bob	3 min 10 s
Carol	3 min 3 s
Daren	2 min 58 s
Eva	2 min 55 s
Frank	3 min 15 s

⑤ How long was the race? _____ metres

⑥ Who won the race? _____

⑦ Who came 2nd? _____

⑧ Who came 5th? _____

⑨ What was the time difference between the
best runner and the second best runner? _____ seconds

Read what Mr Richards says. Then answer the questions.

> Today is Wednesday, May 15. Yesterday, the children practised running from 9:30 a.m. to 11:00 a.m. On the coming Saturday, we will have a swimming gala. It will start at 9:15 a.m. and last 4 hours.

⑩ How long did the children practise running? _____ minutes

⑪ What date will they have a swimming gala? _____

⑫ When will the swimming gala end? _____

UNIT 10 More about Multiplication and Division

Mrs Kerr is dividing her plants into window boxes. Write the numbers.

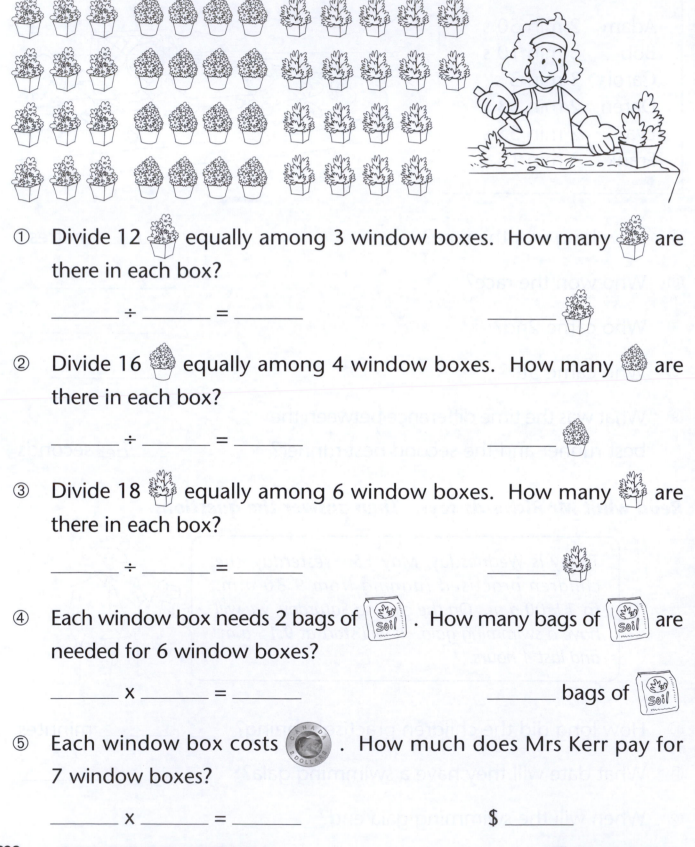

① Divide 12 🌼 equally among 3 window boxes. How many 🌼 are there in each box?

_____ ÷ _____ = _____   _____

② Divide 16 🌸 equally among 4 window boxes. How many 🌸 are there in each box?

_____ ÷ _____ = _____   _____

③ Divide 18 🌿 equally among 6 window boxes. How many 🌿 are there in each box?

_____ ÷ _____ = _____   _____

④ Each window box needs 2 bags of 🟫 . How many bags of 🟫 are needed for 6 window boxes?

_____ x _____ = _____   _____ bags of 🟫

⑤ Each window box costs 🪙 . How much does Mrs Kerr pay for 7 window boxes?

_____ x _____ = _____ $ _____

Look at Peter's baseball cards. Help him solve the problems.

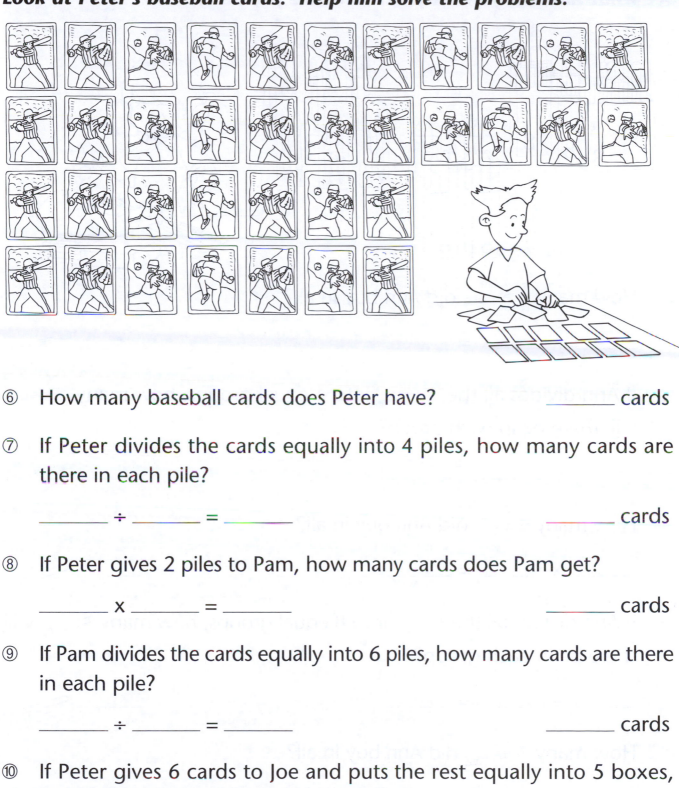

⑥ How many baseball cards does Peter have?   _____ cards

⑦ If Peter divides the cards equally into 4 piles, how many cards are there in each pile?

   _____ ÷ _____ = _____   _____ cards

⑧ If Peter gives 2 piles to Pam, how many cards does Pam get?

   _____ x _____ = _____   _____ cards

⑨ If Pam divides the cards equally into 6 piles, how many cards are there in each pile?

   _____ ÷ _____ = _____   _____ cards

⑩ If Peter gives 6 cards to Joe and puts the rest equally into 5 boxes, how many cards are there in each box?

   _____ ÷ _____ = _____   _____ cards

⑪ How many cards are there in 3 boxes?

   _____ x _____ = _____   _____ cards

ISBN: 978-1-897164-12-9

See what Ann bought. Help her solve the problems.

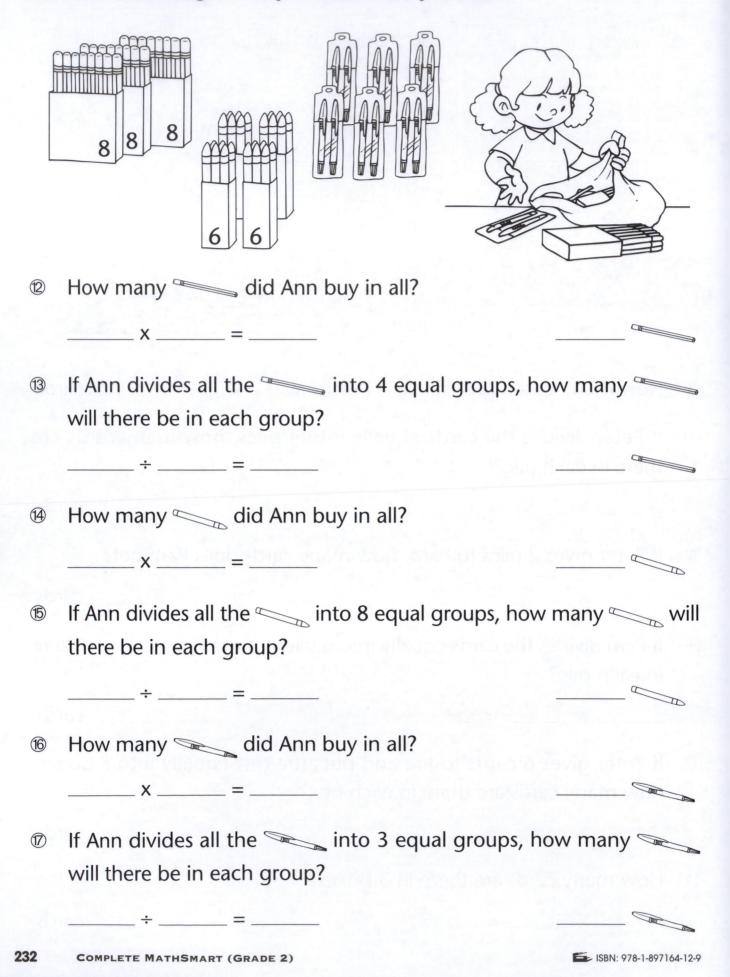

⑫ How many ✏ did Ann buy in all?

_____ x _____ = _____   _____ ✏

⑬ If Ann divides all the ✏ into 4 equal groups, how many ✏ will there be in each group?

_____ ÷ _____ = _____   _____ ✏

⑭ How many 🖍 did Ann buy in all?

_____ x _____ = _____   _____ 🖍

⑮ If Ann divides all the 🖍 into 8 equal groups, how many 🖍 will there be in each group?

_____ ÷ _____ = _____   _____ 🖍

⑯ How many 🖊 did Ann buy in all?

_____ x _____ = _____   _____ 🖊

⑰ If Ann divides all the 🖊 into 3 equal groups, how many 🖊 will there be in each group?

_____ ÷ _____ = _____   _____ 🖊

   ISBN: 978-1-897164-12-9

Darren and his friends plant some saplings every summer. See how many saplings Darren plants and solve the problems.

⑱ Darren plants 7 saplings every hour. How many trees can he plant in 6 hours?

_____ x _____ = _____   _____ saplings

⑲ How long does it take him to plant 28 saplings?

_____ ÷ _____ = _____   _____ hours

⑳ He works 8 hours a day. How many saplings can he plant in one day?

_____ x _____ = _____   _____ saplings

㉑ A row has 10 saplings. How many saplings are there in 3 rows?

_____ x _____ = _____   _____ saplings

㉒ Katie has 16 stakes. She uses 2 for each sapling. How many saplings does she plant?

_____ ÷ _____ = _____   _____ saplings

㉓ Kim can plant 32 saplings in 4 hours. How many saplings can she plant in 1 hour?

_____ ÷ _____ = _____   _____ saplings

Look at the graph and fill in the blanks.

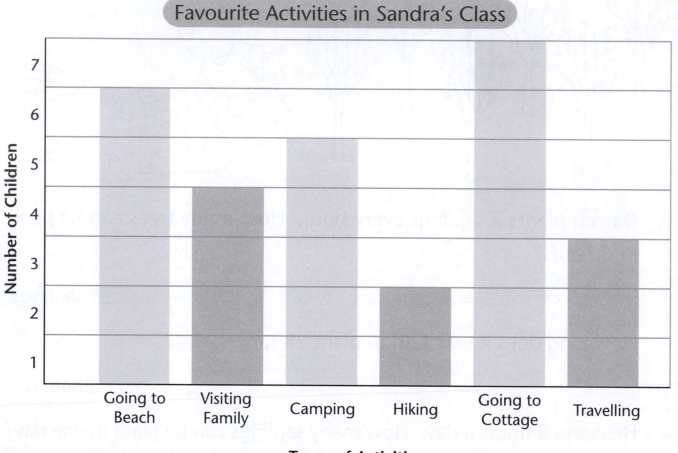

Favourite Activities in Sandra's Class

Number of Children / Types of Activities

① _____ is the most popular activity.

② _____ is the second most popular activity.

③ _____ is the least popular activity.

④ _____ is only liked by 4 children.

⑤ _____ children like going to the beach or cottages.

⑥ _____ more children like camping than hiking.

⑦ _____ types of activities are included in the graph.

⑧ _____ children are in Sandra's class.

Look at the graph and answer the questions.

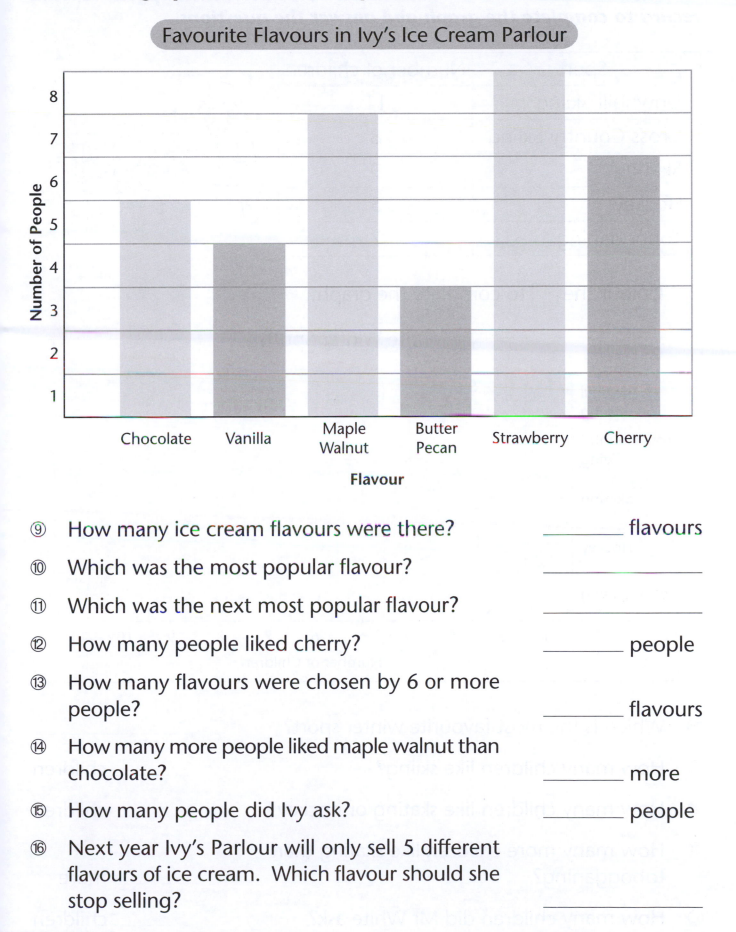

⑨ How many ice cream flavours were there? _____ flavours

⑩ Which was the most popular flavour? _____

⑪ Which was the next most popular flavour? _____

⑫ How many people liked cherry? _____ people

⑬ How many flavours were chosen by 6 or more people? _____ flavours

⑭ How many more people liked maple walnut than chocolate? _____ more

⑮ How many people did Ivy ask? _____ people

⑯ Next year Ivy's Parlour will only sell 5 different flavours of ice cream. Which flavour should she stop selling? _____

Mr White asks the children about their favourite winter sports. Use his record to complete the graph and answer the questions.

Sport	Number of children
Downhill Skiing	11
Cross Country Skiing	8
Skating	9
Hockey	5
Tobogganing	7

⑰ Colour the ☐ to complete the graph.

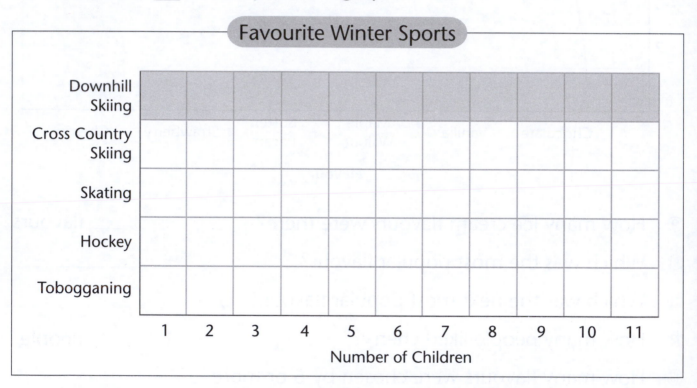

⑱ Which is the most favourite winter sport? _____

⑲ How many children like skiing? _____ children

⑳ How many children like skating or hockey? _____ children

㉑ How many more children like skating than tobogganing? _____ more

㉒ How many children did Mr White ask? _____ children

ISBN: 978-1-897164-12-9

Jamie asks his classmates about the number of children in their families. Use his record to complete the graph and answer the questions.

Number of children in each family	1	2	3	4	5 or more
Number of families	4	6	3	1	2

㉓ Colour the ☐ to complete the graph.

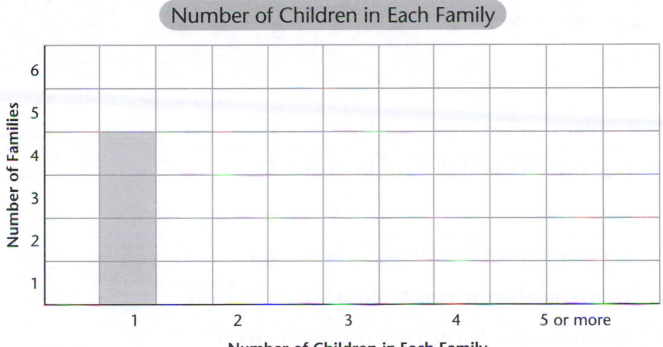

Number of Children in Each Family

㉔ What is the most usual number of children in a family? _____

㉕ How many families have 3 children? _____ families

㉖ How many families have 5 or more children? _____ families

㉗ How many children in the class have no brothers or sisters? _____ children

㉘ How many children did Jamie ask? _____ children

㉙ If Jamie has 3 brothers and no sisters, how many children are there in his family? _____ children

Probability

The 8 cards below are put face down on the table. See what they say and answer the questions.

> *Every time one of us picks a card and puts it back. Then we will shuffle the 8 cards and put them face down for the next player.*

3♦ 4♥ 2♥ 4♠ 3♣ 2♦ 2♠ 6♥

① Is a player more likely to pick a 2 or a 3? _____

② Is a player more likely to pick a 4 or a 6? _____

③ Is a player more likely to pick a ♥ or a ♦ ? _____

④ Is a player more likely to pick a ♠ or a ♣ ? _____

⑤ Which numbers is a player equally likely to pick? _____

⑥ Which number is a player most likely to pick? _____

⑦ Which number is a player unlikely to pick? _____

⑧ Is there any chance for a player to pick a 7 from the 8 cards above? _____

⑨ If the number on the card that a player guesses is the same as the one he or she picks, he or she wins the game. What number should Pam guess so as to have more chance to win? _____

⑩ If the pattern of the card that a player guesses is the same as the one he or she picks, he or she wins the game. What pattern should Pam guess so as to have more chance to win? _____

ISBN: 978-1-897164-12-9

Stanley puts all his lollipops into a bag and picks one out. Help him answer the questions.

Lemon   Lemon   Vanilla   Chocolate   Vanilla

Chocolate   Lemon   Vanilla   Lemon   Orange

⑪ How many lollipops does Stanley have? _____ lollipops

⑫ How many lollipops are lemon flavoured? _____ lollipops

⑬ How many lollipops are chocolate flavoured? _____ lollipops

⑭ How many lollipops are vanilla flavoured? _____ lollipops

⑮ How many lollipops are orange flavoured? _____ lollipops

⑯ Is there more chance to pick a vanilla lollipop or an orange lollipop? _____ lollipop

⑰ Is there more chance to pick a lemon lollipop or a chocolate lollipop? _____ lollipop

⑱ What would be the most likely flavour to be picked from the bag? _____ flavoured

⑲ Is it possible to pick a strawberry lollipop from the bag? _____

⑳ If Stanley puts 2 more vanilla lollipops into the bag, what would be the most likely flavour to be picked from that bag? _____ flavoured

ISBN: 978-1-897164-12-9

Gloria gets some information from the Internet. Help her put the information on the number line and answer the questions.

River	Length (km)
Amazon	7020
Mississippi	6770
Nile	7500
St. Lawrence	3500
Mackenzie	1240

① Write the names and lengths of the rivers in the boxes.

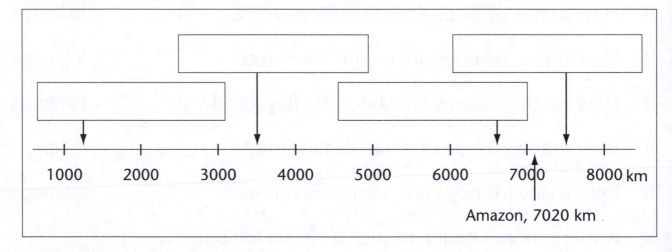

Amazon, 7020 km

② Which river is the longest? _____

③ Which river is the shortest? _____

④ Is the St. Lawrence longer than the Mississippi? _____

⑤ How many rivers are longer than 5000 km? _____ rivers

⑥ Which river is shorter than the St. Lawrence? _____

⑦ Which river is shorter than the Nile, but longer than the Mississippi? _____

⑧ The Yangtze is 5580 km long. Is the Yangtze longer than the Mackenzie? _____

ISBN: 978-1-897164-12-9

Carol makes a cup of coffee and measures its temperature at different times. Write the temperatures.

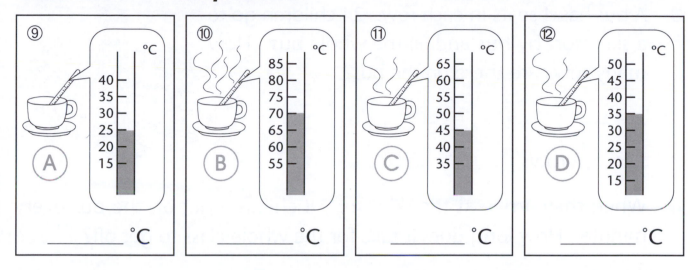

⑨ A _____ °C

⑩ B _____ °C

⑪ C _____ °C

⑫ D _____ °C

⑬ Put the pictures in order. Write the letters.

_____ , _____ , _____ , _____

Carol pours some drinks into the cups and lets Charles pick one cup. Help Charles answer the questions.

⑭ Is Charles more likely to pick pop or juice? _____

⑮ What kind of drink is Charles likely to pick? _____

⑯ What kind of drink is Charles unlikely to pick? _____

⑰ Is there any chance for Charles to pick a cup of coffee? _____

⑱ If Carol takes away 1 cup of pop, what kind of drink is Charles likely to pick? _____

⑲ If Carol takes away 1 cup of iced tea, what kind of drink is Charles unlikely to pick? _____

Mrs Ford's class go skiing. Help them solve the problems.

⑳ A bus has 4 seats in each row. 24 children go to a ski resort by bus and fill the whole bus. How many rows are there on the bus?

_____ ÷ _____ = _____

_____ rows

㉑ When they arrive at the ski resort, 8 children get off the bus every minute. How long does it take for the whole class to get off?

_____ ÷ _____ = _____   _____ minutes

㉒ 21 children ski downhill in groups of 3. How many groups are there ?

_____ ÷ _____ = _____   _____ groups

㉓ 15 children eat lunch at tables for 5 people. How many tables do they need?

_____ ÷ _____ = _____   _____ tables

㉔ Each child eats 2 chicken wings. How many chicken wings do 8 children eat?

_____ x _____ = _____   _____ chicken wings

㉕ Each child drinks 3 boxes of juice. How many boxes of juice do 9 children drink?

_____ x _____ = _____   _____ boxes of juice

㉖ Each toboggan carries 4 children. 20 children play tobogganing at the same time. How many toboggans do they need?

_____ ÷ _____ = _____   _____ toboggans

Mr Bobker's class visit the Museum. Help Mr Bobker solve the problems.

㉗ There are 6 vans going to the Museum. 5 students go in each van. How many students are there in all?

_____ x _____ = _____   _____ students

㉘ The students are divided into 3 equal groups. How many students are there in each group?

_____ ÷ _____ = _____   _____ students

㉙ Each student gets 2 pencils from the Museum. How many pencils does a group of students get?

_____ x _____ = _____   _____ pencils

㉚ There are 8 sections on each floor. How many sections are there on 3 floors?

_____ x _____ = _____   _____ sections

㉛ Each souvenir costs 9¢. Mr Bobker buys 7 souvenirs. How much does he need to pay?

_____ x _____ = _____   _____ ¢

㉜ One of the shows at the Museum starts at 1:05 p.m. and ends at 1:40 p.m. How long does the show last?   _____ minutes

㉝ The show about electricity starts at 12:35 p.m. and last 45 minutes. When does it end?   _____

㉞ The students leave the Museum at 2:45 p.m. and return to school at 3:30 p.m. How long is the ride?   _____ minutes

Jack counted the number of cars in different colours in the parking lot. Read what he says and complete the graph. Then complete the table and fill in the blanks.

Green is the least popular colour and beige is the most popular colour. Black is the second most popular colour. Red and white are equally popular.

Number of Cars in Different Colours

㉟

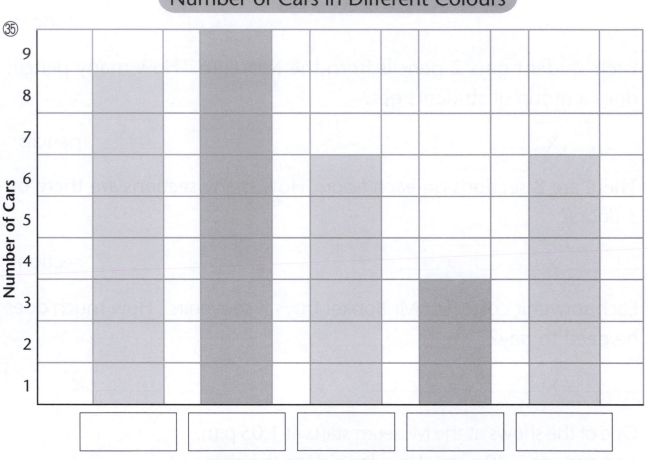

Number of Cars

Colour

㊱

Colour	Black	Beige	Red	Green	White
Number of Cars					

㊲ There were _____ more black cars than red cars in the parking lot.

㊳ There were _____ beige or green cars in the parking lot.

㊴ Jack counted _____ cars in all.

ISBN: 978-1-897164-12-9

Parents' Guide

1. 3-digit Numbers

↦ Children should understand the concept of place value and the use of zero as a place holder; otherwise, they may have difficulty in writing or reading a number with 0.

Examples

607 $\xrightarrow{\text{read}}$ sixty-seven ✗

six hundred and seven ✔

One hundred twenty-eight $\xrightarrow{\text{write}}$ 100208 ✗

128 ✔

2. Addition and Subtraction

↦ To do addition,

1st   align the numbers on the right-hand side.
2nd   add the numbers from right to left (starting with the ones place).
3rd   carry groups of 10 from one column to the next column on the left.

Example

Align the numbers.	Add the ones and carry 1 ten to the tens column.	Add the tens.
67 + 24	1 67 + 24 1	1 67 + 24 91

67 + 24 = 91

↦ To do subtraction,

1st   align the numbers on the right-hand side.
2nd   subtract the numbers from right to left (starting with the ones place).
3rd   if the number is too small to subtract, borrow 10 from the column on the left.

Example

Align the numbers.	Borrow 1 ten from the tens column; subtract the ones.	Subtract the tens.
82 – 19	7 8̶2̶ 12 – 19 3	82 – 19 63

82 – 19 = 63

3. Multiplication

↦ Parents should pay attention to the signs their children use, as quite a few children mix up the signs of multiplication and addition. For example, they will write 3 x 3 = 9 as 3 + 3 = 9.

ISBN: 978-1-897164-12-9

- Children need to understand that multiplication is a quick way to do addition. Initially, children learn to count in twos, fives and tens, and then proceed to count in threes, fours, etc. Parents can let their children use a number line or concrete materials to count by 2's, 5's ... so as to consolidate their concept of multiplication.

  <u>Examples</u> $2 + 2 + 2 + 2 = 8$ $4 \times 2 = 8$

- Multiplying any number by 1, the number stays the same.

  <u>Examples</u> $1 \times 5 = 5$ $1 \times 3 = 3$

- Multiplying any number by 0, the answer is always 0.

  <u>Examples</u> $4 \times 0 = 0$ $0 \times 7 = 0$

4. Division

- Children should understand that division is the opposite of multiplication.

  <u>Example</u> $5 \times 2 = 10$, $10 \div 2 = 5$ and $10 \div 5 = 2$

- Children can use the following steps to do division:

1st Divide	2nd Multiply	3rd Subtract	4th Bring down

  <u>Example</u>

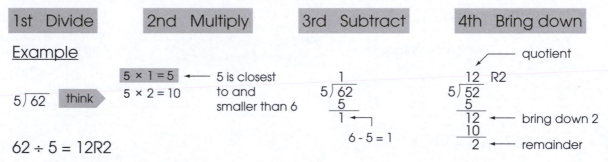

  $62 \div 5 = 12R2$

5. Fractions and Decimals

- Children learn the basic concept of writing a fraction or a decimal. At the beginning, fractions should be limited to halves, thirds, fourths and tenths, and decimal numbers should be limited to one-decimal place only. Parents should encourage their children to use concrete materials and drawings to show the relationship between fractions and decimals.

  <u>Example</u>

 $\frac{3}{10}$ or 0.3 is shaded.

6. Measurement

- Children learn to use centimetres and metres in measuring length and distance, as well as the relationship between centimetres and metres (1 metre = 100 centimetres). Furthermore, they learn how to measure and record the perimeter and area of 2-dimensional shapes. At this stage, it is not necessary to introduce the units of perimeter and area to them.

7. Time and Temperature

➻ Children should understand the relationship between days and weeks, months and years, minutes and hours, and hours and days. Quite a few children, however, have difficulty finding intervals of time. Parents should provide more guidance and daily practice for them.

Examples

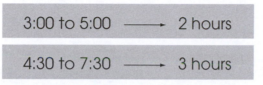

<table>
<tr><td>3:00 to 5:00 ⟶ 2 hours</td></tr>
<tr><td>4:30 to 7:30 ⟶ 3 hours</td></tr>
</table>

➻ Children learn that the thermometer is used to measure temperature. They can use the thermometer to determine whether the temperature is rising or falling and recognize that degree Celsius (°C) is the unit for recording temperature. At this stage, parents should not discuss with children the use of negative numbers to indicate temperatures below 0 °C.

8. Money

➻ Children learn to name and state the value of all coins and show their understanding of the value of each coin. They also need to know how to put coins in equivalent sets up to $1 in value. Parents should remind children that they can use subtraction to work out change.

9. Shapes

➻ At this stage, children learn some 3-dimensional figures such as prism and pyramid. Parents should encourage them to use a variety of materials such as straws and sticks to construct the skeleton of a prism or a pyramid so as to consolidate their concept of 3-dimensional figures. The 2-dimensional figures that the children may have learnt are pentagon, hexagon and octagon. They should be able to describe the attributes of regular polygons using terms such as side/sides and vertex/vertices.

Example

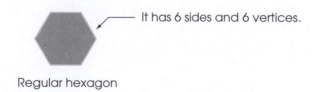

It has 6 sides and 6 vertices.

Regular hexagon

10. Transformations

- Children learn how to demonstrate transformations, such as flips, slides and turns by using concrete materials such as cards and dice.

- Children learn how to find a line of symmetry of a 2-dimensional figure by using paper folding or reflection in a mirror. They should understand that a symmetrical figure can have more than 1 line of symmetry.

Examples

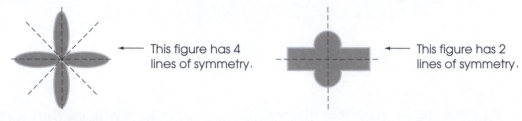

This figure has 4 lines of symmetry.

This figure has 2 lines of symmetry.

11. Pictographs and Block Graphs

- Children need to know how to construct and label simple pictographs and block graphs by using one-to-one correspondence. Parents should encourage them to interpret the graphs and describe the information given by the graphs.

Examples

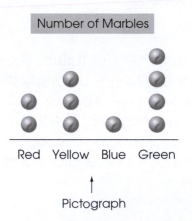

Number of Marbles

Red   Yellow   Blue   Green

↑

Pictograph

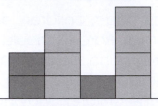

Number of Marbles

Red Yellow Blue Green

↑

Block Graph

1 2-digit Numbers

1. 40 ; 41 ; 43 ; 44   2. 28 ; 26 ; 25 ; 23
3. 58 ; 56 ; 55 ; 52   4. 54 ; 42 ; 37 ; 23
5. 64 ; 50 ; 25 ; 11   6. 90 ; 81 ; 47 ; 30
7.

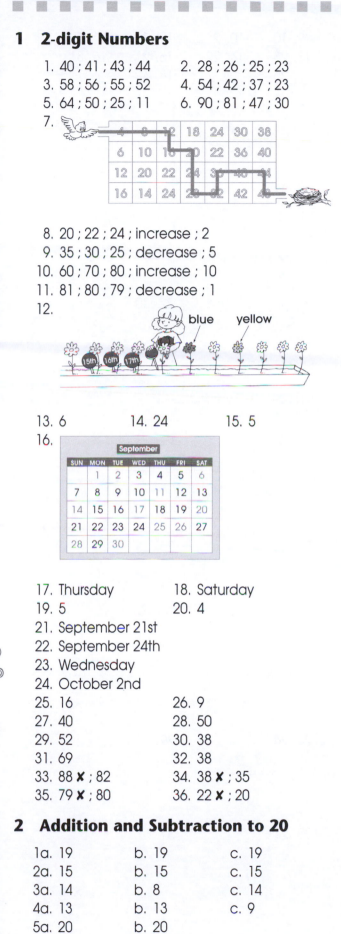

8. 20 ; 22 ; 24 ; increase ; 2
9. 35 ; 30 ; 25 ; decrease ; 5
10. 60 ; 70 ; 80 ; increase ; 10
11. 81 ; 80 ; 79 ; decrease ; 1
12.

13. 6   14. 24   15. 5
16.

17. Thursday   18. Saturday
19. 5   20. 4
21. September 21st
22. September 24th
23. Wednesday
24. October 2nd
25. 16   26. 9
27. 40   28. 50
29. 52   30. 38
31. 69   32. 38
33. 88 ✘ ; 82   34. 38 ✘ ; 35
35. 79 ✘ ; 80   36. 22 ✘ ; 20

2 Addition and Subtraction to 20

1a. 19   b. 19   c. 19
2a. 15   b. 15   c. 15
3a. 14   b. 8   c. 14
4a. 13   b. 13   c. 9
5a. 20   b. 20

6a. 16   b. 7
7a. 17   b. 17
8a. 19   b. 11
9. 12   10. 8
11. 5   12. 9
13. 12 + 8 = 20 ; 20   14. 12 – 8 = 4 ; 4
15. 5 + 9 = 14 ; 14   16. 9 – 5 = 4 ; 4
17. 8 + 9 = 17 ; 17

3 Shapes

1. Hexagon   2. Triangle
3. Rectangle   4. Pentagon

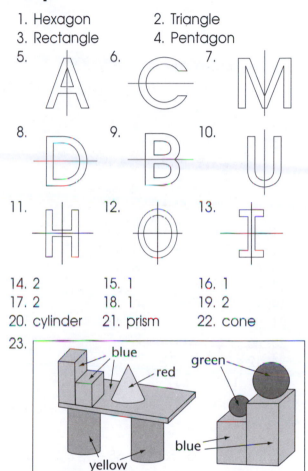

14. 2   15. 1   16. 1
17. 2   18. 1   19. 2
20. cylinder   21. prism   22. cone
23.

4 Addition to 100

1. 35 ; 35
2. 15 ; 32 ; 47   3. 21 ; 30 ; 51

```
    1 5              2 1
  + 3 2            + 3 0
    4 7              5 1
```

4. 13 ; 16 ; 29   5. 22 ; 24 ; 46

```
    1 3              2 2
  + 1 6            + 2 4
    2 9              4 6
```

ISBN: 978-1-897164-12-9

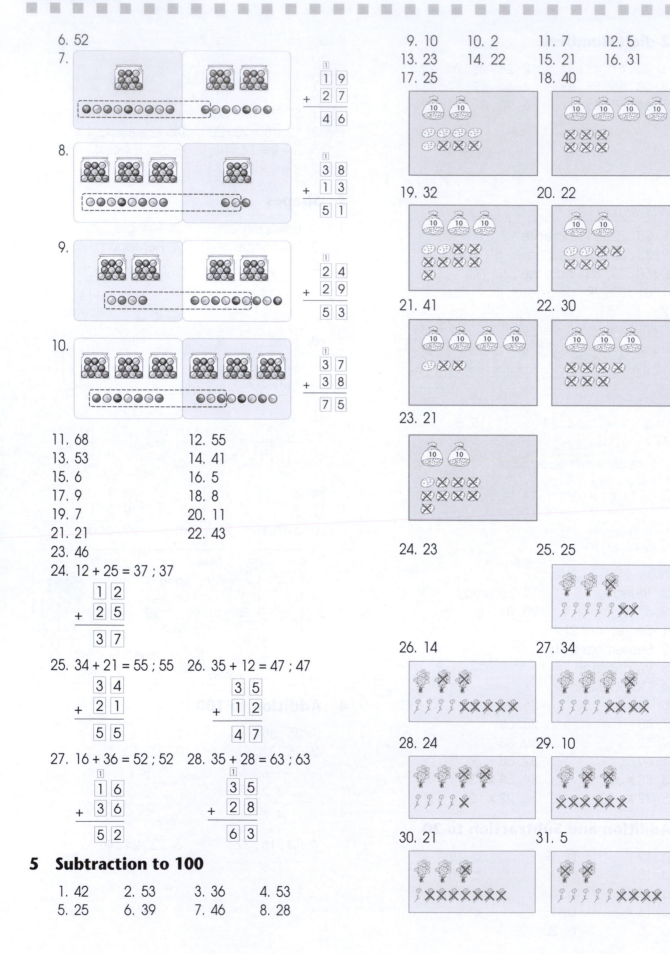

6. 52

7.

$$\begin{array}{r} {\scriptstyle 1} \\ 1\ 9 \\ +\ 2\ 7 \\ \hline 4\ 6 \end{array}$$

8.

$$\begin{array}{r} {\scriptstyle 1} \\ 3\ 8 \\ +\ 1\ 3 \\ \hline 5\ 1 \end{array}$$

9.

$$\begin{array}{r} {\scriptstyle 1} \\ 2\ 4 \\ +\ 2\ 9 \\ \hline 5\ 3 \end{array}$$

10.

$$\begin{array}{r} {\scriptstyle 1} \\ 3\ 7 \\ +\ 3\ 8 \\ \hline 7\ 5 \end{array}$$

11. 68	12. 55
13. 53	14. 41
15. 6	16. 5
17. 9	18. 8
19. 7	20. 11
21. 21	22. 43

23. 46

24. $12 + 25 = 37$; 37

$$\begin{array}{r} 1\ 2 \\ +\ 2\ 5 \\ \hline 3\ 7 \end{array}$$

25. $34 + 21 = 55$; 55

$$\begin{array}{r} 3\ 4 \\ +\ 2\ 1 \\ \hline 5\ 5 \end{array}$$

26. $35 + 12 = 47$; 47

$$\begin{array}{r} 3\ 5 \\ +\ 1\ 2 \\ \hline 4\ 7 \end{array}$$

27. $16 + 36 = 52$; 52

$$\begin{array}{r} {\scriptstyle 1} \\ 1\ 6 \\ +\ 3\ 6 \\ \hline 5\ 2 \end{array}$$

28. $35 + 28 = 63$; 63

$$\begin{array}{r} {\scriptstyle 1} \\ 3\ 5 \\ +\ 2\ 8 \\ \hline 6\ 3 \end{array}$$

5 Subtraction to 100

1. 42	2. 53	3. 36	4. 53
5. 25	6. 39	7. 46	8. 28

9. 10	10. 2	11. 7	12. 5
13. 23	14. 22	15. 21	16. 31
17. 25		18. 40	

19. 32   20. 22

21. 41   22. 30

23. 21

24. 23   25. 25

26. 14   27. 34

28. 24   29. 10

30. 21   31. 5

ISBN: 978-1-897164-12-9

32. 32 − 2 = 30 ; 30

```
  3 2
−   2
  3 0
```

33. 45 − 4 = 41 ; 41

```
  4 5
−   4
  4 1
```

34. 56 − 5 = 51 ; 51

```
  5 6
−   5
  5 1
```

35. 38 − 6 = 32 ; 32

```
  3 8
−   6
  3 2
```

36. 68 − 8 = 60 ; 60

```
  6 8
−   8
  6 0
```

Midway Review

1.
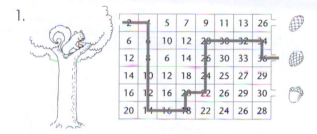

2. 96
3. 8
4. 7
5. 8
6. 66
7. 70
8. 50
9. 14 ; 54
10. 37
11. 35 + 12 = 47
12. 28 + 16 = 44
13. 37 + 9 = 46
14. 57 − 5 = 52
15. 49 − 9 = 40
16. 36 − 12 = 24
17. 58 − 36 = 22
18. 18 + 13 = 31 ; 31
19. 7 + 26 = 33 ; 33
20. 18 + 7 = 25 ; 25
21. 18 − 7 = 11 ; 11
22. 13 + 26 = 39 ; 39
23. 26 − 13 = 13 ; 13
24. 26 − 6 = 20 ; 20
25. 13 + 6 = 19 ; 19
26. 18 − 15 = 3 ; 3
27. 7 + 15 = 22 ; 22
28. cube
29. cylinder
30. cone
31.
32.
33.
34.
35.
36.

6   More about Addition and Subtraction

1. 38
2. 48
3. 57
4. 62
5. 57
6. 41
7. 38
8. 52
9. 58
10. 49
11. 4
12. 8
13. 1
14. 3
15. 4
16. 6
17. 1
18. 10
19. 12
20. 15
21. 71
22. 60
23. 81
24. 72
25. 65
26. 78
27. 58
28. 79
29. 68
30. 59
31. 2
32. 3
33. 5
34. 9
35. 3
36. 7
37. 8
38. 6
39. 12
40. 10
41. 12
42. 13
43. 11 ; 18 ; 18 ; 7
44. 21 − 16 = 5 ; 21 − 5 = 16
45. 30 − 24 = 6 ; 30 − 6 = 24
46. 25 + 10 = 35 or 10 + 25 = 35 ;
    35 − 25 = 10
47. 38 − 35 = 3 or 38 − 3 = 35
48. 29 + 5 = 34 or 5 + 29 = 34 ;
    34 − 29 = 5
49. 81 + 5 = 86 or 5 + 81 = 86 ;
    86 − 81 = 5
50. 83 − 77 = 6 ; 83 − 6 = 77
51. 77 − 69 = 8 ; 77 − 8 = 69
52. 31 + 9 = 40 or 9 + 31 = 40 ;
    40 − 31 = 9
53. 57
54. 34
55. 57 + 34 = 91 ; 91
56. 57 − 34 = 23 ; 23
57. 60 − 57 = 3 ; 3
58. 60 − 34 = 26 ; 26
59. 57 − 15 = 42 ; 42
60. 34 + 15 = 49 ; 49

ISBN: 978-1-897164-12-9

7 Money

1a. 8   b. 8
2a. 6   b. 30
3a. 4   b. 40
4. B   5. C   6. A
7 – 9. (Suggested answers)

7a. 1 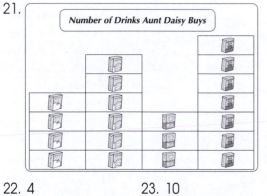 ; 1

b. 1 ; 5

8a. 2 ; 3

b. 1 ; 2 ; 3

9a. 2 ; 1 ; 3

b. 1 ; 3 ; 3

10. 24   11. 42
12. 34   13. 19
14.   15.
16. 10   17. 9
18. 6   19. 66
20. 3   21. 8
22. 59   23. 7
24. 63   25. 1
26. 4   27. 31
28. 36   29. No

8 Measurement

1. ten o'clock   2. half-past four
3. twelve o'clock   4. half-past eight
5. Alan   6. Tim
7. Rita ; Sam ; Tim   8. Tim
9. 4   10. 2
11. 5   12. 3
13. shorter   14. longer
15. B   16. C

9 Probability

1a. A   b. C
2a. C   b. B
3a. B   b. A
4. B   5. B
6. C   7. A
8. A   9. probable
10. impossible

10 Pictographs

1. 7   2. 3
3. 5   4. 4
5. 2   6. 12
7. No   8. 15
9.   10. 3

11. 6   12. 5
13. 7   14. 9
15. 12   16. 3
17. 8   18. 13
19. 5   20. 21
21.

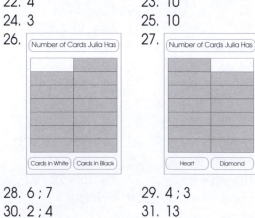

22. 4   23. 10
24. 3   25. 10
26.   27.
28. 6 ; 7   29. 4 ; 3
30. 2 ; 4   31. 13

Final Review

1. 19   2. 12
3. 16   4. longer
5. shorter   6. shortest
7. 3   8. 1
9. 2   10. heaviest

ISBN: 978-1-897164-12-9

11. 78   12. 39
13. 56   14. 95
15. 22   16. 11

17.   18.

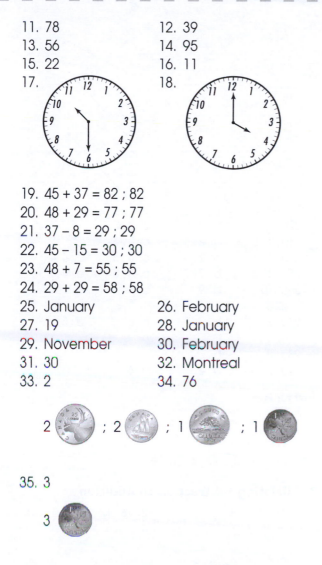

19. 45 + 37 = 82 ; 82
20. 48 + 29 = 77 ; 77
21. 37 − 8 = 29 ; 29
22. 45 − 15 = 30 ; 30
23. 48 + 7 = 55 ; 55
24. 29 + 29 = 58 ; 58
25. January   26. February
27. 19   28. January
29. November   30. February
31. 30   32. Montreal
33. 2   34. 76

2   ; 2   ; 1   ; 1

35. 3

3

36. C   37. A   38. A

ISBN: 978-1-897164-12-9

1 Addition and Subtraction Facts to 20

2. 14	3. 8	4. 17	5. 18
6. 12			
7. 14	8. 5	9. 4	10. 14
11. 18	12. 11	13. 13	14. 13
15. 15	16. 13		
17. 7	18. 5	19. 12	20. 3
21. 6	22. 1	23. 2	24. 0
25. 4	26. 2		
27. +	28. –	29. +	30. –
31. –	32. +	33. –	34. –
35. –	36. +	37. +	38. –

39.

12 – 6   18 – 10   6 + 2

40.

6 + 7   16 – 3   17 – 5

41.

12 + 5   20 – 4   9 + 8

42.

6 + 5   15 – 3   17 – 5

43.

19 – 8   3 + 7   16 – 6

44a. 13	b. 14	c. 15	d. 16
45a. 9	b. 10	c. 11	d. 12
46. 12 + 6 ; 18 ; 18		47. 16 – 12 ; 4 ; 4	
48. 20 – 12 ; 8 ; 8		49. 10 + 5 ; 15 ; 15	

Just for Fun

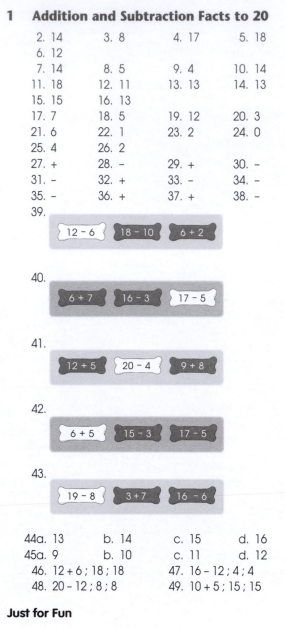

2 More about Addition Facts

1b. 5	c. 5		
2a. 8	b. 8	c. 8	
3a. 10	b. 10	c. 10	
4a. 5	b. 5	c. 5	
5a. 8	b. 8	c. 8	
6. 3	7. 7	8. 4	9. 8
10. 7	11. 6	12. 6	13. 13
14. 6	15. 17		

16. 10 + 8 = 8 + 10 → 17
17. 12 + 5 = 5 + 12 → 14
18. 4 + 15 = 15 + 4 → 18
19. 5 + 9 = 9 + 5 → 16
20. 14 + 6 = 6 + 14 → 19
21. 3 + 13 = 13 + 3 → 20

22a. 1 , 6	b. 2 , 5	c. 3 ,4	
23a. 1 , 5	b. 2 , 4	c. 3 , 3	
24a. 1 , 7	b. 2 , 6	c. 3 , 5	d. 4 ,4
25a. 1 , 8	b. 2 , 7	c. 3 , 6	d. 4 ,5
26a. 10	b. 9	c. 8	d. 7
e. 6			
27a. 8	b. 7	c. 6	d. 5
e. 4			
28a. 8	b. 8		
29a. 2 ; 6	b. 2	c. 6	

Just for Fun

2 ③ ⑧ 7 ⑥ ⑤ 4
④ ⑦ 5 ⑨ ② 3 6
6 9 ⑩ ⑪ 4 ⑩ ⑪

3 Relating Subtraction to Addition

1. 12 ; 4 ; 8	2. 18 ; 12
3. 15 ; 6	4. 17 ; 8
5. 11 ; 6	

6. 6 ; 14 ; 8 ; 14 ; 6 ; 6
7. 5 , 6 ; 11 ; 6 , 5 ; 11 ; 11 , 6 ; 5 ; 11 , 5 ; 6
8. 4 , 9 ; 13 ; 9 , 4 ; 13 ; 13 , 4 ; 9 ; 13 , 9 ; 4
9. 12 , 7 ; 19 ; 7 , 12 ; 19 ; 19 , 7 ; 12 ; 19 , 12 ; 7
10. 7 , 9 ; 16 ; 9 , 7 ; 16 ; 16 , 7 ; 9 ; 16 , 9 ; 7
11. 11 , 6 ; 17 ; 6 , 11 ; 17 ; 17 , 11 ; 6 ; 17 , 6 ; 11

12. 5 ; 5	13. 7 ; 7	14. 9	15. 10
16. 7	17. 16	18. 11	19. 8
20. 7 ; 7	21. 3 ; 3		
22. 9 ; 9	23. 8 ; 8	24. 6 ; 6	25. 4 ; 4
26. 8 ; 8	27. 7 ; 7	28. 5 ; 5	29. 9 ; 9
30. 6 ; 6	31. 6 ; 6		

Just for Fun

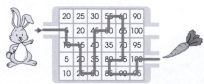

■ red
● green
▲ blue
▢ yellow

4 Adding and Subtracting Using Counting

1. 23	2. 24	3. 21	4. 16
5. 24	6. 27	7. 22	8. 21

ISBN: 978-1-897164-12-9

9. 19   10. 28   11. 18   12. 26
13. 29   14. 22   15. 26   16. 18
17. 30   18. 14
19. 57   20. 67   21. 58   22. 75
23. 72   24. 89   25. 86   26. 79
27. 66   28. 56
29. 61   30. 84   31. 79   32. 74
33. 88   34. 82   35. 55   36. 80
37a. 4 ; 24   b. 14 ; 24   38a. 6 ; 36   b. 16 ; 36
39a. 8 ; 48   b. 18 ; 48   40a. 5 ; 55   b. 15 ; 55
41a. 0 ; 40   b. 10 ; 40   42a. 0 ; 50   b. 10 ; 50
43. 10
44.

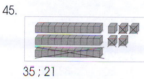

37 ; 10

45.

35 ; 21

46.

29 ; 13

47.

33 ; 11

48.

28 ; 13

49.

42 ; 11

50.

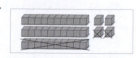

34 ; 22

Just for Fun

1.

2.

---

5   Adding without Regrouping I

1. 39

2.	3.	4.	5.
4 2 + 4 4 6	4 + 5 3 5 7	6 3 + 5 6 8	6 + 4 3 4 9

6. 29   7. 49   8. 38   9. 68
10. 57   11. 77   12. 89   13. 19
14. 38   15. 59   16. 67   17. 78
18. 48   19. 86   20. 29   21. 95
22. 16   23. 38   24. 68   25. 48
26. 27   27. 56   28. 27   29. 18
30. 38   31. 28   32. 66   33. 59
34. 48   35. 75   36. 87   37. 27
38. 96
39. policeman
40. 32 + 4 ; 36 ; 36   41. 20 + 6 ; 26 ; 26
42. 45 + 3 ; 48 ; 48   43. 23 + 6 ; 29 ; 29

Just for Fun

    28 ; 27 ; 39 ; 19

---

6   Adding without Regrouping II

1. 57

2.	3.	4.
2 2 + 1 6 3 8	3 4 + 1 4 4 8	2 0 + 3 0 5 0

 5. 38   6. 77   7. 67   8. 78
 9. 67   10. 58   11. 91   12. 92
13. 47   14. 73   15. 78   16. 76
17. 93   18. 88   19. 46   20. 36
21. 44   22. 47   23. 86   24. 68
25. 86   26. 88   27. 59   28. 96
29. 47   30. 38   31. 59   32. 69
33. 57   34. 78   35. 88   36. 68
37. 99
38. 38 ; 47 ; 57 ; 59 ; 68 ; 69 ; 78 ; 88 ; 99
39. 44 + 32 ; 76 ; 76   40. 53 + 46 ; 99 ; 99
41. 22 + 36 ; 58 ; 58   42. 15 + 30 ; 45 ; 45

Just for Fun

---

7   Adding with Regrouping I

1. 32

2.	3.	4.
4 6 + 8 5 4	3 4 + 9 4 3	6 + 4 5 5 1

 5. 24   6. 32   7. 40   8. 53
 9. 65   10. 72   11. 28   12. 71
13. 83   14. 52   15. 36   16. 60
17. 44   18. 61   19. 56   20. 33
21. 61   22. 44   23. 51   24. 35

25. 70 26. 81 27. 94 28. 40
29. 43 30. 53 31. 35 32. 60
33. 72 34. 28 35. 83 36. 42
37. 34 38. 90 39. 61 40. 55
41. 70 42. 81
43. 18 + 6 ; 24 ; 24   44. 37 + 5 ; 42 ; 42
45. 28 + 8 ; 36 ; 36   46. 45 + 9 ; 54 ; 54

Just for Fun

8 Adding with Regrouping II

1. 43
2.
$$\begin{array}{r} 37 \\ + 26 \\ \hline 63 \end{array}$$
3.
$$\begin{array}{r} 35 \\ + 17 \\ \hline 52 \end{array}$$
4.
$$\begin{array}{r} 29 \\ + 32 \\ \hline 61 \end{array}$$

5. 56 6. 64 7. 70 8. 82
9. 80 10. 83 11. 91 12. 63
13. 85 14. 84 15. 71 16. 96
17. 92 18. 95 19. 60 20. 70
21. 83 22. 85 23. 81 24. 84
25. 93 26. 64 27. 82 28. 91

29.
| 44 | 18 + 26 | 27 + 15 | 27 + 17 |

30.
| 65 | 32 + 33 | 36 + 29 | 22 + 33 |

31.
| 52 | 26 + 16 | 15 + 37 | 17 + 35 |

32.
| 63 | 25 + 38 | 34 + 27 | 27 + 36 |

33.
| 81 | 54 + 27 | 63 + 28 | 45 + 36 |

34.
| 74 | 36 + 38 | 29 + 45 | 27 + 37 |

35.
| 91 | 46 + 45 | 33 + 59 | 62 + 29 |

36.
| 46 | 23 + 13 | 19 + 27 | 36 + 10 |

37. 15 + 9 ; 24 ; 24   38. 36 + 49 ; 85 ; 85
39. 54 + 38 ; 92 ; 92   40. 27 + 45 ; 72 ; 72

Just for Fun

6 ; 15 ; 28 ; 45 ; 66 ; 91

Midway Review

1. 7 ; 13 2. 5 : 11 3. 9 ; 17 4. 9 ; 13
5. 7 ; 12 6. 8 ; 8 7. 8 ; 12 8. 11 ; 11
9a. 1 , 9 b. 2 , 8 c. 3 , 7 d. 4 , 6
 e. 5 , 5
10a. 10 b. 9 c. 8 d. 7
 e. 6
11. 7 ; 15 ; 8 ; 15 ; 7 ; 7
12. 3 , 10 ; 13 ; 10 , 3 ; 13 ; 13 , 3 ; 10 ; 13 , 10 ; 3
13. 6 ; 6 14. 6 ; 6 15. 13 16. 16
17. 7 ; 7 18. 8 ; 8 19. 21 20. 18
21. 9 ; 9 22. 7 ; 7
23. 24 24. 41 25. 40 26. 58
27. 11 28. 63 29. 93 30. 6
31. 50 32. 74 33. 90 34. 89
35. 28 36. 22 37. 30 38. 30
39. 79 40. 75 41. 62 42. 81
43. 49 44. 85 45. 56 46. 7
47. 60 ; 60
48. 58   49. 41   50. 39
$$\begin{array}{r} 35 \\ + 23 \\ \hline 58 \end{array}$$
$$\begin{array}{r} 25 \\ + 16 \\ \hline 41 \end{array}$$
$$\begin{array}{r} 23 \\ + 16 \\ \hline 39 \end{array}$$

9 Subtracting without Regrouping I

1. 44
2.
$$\begin{array}{r} 39 \\ - 3 \\ \hline 36 \end{array}$$
3.
$$\begin{array}{r} 26 \\ - 3 \\ \hline 23 \end{array}$$
4.
$$\begin{array}{r} 54 \\ - 2 \\ \hline 52 \end{array}$$
5.
$$\begin{array}{r} 25 \\ - 5 \\ \hline 20 \end{array}$$

6. 31 7. 21 8. 43 9. 92
10. 52 11. 70 12. 82 13. 43
14. 66 15. 21 16. 55 17. 31
18. 72 19. 12 20. 93 21. 40
22. 50 23. 24 24. 32 25. 62
26. 71 27. 84 28. 91 29. 40
30. 44 31. 34 32. 53 33. 62
34. 50 35. 35 36. 81 37. 90
38. 21 39. 41 40. 81 41. 31
42. 63 43. 63 44. 52
45. 28 – 6 ; 22 ; 22
46. 59 – 5 ; 54 ; 54
47. 46 – 4 ; 42 ; 42
48. 37 – 3 ; 34 ; 34

Just for Fun

ISBN: 978-1-897164-12-9

10 Subtracting without Regrouping II

1. 23

2.
```
   67
 - 43
   24
```

3.
```
   55
 - 15
   40
```

4.
```
   36
 - 24
   12
```

5. 24   6. 23   7. 24   8. 41
9. 32   10. 30   11. 31   12. 4
13. 21   14. 22   15. 12   16. 54
17. 15   18. 10   19. 4   20. 32
21. 23   22. 22   23. 46   24. 40
25. 11   26. 14   27. 16   28. 13
29a. 34   b. 23   c. 34 ; colour a and c
30a. 22   b. 23   c. 23 ; colour b and c
31a. 16   b. 26   c. 16 ; colour a and c
32a. 45   b. 45   c. 44 ; colour a and b
33. 16 ; 16   34. 24   35. 12   36. 32

```
   96          28          67
 - 72        - 16        - 35
   24          12          32
```

Just for Fun

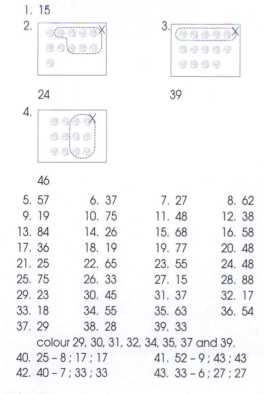

11 Subtracting with Regrouping I

1. 15

2. [diagram]   3. [diagram]

24   39

4. [diagram]

46

5. 57   6. 37   7. 27   8. 62
9. 19   10. 75   11. 48   12. 38
13. 84   14. 26   15. 68   16. 58
17. 36   18. 19   19. 77   20. 48
21. 25   22. 65   23. 55   24. 48
25. 75   26. 33   27. 15   28. 88
29. 23   30. 45   31. 37   32. 17
33. 18   34. 55   35. 63   36. 54
37. 29   38. 28   39. 33

colour 29, 30, 31, 32, 34, 35, 37 and 39.
40. 25 – 8 ; 17 ; 17   41. 52 – 9 ; 43 ; 43
42. 40 – 7 ; 33 ; 33   43. 33 – 6 ; 27 ; 27

Just for Fun

54 ; 42 ; 29 ; 15 ; 0

12 Subtracting with Regrouping II

1. 26

2. [diagram]

14

3. [diagram]

18

4. 16   5. 38   6. 16   7. 45
8. 18   9. 28   10. 8   11. 29
12. 17   13. 19   14. 37   15. 27
16. 16   17. 13   18. 9   19. 28
20. 17   21. 28   22. 25   23. 37
24. 47   25. 23   26. 12   27. 26
28a. 36   b. 23   c. 36 ; colour a and c
29a. 27   b. 37   c. 37 ; colour b and c
30a. 14   b. 14   c. 15 ; colour a and b
31a. 26   b. 25   c. 25 ; colour b and c
32a. 44   b. 34   c. 44 ; colour a and c
33. 92 – 37 ; 55 ; 55
34. 43 – 27 ; 16 ; 16
35. 55 – 39 ; 16 ; 16
36. 61 – 46 ; 15 ; 15

Just for Fun

SINGER

13 Estimating Sums and Differences

1. 30   2. 40   3. 50   4. 40
5. 60   6. 80   7. 80   8. 90
9. 40   10. 20
11. 30   12. 20   13. 50   14. 60
15. 10   16. 80   17. 10   18. 50
19. 10   20. 70   21. 100 22. 0
23a. 66   b. 70
24a. 44   25a. 53
b.   b.
```
   20              10
 + 30            + 50
   50              60
```
26a. 65   27a. 33
b.   b.
```
   50              30
 + 10            + 10
   60              40
```
28a. 89
b.
```
   30
 + 60
   90
```
29a. 92   b. 70 , 20 ; 90
30a. 88   b. 20 , 70 ; 90
31a. 79   b. 30 , 50 ; 80
32a. 95   b. 50 , 40 ; 90
33a. 91   b. 60 , 30 ; 90
34a. 58   b. 10 , 50 ; 60
35a. 24   b. 20

ISBN: 978-1-897164-12-9

36a. 15
b.
```
   40
 - 20
   20
```

37a. 32
b.
```
   70
 - 40
   30
```

38a. 26
b.
```
   70
 - 50
   20
```

39a. 41
b.
```
   60
 - 10
   50
```

40a. 36
b.
```
   90
 - 50
   40
```

41a. 47   b. 90 , 50 ; 40
42a. 33   b. 50 , 10 ; 40
43a. 48   b. 80 , 30 ; 50
44a. 45   b. 60 , 20 ; 40
45a. 48   b. 80 , 30 ; 50
46a. 28   b. 40 , 10 ; 30
48. less than 90
49. more than 80
50. less than 30
51. less than 50
52. more than 60

Just for Fun

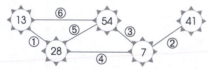

14 Checking Subtraction by Using Addition

1a. 12   b. 12 ; 28
2a. 26   b. 26 ; 63
3a. 22   b. 22 ; 48
4a. 18   b. 18 ; 51
5a. 35   b. 35 ; 77
6a. 23   b. 23 ; 82
7a. 44   b. 44 , 8 ; 52
8a. 22   b. 22 , 17 ; 39
9a. 22   b. 22 , 23 ; 45
10a. 27   b. 27 , 39 ; 66
11a. 42   b. 42 , 45 ; 87
12a. 7   b. 7 , 16 ; 23
13a. 38   b. 38 , 33 ; 71
14a. 35   b. 35 , 63 ; 98
15a. 18   b. 18 , 14 ; 32
16a. 21   b. 21 , 6 ; 27
17a. 25   b. 25 , 31 ; 56
18a. 16   b. 16 , 29 ; 45
19a. 39   b. 39   c. 39
20a. 21   b. 21 , 17 ; 38   c. 38 , 21 ; 17
21a. 17   b. 17 , 32 ; 49   c. 49 , 17 ; 32
22a. 26   b. 26 , 25 ; 51   c. 51 , 26 ; 25
23a. 13   b. 13 , 9 ; 22   c. 22 , 13 ; 9

24a. 71   b. 71 , 15 ; 86   c. 86 , 71 ; 15
25a. 25   b. 25 , 65 ; 90   c. 90 , 25 ; 65
26a. 27   b. 27 , 48 ; 75   c. 75 , 27 ; 48
27. 56 , 39 ; 17 ; 17
```
   17
 + 39
   56
```
28. 48 , 26 ; 22 ; 22
```
   22
 + 26
   48
```
29. 15 , 8 ; 7 ; 7
```
    7
 +  8
   15
```

Just for Fun

1. 20 ; 35 ; 45
2. 40 ; 44 ; 46
3. 40 ; 50 ; 80

15 More Addition and Subtraction

1. 9 ; 6   2. 2 ; 10   3. 14 ; 5   4. 6 ; 12
5. 16 ; 2   6. 35 ; 29   7. 82 ; 80   8. 29 ; 36
9. 70 ; 52   10. 80 ; 34
12. 60   13. 36   14. 46   15. 36
16. 46   17. 13
18. 24 ; 44   19. 32 ; 62   20. 33 ; 53   21. 14 ; 54
22. 2 ; 12
23. 20 ; 40   24. 20 ; 40   25. 14 ; 44   26. 12 ; 42
27. 30   28. 10   29. 44   30. 40
31. 43   32. 20   33. 30   34. 26
35. 30   36. 18   37. 20   38. 30
39a. 3   b. 13   c. 23   d. 33
e. 43
40a. 6   b. 16   c. 26   d. 36
e. 46
41a. 64   b. 54   c. 44   d. 34
e. 24
42a. 58   b. 48   c. 38   d. 28
e. 18
43. 8 + 4 - 5 ; 7
44. 9 - 3 + 5 ; 11
45. 7 + 6 - 4 ; 9

Just for Fun

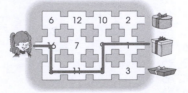

16 Addition and Subtraction with Money

1. 65   2. 42   3. 52   4. 37
5. 28
7. ✓

ISBN: 978-1-897164-12-9

8. 50 , 49 ; 1   9. 100 , 85 ; 15
10. 45 , 36 ; 9   11. 75 , 56 ; 19
12. 67 , 36 ; 31   13. 76 , 46 ; 30
14. 72 , 47 ; 25   15. 28 , 16 ; 12

	25¢	10¢	5¢	1¢
16.	2			4
17.		2		2
18.	3		1	
19.	1	2		2
20.	1	1		1

21. 57   22. 66   23. 32   24. 41
25. 34 ; 34
26. 98
```
    57
 +  41
    98
```
27. 89
```
    57
 +  32
    89
```
28. 34
```
    66
 -  32
    34
```
29. 25
```
    66
 -  41
    25
```

Just for Fun

   2 , 4

Final Review

1. 41   2. 45   3. 32   4. 43
5. 28   6. 18   7. 57   8. 66
9. 71   10. 55   11. 80   12. 19
13. 36   14. 69   15. 43   16. 70
17. 73   18. 27   19. 16   20. 91
21. 56   22. 42   23. 25   24. 49
25a. 63   26a. 17
  b.   b.
```
    30              40
 +  40            - 30
    70              10
```
27a. 26   b. 70 – 40 ; 30
28a. 58   b. 40 + 20 ; 60
29a. 23   30a. 23
  b.   b.
```
    23              23
 +  14            + 29
    37              52
```
31a. 16   b. 16 + 48 ; 64
32a. 46   b. 46 + 33 ; 79
33a. 32   b. 32 + 54 ; 86
34a. 25   b. 25 + 28 ; 53
35. 1 ; 11   36. 25 ; 45   37. 12 ; 42   38. 23 ; 63
39a. 3   b. 13   c. 23   d. 33
40a. 53   b. 43   c. 33   d. 23
41.   42.   43.
```
   4 3           3 8           5 5
 + 1 9         + 2 7         + 1 6
   6 2           6 5           7 1
```

44.   45.   46.
```
   6 2           5 1           5 8
 - 4 2         - 3 7         - 3 3
   2 0           1 4           2 5
```
47. 10   48. 20   49. 11   50. 5
51. 46 ; 63   52. 49 ; 23   53. 58 ; 9   54. 14 ; 27
55. B ; C   56. B ; D   57. A
58. 33 ; 33
59. 42   60. 35   61. 9   62. 34
```
    23          92          26          69
 +  19        - 57        - 17        - 35
    42          35           9          34
```
63. 83
```
    38
 +  45
    83
```

ISBN: 978-1-897164-12-9

Review

1. Card A : Square ; 25
   Card B : Rectangle ; 32
   Card C : Triangle ; 9
2. Mary ; George ; Freda ; Stephen
3. Tina ; Rose ; Wayne ; Sophia
4. Ivy ; Alfred ; Yvonne ; Jill

5.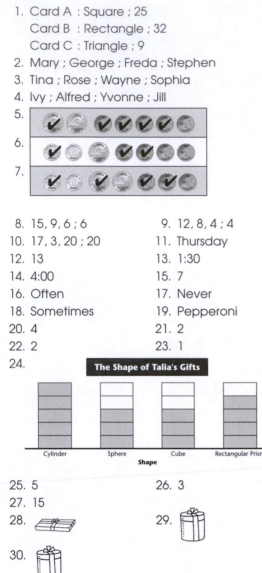
6.
7.

8. 15, 9, 6 ; 6
9. 12, 8, 4 ; 4
10. 17, 3, 20 ; 20
11. Thursday
12. 13
13. 1:30
14. 4:00
15. 7
16. Often
17. Never
18. Sometimes
19. Pepperoni
20. 4
21. 2
22. 2
23. 1
24.

The Shape of Talia's Gifts

(bar graph: Cylinder, Sphere, Cube, Rectangular Prism)

Shape

25. 5
26. 3
27. 15
28. (gift)
29. (gift)
30. (gift)

1 Numbers to 50

1. 18 ; eighteen
2. 14 ; fourteen
3. 17 ; seventeen
4. 16 ; sixteen
5. 18 ; 17 ; 16 ; 14
6. 16 ; 15 ; 13 ; 12
7. 17 ; 14 ; 13 ; 11
8a. 36, 37, 38, 39, 40, 41   b. 5
9a. 28, 29, 30, 31, 32, 33, 34
  b. 6
10. 5 ; 3
11. 4 ; 7
12. 8 ; 5
13. 6 ; 0
14. 3 ; 9
15. 36
16. 63
17. 91
18. 83
19. 60
20. 52
21. 19, 30, 40, 48

22. 6, 13, 15, 29
23. 14, 26, 33, 44
24. 16, 26, 38, 46
25. 3rd ; 5th ; 6th ; 9th ; 10th ; 13th ; 14th ; 15th ; 17th ; 18th
26. chips
27. fudgicles
28. chocolate bars
29. 9
30. 5
31. 3
32. 1st, 5th, 9th,13th, 17th
33. 2nd, 6th, 10th, 14th, 18th
34. 3rd, 4th, 7th, 8th, 11th, 12th, 15th, 16th, 19th
35a. chocolate bars   b. fudgicles
  c. chips   d. chocolate bars
36.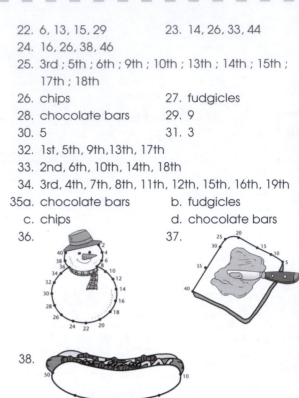
37.
38.

Mind Boggler

40

2 Addition

1. 7, 9 ; 16
   9, 7 ; 16
2. 3, 8 ; 11
   8, 3 ; 11
3. 7, 8 ; 15
   8, 7 ; 15
4. 4, 9 ; 13
   9, 4 ; 13
5. 6 ; 15
6. 7 ; 12
7. 7 ; 15
8. 9 ; 12
9. 30
10. 50
11. 10, 40 ; 50
12. 30, 10 ; 40
13.   15
    +   6
    ——
      21
14.   24
    + 25
    ——
      49
15. 37
16. 38
17. 46
18. 49
19. 48
20. 48
21. 37
22. 39
23. 49
24. 38
25. 27
26. 37
27. 34
28. 48
29.

(dot/star diagram and addition box)

		①
	2	6
+	1	5
	4	1

ISBN: 978-1-897164-12-9

30.

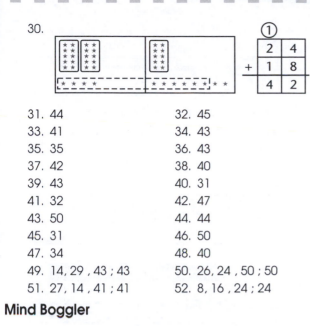

①		
	2	4
+	1	8
	4	2

31. 44	32. 45
33. 41	34. 43
35. 35	36. 43
37. 42	38. 40
39. 43	40. 31
41. 32	42. 47
43. 50	44. 44
45. 31	46. 50
47. 34	48. 40
49. 14, 29 , 43 ; 43	50. 26, 24 , 50 ; 50
51. 27, 14 , 41 ; 41	52. 8, 16 , 24 ; 24

Mind Boggler

①
```
  2 [6]
+ [1] 5
  4 1
```
②
```
  [1] 3
+ 1 [7]
  3 0
```
③
```
  [1] 6
+ 3 [4]
  5 0
```

3 Subtraction

1. A 22 ; B 12 ; C 23 ; D 44 ; E 44 ; F 31 ; G 41 ;
   H 10 ; I 32 ; J 44 ; K 45 ; L 32
   A → B → C → F → H → I → L → ✸

2. 11	3. 15
4. 21	5. 6
6. 12	7. 24
8. 29	9. 28
10. 39	11. 21
12. 19	13. 29
14. 38	15. 42
16. 17	17. 25
18. 38	19. 31
20. 14	21. 5
22. 4 ; 14	23. 4 ; 24
24. 3 ; 13	25. 9 ; 19
26A. 17	B. 5
C. 17	D. 17
E. 4	F. 9
G. 19	H. 39
I. 18	J. 8
K. 14	L. 37
27. H	28. E
29. 32 ; 34 ; 40	30. 50, 32, 18 ; 18
31. 48, 34, 14 ; 14	32. 40, 17, 23 ; 23
33. 40, 32, 8 ; 8	

Mind Boggler

33 ; 15

4 Patterning

1.-12. (Suggested answers)
1. 1 2 1 2 1 2 1 2
2. 1 1 2 1 1 2 1 1
3. 1 2 2 3 1 2 2 3
4. A B C A B C A B C
5. A B B A B B A B B
6. A B B C A B B C A
7. 1 1 2 3 1 1 2 3 1 1
8. A B A C A B A C A B
9. 1 2 3 1 2 3 1 2 3
10. 1 1 2 1 1 2 1 1 2
11. 1 2 3 1 2 3 1 2 3
12. 1 2 3 4 1 2 3 4 1
13. ☐ 14. △
15. ▭ 16. ●

17.-18. (Suggested answers)
17. 1 2 2 1 2 2 2 1 2	18. A B A A B A A B
19A. 1	B. 10
C. down ; 1	D. down ; 10
E. up ; 11	
20a. 2	b. 13 ; 15
21a. up	b. 35 ; 40
22a. down ;10	b. 30 ; 20
23a. up ; 10	b. 66 ; 76
24a. down ; 2	b. 48 ; 46

Mind Boggler

| 1. 6 ; 5 ; 4 ; 3 ; 2 | 2. 6 ; 5 ; 4 ; 3 ; 2 |

5 Measurement I

1. B	2. A
3. A	4. B
5. 14 ; 2	6. 13 ; 1
7. 10 ; 2	
8a. longer	b. 1 m
9a. longer	b. 3 m
10. m	11. cm
12. cm	13. m
14. cm	15. m
16. 11	17. 9
18. 15	19. 20
20. B	21. D
22. C	23. A
24. 2 ; 1 ; 3 ; 4	25. 5
26. 4	27. 3

Mind Boggler

1. T   2. F   3. T

6 Geometry I

1. 2 ; 4
2. 2 ; 3
3. 5 ; 4
4. 3 ; 3
5. Triangle ; Rectangle ; Pentagon ; Hexagon ; Octagon
6. 3 ; 4 ; 5 ; 6 ; 8
7. 3 ; 4 ; 5 ; 6 ; 8
8a. 3
  b. A ; B
9a. 6
  b. A ; B
  c. A
10a. 5
   b. B ; A
   c. B
11a. 8
   b. A ; B
   c. A
12. Square ; Rectangle
13. Hexagon ; Triangle
14. Pentagon ; Square

15.
Rectangle

16.
Hexagon

17.
Triangle

18.
Pentagon

19.
Square

20.
Octagon

21. right ; down
22. right ; up
23. left ; up
24. left ; down
25. Reflection
26. Rotation
27. Translation

Mind Boggler

D ; E

7 Data Management

1.
🍎	🍐	🍓	🍊	🍌
IIII II	IIII IIII	IIII III	IIII I	IIII

2.
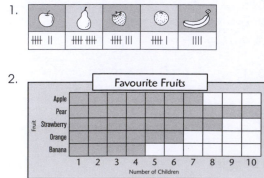

3. 1
4. 2
5. Banana
6. Pear

7.
Chocolate	Vanilla	Strawberry	Cherry
IIII IIII	IIII I	IIII IIII II	III

8. Number of Ice Cream Cones Sold
9. 4
10. Strawberry
11. Cherry
12. 9
13. 15
14. 3
15. 30

16.
III	IIII III	IIII	IIII

17.
Hannah's Hat Collection

18. Hannah's Hat Collection
19. 12
20. 17
21. 9
22. 20
23. III ; III ; IIII ; II ; IIII ; I

24.
The Greens' Food Selections

25. The Greens' Food Selections
26. 3
27. 5
28. 6

Mind Boggler

1. No
2. No

Progress Test

1. fifteen ; sixteen ; eighteen
2. 34 ; 36 ; 38 ; 39
3. ⬡ ; ⬡ ; △
4. ◨ ; ◨ ; ◨
5. 8 ; 10 ; 16 ; 20
6. 45 ; 43 ; 41 ; 40 ; 39
7. 34
8. 12
9. 11
10. 50
11. 14
12. 41
13. 47
14. 10
15. 6
16. 50

ISBN: 978-1-897164-12-9

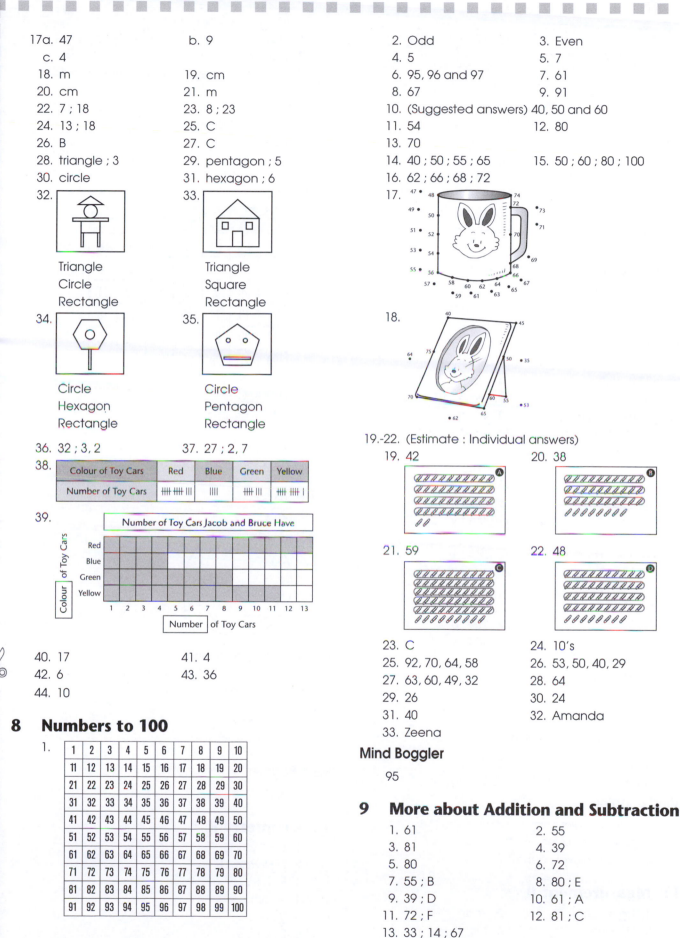

17a. 47   b. 9
  c. 4
18. m   19. cm
20. cm   21. m
22. 7 ; 18   23. 8 ; 23
24. 13 ; 18   25. C
26. B   27. C
28. triangle ; 3   29. pentagon ; 5
30. circle   31. hexagon ; 6

32.
Triangle
Circle
Rectangle

33.
Triangle
Square
Rectangle

34.
Circle
Hexagon
Rectangle

35.
Circle
Pentagon
Rectangle

36. 32 ; 3, 2   37. 27 ; 2, 7

38.

Colour of Toy Cars	Red	Blue	Green	Yellow
Number of Toy Cars	⊞ ⊞ III	IIII	⊞ III	⊞ ⊞ I

39.

Number of Toy Cars Jacob and Bruce Have

Colour of Toy Cars
Red
Blue
Green
Yellow

1 2 3 4 5 6 7 8 9 10 11 12 13
Number of Toy Cars

40. 17   41. 4
42. 6   43. 36
44. 10

8 Numbers to 100

1.

1	2	3	4	5	6	7	8	9	10
11	12	13	14	15	16	17	18	19	20
21	22	23	24	25	26	27	28	29	30
31	32	33	34	35	36	37	38	39	40
41	42	43	44	45	46	47	48	49	50
51	52	53	54	55	56	57	58	59	60
61	62	63	64	65	66	67	68	69	70
71	72	73	74	75	76	77	78	79	80
81	82	83	84	85	86	87	88	89	90
91	92	93	94	95	96	97	98	99	100

2. Odd   3. Even
4. 5   5. 7
6. 95, 96 and 97   7. 61
8. 67   9. 91
10. (Suggested answers) 40, 50 and 60
11. 54   12. 80
13. 70
14. 40 ; 50 ; 55 ; 65   15. 50 ; 60 ; 80 ; 100
16. 62 ; 66 ; 68 ; 72
17.

18.

19.-22. (Estimate : Individual answers)
19. 42   20. 38

21. 59   22. 48

23. C   24. 10's
25. 92, 70, 64, 58   26. 53, 50, 40, 29
27. 63, 60, 49, 32   28. 64
29. 26   30. 24
31. 40   32. Amanda
33. Zeena

Mind Boggler

95

9 More about Addition and Subtraction

1. 61   2. 55
3. 81   4. 39
5. 80   6. 72
7. 55 ; B   8. 80 ; E
9. 39 ; D   10. 61 ; A
11. 72 ; F   12. 81 ; C
13. 33 ; 14 ; 67

14. 88
```
     49
  +  39
    ‾‾‾‾
     88
```

15. 17
```
     67
  -  50
    ‾‾‾‾
     17
```

16. 32
```
     49
  -  17
    ‾‾‾‾
     32
```

17. 27
```
     50
  -  23
    ‾‾‾‾
     27
```

18. 46 – 27 = 19 ; 19
19. 46 + 39 = 85 ; 85
20. 35 + 38 = 73 ; 73
21. 73 – 24 = 49 ; 49
22. 70 – 14 = 56 ; 56
23. 15 + 29 = 44 ; 44
24. 50 – 6 = 44 ; 44
25. 45 + 45 = 90 ; 90
26. 12 + 12 = 24 ; 24

Mind Boggler

1. Mrs. Venn
2. Mrs. Green

10 Money

1. nickel ; 5
2. penny ; 1
3. toonie ; 2
4. loonie ; 1
5. quarter ; 25
6. dime ; 10
7. ✔,✔,✔,✔
8. ✔,✔
9. ✔,✔,✔,✔,✔
10. ✔,✔,✔,✔,✔
11. ✔,✔

12.-15. (Estimate : Individual answers)

12. 6 ; 62
13. 12 ; 74
14. 8 ; 83
15. 8 ; 47
16. Louis
17. Jimmy
18. No
19. 25¢ : 1
    10¢ : 0
    5¢ : 1
    1¢ : 4
20. 25¢ : 1
    10¢ : 0
    5¢ : 0
    1¢ : 1
21. 25¢ : 1
    10¢ : 1
    5¢ : 0
    1¢ : 3
22. 25¢ : 0
    10¢ : 1
    5¢ : 1
    1¢ : 3
23. 25¢ : 1
    10¢ : 0
    5¢ : 1
    1¢ : 2
24. 85 ; 20
25. 95 ; 57
26. 58 ; 32
27. 55 ; 30

Mind Boggler

1. quarter ; dime
2. nickels ; quarter
3. dimes ; nickel ; penny

11 Measurement II

1. Hour
2. Year
3. Second
4. Month

5. Day
6. 7
7. Monday
8. Friday
9. 5 ; June 1, June 8, June 15, June 22 and June 29
10. 4 ; July 4, July 7, July 16, and July 25
11. 4
12. February ; April
13. August ; September
14. September ; December
15. August
16. June
17. 31
18. 7
19. 366
20.

October						
Sun	Mon	Tue	Wed	Thu	Fri	Sat
			1	2	3	4
5	6	7	8	9	10	11
12	13	14	15	16	17	18
19	20	21	22	23	24	25
26	27	28	29	30	31	

21. Sunday
22. Friday
23. Saturday
24. 7
25. 12
26. 60
27. 24
28a. 12:15
b. 01:00
c. 45
29a. 03:45
b. 05:45
c. 2
30a.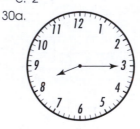
b.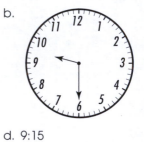
c. 1 hour 15 minutes
d. 9:15
31a. B
b. lower
c. drops ; 15°C
32a. A
b. higher
c. rises ; 10°C

Mind Boggler

5:35

12 Geometry II

1. C ; Cylinder
2. D ; Pyramid
3. F ; Rectangular Prism
4. A ; Sphere
5. B ; Cone
6. E ; Cube

ISBN: 978-1-897164-12-9

7. cube
8. cone
9. sphere
10. 6, 5, 1, 6, 5, 2
11. 8, 6, 1, 8, 5, 0
12. 6   13. 2
14. 4   15. Cone
16. Pyramid   17. Cylinders
18. Spheres
19a. No   b. Yes
  c. No
20. A   21. C
22. D   23. A
24. Yes   25. No
26. Yes   27. Yes
28. Yes   29. No
30. No   31. Rectangular prism
32. Pyramid   33. Cube
34. Cone   35. Cylinder
36. Rectangular prism

Mind Boggler

1. Circle   2. Rectangle

13 Fractions

1. A ; C ; E ; G

2. $\frac{1}{4}$; One quarter   3. $\frac{2}{3}$; Two thirds

4. $\frac{3}{4}$; Three quarters

5. $\frac{4}{5}$; Four fifths

6.   7.

8.

9. $\frac{3}{6}$; $\frac{1}{2}$; equal   10. $\frac{4}{6}$; $\frac{2}{3}$; equal

11a. 3 ; 8   b. $\frac{3}{8}$

12a. 5 ; 12 ; $\frac{5}{12}$ b. 7 ; 12 ; $\frac{7}{12}$

13a. 2 ; 10 ; $\frac{2}{10}$ b. 8 ; 10 ; $\frac{8}{10}$

14a. $\frac{2}{5}$ b. $\frac{3}{5}$

15a. $\frac{3}{4}$ b. $\frac{1}{4}$
16a. $\frac{1}{6}$ b. $\frac{3}{6}$
c. $\frac{2}{6}$

17a. 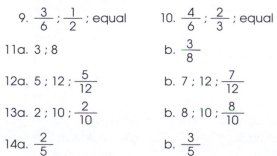   b. 1   c. 50   d. 50

18a.   b. 1   c. 25   d. 25

19a.   b. 1   c. 75   d. 75

20a.   b. 25   c. 10   d. 10

21. 15 ; a quarter   22. 40 ; two thirds
23. 30 ; one half
24. 45   25. 30
26. 20   27. Joe

Mind Boggler

1. $\frac{6}{9}$ 2. $\frac{4}{8}$

3. $\frac{2}{6}$ 4. $\frac{1}{4}$

14 Probability

1. likely   2. likely
3. not likely   4. ✔
5. ✗   6. ✔
7. ✗   8. not likely
9. probably   10. likely
11a. Often   b. Sometimes
  c. Never
12a. Often   b. Never
  c. Sometimes
13a. Sometimes   b. Never
  c. Often
14a. Often   b. Sometimes
  c. Never
15a. A   b. B
16a. C   b. B
17a. C   b. A
18a. No   b. A
19A. 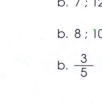   B.

C.   D.

ISBN: 978-1-897164-12-9

20. D   21. A
22. No

Mind Boggler

Spinner B. It is the only spinner with sections having the same size.

Final Test

1. 51
2. 11
3. 66
4. 17
5. 74
6. 74
7. 2
8. 86
9. 51
10. 54
11. 28
12. 83
13. 99 ;

14. 68 ;

15. 78 ;

16. 39 ;

17. $\frac{3}{6}$
18. $\frac{5}{8}$
19. $\frac{5}{9}$
20. $\frac{1}{6}$
21. $\frac{4}{8}$
22. $\frac{2}{3}$
23. Cone ; Cube ; Pyramid ; Cylinder ; Sphere
24. 1 ; 6 ; 5 ; 2 ; 0
25. 0 ; 0 ; 4 ; 0 ; 0
26. 1 ; 8 ; 5 ; 0 ; 0
27. ✔ ; ✗ ; ✗ ; ✔ ; ✔
28.

29. Rectangular prism
30. 6
31. 4
32. Yes
33a.

b. 30   c. 30

34a.

b. 10   c. 10

35a.

b. 6   c. 6
36. 77 – 56 = 21 ; 21
37. 80 – 45 = 35 ; 35
38. 37 + 40 = 77 ; 77
39.-42. (Suggested drawings)
39.

$\frac{2}{5}$

40.

$\frac{2}{3}$

41.

$\frac{3}{6}$

42.

$\frac{7}{8}$

43. Sometimes
44. Never
45. Sometimes
46. Often
47. A
48. C
49a.

b.

c. 45

50a.

b.

c. 30

51. I ; II ; III ; IIII ; ⊬ ; ⊬I

52.

53. Number of Juice Boxes on Each Shelf
54. 21
55. up ; 1
56. 7
57. 31
58. 9
59. 7
60. cone
61. 1:15
62. 3:45
63. 2 h 30 min
64. 15
65. rectangles
66. triangles
67. hexagons
68. 6
69. rectangular prism
70. September
71. 45

1 3-digit Numbers

1. Sam   2. Craig
3. One hundred forty-five
4. Two hundred thirteen
5. 145, 178, 180, 193, 213
6. 3   7. 2
8. Peggy   9. Max
10. July   11. May
12. July and August
13. May, June and September
14. 100   15. 6
16. July, August, June, September, May
17. Six hundred seventy-four

2 Addition and Subtraction

1. 39 + 23 = 62 ; 62
2. 32 + 19 = 51 ; 51
3. 36 + 25 = 61 ; 61
4. 39 – 23 = 16 ; 16
5. 32 – 19 = 13 ; 13
6. 23 + 19 + 25 = 67 ; 67
7. 520 + 100 = 620 ; 620
8. 100 + 180 = 280 ; 280
9. 520 – 100 = 420 ; 420
10. 180 – 130 = 50 ; 50
11. 520 + 100 + 180 = 800 ; 800
12. 800 - 450 = 350 ; 350
13. 450 – 350 = 100 ; 100
14. 2nd   15. 1st
16. 2nd   17. A
18. A   19. B
20. 158 – 138 = 20 ; 20
21. 158 + 138 = 296 ; 296
22. 109 – 105 = 4 ; 4
23. 109 + 105 = 214 ; 214
24. 147 – 123 = 24 ; 24
25. 147 + 123 = 270 ; 270
26. 138 + 109 + 123 = 370 ; 370
27. 158 + 105 + 147 = 410 ; 410
28. 138 – 75 = 63 ; 63
29. 147 – 89 = 58 ; 58

3 Multiplication

1a. 2	b. 2 ; 12	c. 6
d. 6 ; 12	e. 12	
2a. 3	b. 3 ; 9	c. 9
3a. 4 ; 8	b. 8 ; 32	c. 8 ; 4
d. 4 ; 32	e. 32	
4a. 4	b. 4 ; 12 ; 12	
5a. 2	b. 5 x 2 = 10 ; 10	
6a. 6	b. 2 x 6 = 12 ; 12	
7a. 8	b. 4 x 8 = 32 ; 32	
8a. 5	b. 3 x 5 = 15 ; 15	
9a. 3	b. 6 x 3 = 18 ; 18	
10a. B	b. 4 ; 8 ; 8	
11a. A	b. 5 x 4 = 20 ; 20	
12a. C	b. 3 x 6 = 18 ; 18	
13a. B	b. 4 x 3 = 12 ; 12	

14. 8 x 6 = 48 ; 48
15. 7 x 6 = 42 ; 42
16. 9 x 2 = 18 ; 18
17. 4 x 6 = 24 ; 24
18. 5 x 5 = 25 ; 25
19. 5 x 4 = 20 ; 20
20. 2 x 3 = 6 ; 6

4 Money

1.
37
2.
42
3.
37
4.
32

5a. 6	b. 12	c. 8
6a. 5	b. 30	c. 20
7a. 4	b. 56	c. 4

8. 39
9. 23
10. 34

ISBN: 978-1-897164-12-9

11. 19

12. 23 + 19 = 42 ; 42

```
  23
+ 19
  42
```

13. 50 – 39 = 11 ; 11

```
  50
- 39
  11
```

14. 34 – 19 = 15 ; 15

```
  34
- 19
  15
```

15. 39 + 39 = 78 ; 78

```
  39
+ 39
  78
```

16. 23 + 39 = 62 ; 62

```
  23
+ 39
  62
```

17. 85 – 19 = 66 ; 66

```
  85
- 19
  66
```

18. 34 + 34 + 23 = 91 ; 91

```
  34
  34
+ 23
  91
```

19. 50 – 16 = 34 ; brownie

```
  50
- 16
  34
```

5 Pictographs

1. Dress shoes
2. Running shoes
3. Sandals
4. Dress shoes
5. Boots
6. 4
7. 13
8. 25
9. The Cubs
10. The Rangers
11. 3
12. The Jays
13. The Herons
14. The Lotus
15. 7

16.

Number of Games Won
Toronto | Rochester | Philadelphia Team | Buffalo | New York

17. Rochester
18. Philadelphia
19. Buffalo
20. 3
21. 5
22. 12

23.

Favourite Sandwiches
Ham | Corned Beef | Roast Beef | Egg Salad | Chicken | Tuna Salad
Sandwich

24. Ham
25. Tuna Salad
26. 10
27. 8
28. 2

6 More about Addition and Subtraction

1. Dan
2. Roberta
3. Roberta
4. Ada
5. 145 + 108 = 253 ; 253
6. 213 + 96 = 309 ; 309
7. 177 – 82 = 95 ; 95
8. 134 – 59 = 75 ; 75
9. Toronto
10. Oakville
11. 150 + 32 = 182 ; 182

12. 165 + 64 = 229 ; 229
13. 178 + 45 = 223 ; 223
14. 197 + 58 = 255 ; 255
15. 255 – 182 = 73 ; 73
16. 154 – 72 = 82 ; 82
17. 302 – 124 = 178 ; 178
18. 326 – 97 = 229 ; 229
19. 105 – 35 = 70 ; 70
20. 154 + 326 = 480 ; 480
21. 380 – 166 = 214 ; 214
22. 85 + 17 = 102 ; 102
23. 380 – 85 = 295 ; 295
24. 106 + 215 = 321 ; 321
25. 215 – 80 = 135 ; 135
26. 159 + 159 = 318 ; 318

Midway Review

1. 9 ; 27 ; 27
2. 5 x 4 = 20 ; 20
3. 4 x 6 = 24 ; 24
4. 7 x 2 = 14 ; 14
5. 5 x 6 = 30 ; 30
6. 8 x 2 = 16 ; 16
7. 8 ; 8
8. Pam ; Dora
9. Dora ; Pam
10. 93 ; 86
11. Pam ; Dora
12. 82
13. 3
14. 11
15. 8
16. 295 ; Three hundred twelve
17. 273 ; Two hundred ninety-eight
18. Three hundred one ; 290
19. Glenview School ; Trafalgar School ; Meadows School
20. Trafalgar School ; Meadows School ; Glenview School
21. Glenview School
22. 607
23. 571
24. 591
25. 17
26. Simon
27. Janet
28. 2
29. 3

30. 5
31. No
32. 3
33. 2

7 4-Digit Numbers

1. 2321
2. 3212
3. 1421
4. 2142
5. 3134
6. 2043
7. Orange
8. Peach
9. 2
10. One thousand three hundred twenty-one
11. One thousand nine hundred twenty-one
12. Diplodocus
13. Brachiosaurus
14. 1000
15. 2000
16. Giganotosaurus
17. Two thousand one hundred centimetres
18. One thousand three hundred centimetres
19. 7300 ; 5206 ; 3249 ; 2375 ; 1854
20. 5208 ; 3153 ; 2005 ; 1656 ; 1054
21. One thousand eight hundred fifty-four
22. Five thousand two hundred eight
23. 2 ; 3249 and 5206
24. 3 ; 1054, 1656 and 3153
25. 2314
26. 3105
27. 1 ; 4 ; 7
28. 2 ; 0 ; 9
29. Toby's Shop
30. Ranis Retail
31. 8
32. 7
33. 5000

8 Division

1. 4 ; 4
2. 3 ; 3
3. 3 ; 3
4. 6 ; 6
5. 2 ; 2

6. 25 ÷ 5 = 5 ; 5

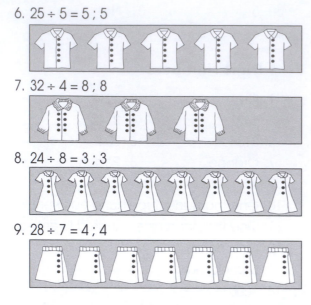

7. 32 ÷ 4 = 8 ; 8

8. 24 ÷ 8 = 3 ; 3

9. 28 ÷ 7 = 4 ; 4

10. 20 ÷ 4 = 5 ; 5
11. 27 ÷ 3 = 9 ; 9
12. 72 ÷ 8 = 9 ; 9
13. 21 ÷ 7 = 3 ; 3
14. 20 ÷ 4 = 5 ; 5
15. 10 ÷ 5 = 2 ; 2
16. 40 ÷ 4 = 10 ; 10
17. 40 ÷ 5 = 8 ; 8
18. 14 ÷ 2 = 7 ; 7
19. 24 ÷ 3 = 8 ; 8
20. 35 ÷ 7 = 5 ; 5
21. 20 ÷ 4 = 5 ; 5

9   Measurement

1a. 8:30 ; 10   b. 6:00 ; 15
  c. lower
2a. 8:45 ; 25   b. 6:15 ; 20
  c. higher
 3. Tuesday   4. Monday
 5. 400   6. Adam
 7. Eva   8. Bob
 9. 5   10. 90
11. May 18   12. 1:15 p.m.

10 More about Multiplication and Division

1. 12 ÷ 3 = 4 ; 4
2. 16 ÷ 4 = 4 ; 4

3. 18 ÷ 6 = 3 ; 3
4. 6 x 2 = 12 ; 12
5. 7 x 2 = 14 ; 14
6. 36
7. 36 ÷ 4 = 9 ; 9
8. 2 x 9 = 18 ; 18
9. 18 ÷ 6 = 3 ; 3
10. 30 ÷ 5 = 6 ; 6
11. 3 x 6 = 18 ; 18
12. 3 x 8 = 24 ; 24
13. 24 ÷ 4 = 6 ; 6
14. 4 x 6 = 24 ; 24
15. 24 ÷ 8 = 3 ; 3
16. 6 x 2 = 12 ; 12
17. 12 ÷ 3 = 4 ; 4
18. 6 x 7 = 42 ; 42
19. 28 ÷ 7 = 4 ; 4
20. 8 x 7 = 56 ; 56
21. 3 x 10 = 30 ; 30
22. 16 ÷ 2 = 8 ; 8
23. 32 ÷ 4 = 8 ; 8

11 Bar Graphs

1. Going to Cottage
2. Going to Beach
3. Hiking
4. Visiting Family
5. 13   6. 3
7. 6   8. 27
9. 6   10. Strawberry
11. Maple Walnut   12. 6
13. 3   14. 2
15. 33   16. Butter Pecan
17.

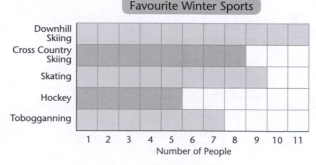

Favourite Winter Sports

18. Downhill skiing 19. 19
20. 14 21. 2
22. 40
23.

Number of Children in Each Family

24. 2 25. 3
26. 2 27. 4
28. 16 29. 4

12 Probability

1. 2 2. 4
3. ♥ 4. ♠
5. 3, 4 6. 2
7. 6 8. No
9. 2 10. ♥
11. 10 12. 4
13. 2 14. 3
15. 1 16. Vanilla
17. Lemon 18. Lemon
19. No 20. Vanilla

Final Review

1.

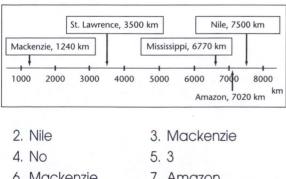

2. Nile 3. Mackenzie
4. No 5. 3
6. Mackenzie 7. Amazon
8. Yes 9. 25
10. 70 11. 45
12. 35 13. B ; C ; D ; A

14. Pop 15. Pop
16. Iced tea 17. No
18. Pop 19. Juice
20. $24 \div 4 = 6$; 6
21. $24 \div 8 = 3$; 3
22. $21 \div 3 = 7$; 7
23. $15 \div 5 = 3$; 3
24. $8 \times 2 = 16$; 16
25. $9 \times 3 = 27$; 27
26. $20 \div 4 = 5$; 5
27. $6 \times 5 = 30$; 30
28. $30 \div 3 = 10$; 10
29. $10 \times 2 = 20$; 20
30. $3 \times 8 = 24$; 24
31. $7 \times 9 = 63$; 63
32. 35
33. 1:20 p.m.
34. 45
35.

Number of Cars in Different Colours

36. 8 ; 9 ; 6 ; 3 ; 6
37. 2
38. 12
39. 32

ISBN: 978-1-897164-12-9

ISBN: 978-1-897164-12-9